LP Clerc's PHOTOGRAPHY
THEORY AND PRACTICE

Edited by DA Spencer PhD, DI, FRIC, FIBP, Hon. FRPS

PHOTOGRAPHY
THEORY AND PRACTICE

I Fundamentals:
Light. Image. Optics.

Revised by LA Mannheim MA (Oxon)

FOCAL PRESS London & New York

Completely revised and enlarged edition.

Originally published by Sir Isaac Pitman & Sons Ltd.

First Edition 1930
Second Edition 1937
Reprinted 1940
Reprinted 1942
Reprinted 1944
Reprinted 1946
Reprinted 1947
Third Edition 1954
Completely revised Edition 1970

© 1970 FOCAL PRESS LIMITED

SBN 240 50684 7

Printed and bound in Great Britain at the Pitman Press, Bath

Preface

There have been few really classical text books in photography. One of these, Louis Philippe Clerc's *La Technique Photographique*, was first published in 1926, and went through six French editions. The last of these was published just after the author's death in 1959. It was as unique a work as L. P. Clerc's personality was as a man. For *La Technique Photographique* was the first comprehensive treatise on photographic theory and practice, covering the whole field concisely yet precisely, scientifically yet in clearly understandable form.

The key to these qualities is that L. P. Clerc was probably the last photographic scientist to be able to keep an overall view over a discipline which – since his death in 1959 – has expanded far beyond the scope of any single man or mind.

L. P. Clerc himself devoted a long life to photographic research and writing. He accumulated the leading honours awarded in photographic activities – from membership of the Council of the *Société Française de Photographie et de Cinématographie* and honorary professorship at the *Institut d'Optique* to the progress medal of the *Royal Photographic Society* and the honorary Fellowships of the *R.P.S.* and the *Photographic Society of America*. At the same time he gained some of the highest distinctions in public service – including the *Croix de Guerre* and *Chevalier de la Legion d'Honneur*.

His qualification for the unique coverage of *La Technique Photographique* was his encyclopaedic and versatile knowledge of photographic science and technology which ensured his leading position in the French photographic industry as scientific consultant, research leader, teacher, lecturer and author. In this connection he read for over fifty years almost everything published on photography in the majority of international technical journals. The worthwhile and significant parts of this information appeared in the journal *Le procédé* which he started in 1898, and later in *Science et Industries Photographique*, which he founded in 1921 and which is still being continued by one of his close collaborators.

Three English editions of *La Technique Photographique* – with a number of intermediate reprints – appeared as *Photography: Theory and Practice* between 1930 and 1954. The last of these had to face the problem that one man could no longer span the whole photographic field, and it became the joint work of a number of expert photographic scientists and writers who brought their specialised knowledge to the sections they covered. The present edition necessarily continues this principle. It also has two specific purposes.

The first is to make *Photography: Theory and Practice* once more the exhaustive current textbook which *La Technique Photographique* was in its day. It has therefore been very extensively rewritten. But even with this radical revision the express aim remained to follow Clerc's original style and presentation as far as possible. Inevitably the work has grown to just over double the size of the third English edition, even though certain very marginal sections have been dropped.

The second purpose is to make *Photography: Theory and Practice* easily accessible to students of scientific as well as professional photography at photographic schools and courses – for whom such a comprehensive text and reference book should prove particularly valuable. To this end the book is being published in separate sections which the student can buy at an economic price and handle more easily.

The present volume, introducing the series by way of fundamental matters concerning image formation, will be followed in rapid succession by others covering all aspects of the subject in full detail. Eventually, the complete work will be issued in a hardboard version.

Two points of detail remain to be made:

(1) The sections, though part of a whole, are self-contained. Their sequence is logical, but not a compulsory order of study, especially for students with a certain basic knowledge of the subject. Even the paragraphs – though following a rational progression within each section – present essentially distinct aspects, steps of exposition or items of information. They are of course cross-referenced where necessary. For this reason the paragraphs are numbered; this numbering is also the form of reference in the index at the end.

(2) As in previous editions, no bibliographical references are included. The reason is that such references would have added enormously to the bulk of the book – with comparatively little advantage to most readers, in view of the limited accessibility of original literature sources in other than specialised libraries. The references have therefore been confined to a mention of the names of authors (and dates) of various discoveries, improvements, etc. This will serve to narrow down the scope of any bibliographic search which some readers may wish to carry out.

Contents

76 Spherical aberration   77 Focus shift   78 Astigmatism   79 Tangential and radial images
80 Coma   81 Curvature of the field   82 Distortion   83 More advanced aberrations
84 Influence of temperature   85 Influence of diaphragm aperture on the different aberrations
86 Distribution of light in the field   87 Field illuminated; field covered   88 Loss of light
in passing through a lens   89 Anti-reflection coatings   90 Effect of internal reflection
91 Stereoscopic effects   92 Faults in lenses

Chapter IX
Focal length of lenses – image scale – conjugate points

93 Conjugate points   94 Relations between the size of object and image   95 Graphical
construction of the image formed by an optical system   96 Image of a plane inclined to the axis
97 Experimental determination of the focal length of a lens   98 Direct determination of the
position of the nodal points and the focal length   99 Automatic adjustment of object and
image   100 Optical automatic focusing   101 Combination of lenses or optical systems

Chapter X
Diaphragm and relative aperture – effect on perspective and intensity

102 Relative aperture of a diaphragm   103 Aperture scale   104 Numerical aperture
105 Different types of diaphragm   106 Centre stops   107 Pupils of an optical system
108 Photographic perspective   109 Perspective and viewpoint   110 Depth of field   111 Relative depth of field   112 Absolute depth of field   113 Depth of field indicators   114 Factors
affecting depth of field   115 Depth with interchangeable lenses   116 Choice of lenses for
depth   117 Close-up depth of field   118 Hyperfocal distance   119 Absolute hyperfocal
distance   120 Direct hyperfocal distance calculation   121 Depth of field limits from the
hyperfocal distance   122 Influence of the corrections of the lens on the depth of field and
hyperfocal distance   123 Accuracy of depth of field tables   124 Fixed focus cameras   125
Focusing scales   126 Depth of focus   127 Effect of relative aperture on the brightness of
the image   128 Effect of the scale of an image on its brightness   129 Measurement of the
effective aperture   130 Measurement of the pupillary magnification

Chapter XI
Choice of a lens – lens types

131 Preliminary remarks   132 Definition requirements   133 Requirements of lens speed
134 Focal length and image size   135 Choice of focal length and angle   136 Angles of
coverage with camera movements   137 Optical glass types in lens design   138 Survey of
principal lens types   139 Single lenses   140 Petzval portrait lens   141 Rectilinear lenses
142 Wide-angle rectilinears   143 Anachromatic symmetrical lens   144 Antiplanats   145
The first anastigmats   146 Convertible anastigmats   147 Triplet type anastigmats
148 Symmetrical anastigmats of separated lenses   149 Wide-angled lenses   150 Fish-eye
lenses   151 Ultra-speed lenses   152 Variable power telephotos   153 Fixed focus telephotos   154 Modern telephoto lenses   155 Mirror optical system   156 Inverted telephoto
systems   157 Practical retrofocus systems   158 Modern convertible lens systems   159
Focus variation: front cell focusing   160 Variable focus (zoom) lenses   161 Focusing with
zoom lenses   162 Zoom lenses for still cameras   163 Projection zoom lenses   164 Lenses
for extended spectral ranges   165 Lenses for extreme resolution   166 Aspheric lenses
167 Plastic lenses   168 Lens mount types

Chapter XII
Lens performance, testing and design

169 Resolving power   170 Theoretical and practical resolution limits   171 Visual sharpness
and edge gradient   172 Spread function   173 Contrast transfer function   174 Frequency
response and optical transfer function   175 Cascading functions   176 Simplified merit
values   177 Lens testing in practice   178 Aspects of lens design   179 The care of lenses

Chapter XIII
Lens accessories and attachments

180 Optical lens attachments   181 Supplementary close-up lenses   182 Negative supplementary lenses   183 Tele-converters   184 Afocal attachments   185 Anamorphic attachments   186 Colour filters   187 The best position for mounting colour filters   188 Care
of colour filters   189 Polarisers   190 Soft focus diffusers   191 Prisms and mirrors
192 Lens hoods   193 Graduated filters or sky shades

SECTION I
FUNDAMENTALS OF VISION AND PHOTOGRAPHY

CHAPTER I

LIGHT AND COLOUR

1. White light—its composite nature—the spectrum. 2. Light waves—wavelength of radiation—frequencies. 3. Spectrum lines and their origin. 4. Luminosity of spectrum colours—visual impression and mechanism of vision—colour sensitivity of the eye. 5. Ultra-violet and intra-red radiation—ultra-violet and infra-red transmitting media—ultra-violet and infra-red applications. 6. Colours in nature—colour by reflection. 7. Accurate description of object colours—standards of illuminance—standard observer—relative stimulation of receptors—I.C.I. colour triangle—chromaticity values. 8. Colours by transmitted light—absorption—filters. 9. Daylight and its colour. 10. Artificial light sources—incandescent lamps—tungsten-halogen lamps—flash—discharge lamps—carbon arcs—lasers. 11. Colour temperature—mireds—spectral energy curves—equal energy spectrum.

1. White Light. The illuminant which is usually considered normal for both visual and photographic purposes is the so-called "white light." This can come from a number of sources or combinations of sources, but in all cases will have similar properties. If a beam of white light be passed through a prism of glass or other suitable transparent medium it will be split up into its component colours. The spectrum, or band of colours produced by the prism, can be seen to consist of three main regions, each of which blends gradually into the next, over two narrow transition regions. The three broad divisions are the blue-violet, green, and red. Between these bands occur the transition regions of blue-green and yellow. This is best seen in the spectrum formed by a diffraction grating, which does not spread out the colours unequally as does a prism but gives an evenly spaced spectrum.

Light appears white when the amounts of blue, green, and red are approximately equal. If there is one part of the spectrum which predominates then the light appears coloured.

When a spectrum is carefully examined it will be seen that the three primary divisions are purely arbitrary; the bands can be further divided, as is often done, into violet, indigo, blue, green, yellow, orange, and red. Further subdivision leads to such vague terms as bluish-green, reddish-orange, and so on. When this stage is reached it is no longer possible to specify a colour accurately by name, since the naming of colours is dependent on memory-matching, and few people have this ability. However, it is possible to identify a spectrum colour by a perfectly accurate description. Light is one of the many forms of electromagnetic radiation of a wave-form nature. Colours can therefore be specified by their wavelength or by a band of wavelengths.

2. Light Waves — Wavelength. Electro-magnetic radiation can be regarded as a spatial vibration, i.e. a regular variation of intensity with distance. This is a characteristic of all wave motion. The simplest kind of wave is the sinusoidal wave (Fig. 1.1), so called because it plots the mathematical relationship of the sine of an angle against the angle itself. Considerably more complex wave forms also exist, but they can nearly all be analysed mathematically in terms of simple sine waves.

In its graphical form the wave has regularly recurring peaks and troughs which can be taken as positive and negative intensities. The distance from one peak to the next, or the distance between any two equivalent successive points of the wave, is the wavelength.

Electro-magnetic radiations can have wavelengths ranging from several kilometres (long-wave radio) down to a thousand millionth of a millimetre, as is the case with cosmic rays. In between there are bands of wavelengths used in short-wave radio and television transmission,

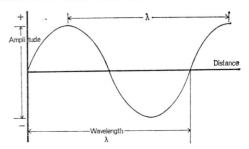

FIG. 1.1. SIMPLEST WAVEFORM—THE SINE WAVE

X-rays, gamma rays and also one comparatively narrow band which our eyes perceive as light.

All electro-magnetic radiation can travel in empty space, such as a vacuum. This is in contrast to sound waves which are mechanical vibrations of matter and therefore need matter to transmit them. Sound cannot travel through a vacuum.

A complete wave—the curve from one peak to the next in Fig. 1.1—is also known as a cycle. The wave travels at a certain constant speed, and in one second therefore vibrates through a number of cycles. This is thus a second way of specifying electro-magnetic radiation. The simplest relationship between frequency and wavelength is:

$$\text{Velocity} = \text{wavelength} \times \text{frequency}$$

In a vacuum the velocity of electro-magnetic radiation is approximately 3×10^{10} metres per second. A radiation with a frequency of 6×10^{15} cycles per second then has a wavelength of 0.5×10^{-6} metres. This is the wavelength of green light. The universal symbol for denoting the wavelength of light is the Greek letter λ (lambda). Wavelengths may be specified in any of several units.

As the very early researches into light radiation were of low accuracy it was not necessary to use many significant figures and in fact wavelengths were specified in microns ($\mu = 1/1,000$ mm) and the spectrum ranged from 0.4 to $0.7\ \mu$. The researches of Ångström into spectroscopy opened up a field in which the wavelength of spectral lines had to be very precisely defined. As a result the Angström units ($\text{Å} = 10^{-7}$ mm) were introduced, the spectrum ranging from 4,000 to 7,000 Å. Often it is adequate to use a slightly simpler unit, the millimicron ($\text{m}\mu = 10^{-6}$ mm), which is often also called the nanometer (nm, derived from 10^{-9} metre, which is the same thing). In these units the spectrum ranges from 400 to 700 $\text{m}\mu$ or nm. Fig. 1.2 shows the distribution of wavelengths in a linear spectrum and the colours which are commonly attached to these broad regions of the spectrum.

3. Spectrum Lines. The spectrum formed by dispersing either sunlight or artificial light such as that from a tungsten-filament lamp, gives a spectrum in which there is continuous gradation of colour and brightness from one end to the other. If, however, the light comes from an electric current arcing between two electrodes or an electric discharge between electrodes through a gas, the energy of the discharge raises the energy level of the individual atoms of the material (the electrodes or the intervening gas) in certain well-organized ways. This arises from the fact that atoms can exist only at specified energy levels. When such an atom returns to a lower energy level (as the condition of the higher levels is unstable) the energy released has to be a specific amount for each atom. This energy is given off as radiation of a given frequency and therefore associated wavelength. In the atomic structure there are a number of levels and interchange can go on between many of these. Each of these will produce a radiation of specific frequency.

As a result, the spectra of these sources are restricted to a number of narrow bands at particular frequencies which are characteristic of the materials used and the energy level changes involved. These narrow bands are called spectrum lines. The photographic applications of discharge or arc sources will be dealt with later in more detail.

4. Luminosity of Different Spectrum Colours. If a number of people are tested so as to ensure that they are not colour-blind, it is possible, by a series of experiments, to compile a series of curves which represent the sensitivity of their eyes to different wavelengths. These graphs will differ from one to another slightly, and an average curve can be drawn. This curve can also be thought of as representing the luminosity of different spectrum colours as seen by the eye. In 1931 the International Committee of Illumination specified such a standard curve, based on much accurate work using the above methods. Further research has shown that this curve is not accurate for the blue part of the spectrum. More

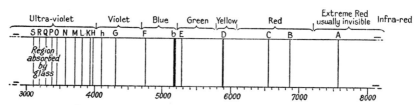

FIG. 1.2. DISTRIBUTION OF COLOURS IN THE SOLAR SPECTRUM WITH ABSORPTION (FRAUNHOFER) LINES *A* TO *S*

precise measurements have indicated a variation from the smooth curve due to pigmentation in the macular region of the retina. This is another characteristic which varies between observers. The curve for the standard observer will, however, stand for a long time yet.

Light impressions are registered by the eye by means of light-sensitive cells in the retina. These cells contain pigments which are decomposed by the action of light; the chemical reaction results in the stimulus which is passed on to the brain. There are two main groups of such cells, called—because of their shape—cones and rods. The cones are the less sensitive of the two, but are able to discriminate colour and probably give rise to stronger visual stimuli. Vision in daylight and at all other fairly high lighting levels works primarily through the cones, as the stimulus provided by the rods is appreciably lower. The luminosity response curve of the cones has its maximum in the yellow green at 555 mμ.

At night, and at all brightness levels below the sensitivity limit of the cones, the rods in the retina take over. These are much more sensitive, but have no ability of colour discrimination. Their luminosity curve is similar in shape to that of daylight vision, but the wavelength of maximum luminosity is displaced from 555 to 515 mμ (Fig. 1.3) This shift is known as the Purkinje shift. The only significance of it in photography is that it is fully used in darkrooms where the illumination is low. The darker green safelights which are used for fast panchromatic materials are designed to transmit a light to which the eye is most sensitive and therefore it is blue-green light of wavelength 515 mμ which these dark panchromatic screens transmit most.

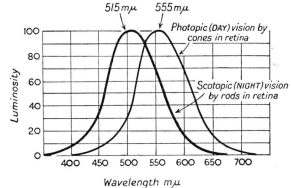

FIG. 1.3. THE LUMINOSITY CURVES OF THE EYE FOR DAY AND NIGHT VISION, SHOWING THE SHIFT IN MAXIMUM INTENSITY
(Purkinje shift)

The cones are present all over the retina of the eye, but are concentrated in the central region known as the fovea. In this region their high concentration also provides the maximum acuity and detail discrimination of vision: we see detail most clearly by looking straight at it. Outside the central region, in the extrafoveal or para-foveal region, the rods begin to appear. They are less closely spaced; hence detail discrimination and acuity are lower at night. Their extrafoveal distribution is also responsible for the fact that we tend to notice low intensity visual impressions more "out of the corner of the eye" than by looking directly at them.

The cones of the eye are also responsible for colour vision. At the beginning of the 19th century Thomas Young had suggested that there are three differentially colour sensitive receptor cells in the eye. These respond broadly to red, green and blue light respectively. H. Helmholtz further postulated that different colour impressions are obtained by different intensities of stimulation of these receptors, ranging from visual impressions of the primary red, green and blue to inumerable intermediate mixtures (for example the impression of yellow by the stimulation of the red and the green receptors). The response curves of the differentially sensitive cones overlap (Fig. 1.5); it is this overlapping which makes an infinite number of differential stimulations possible.

The actual presence of three colour receptors in the eye has been proved only as recently as 1965. But this principle of trichromatic analysis of all visible colours is the basis of all modern systems of colour photography (§ 44).

5. **Ultra-Violet and Infra-Red Radiation.** The human eye is sensitive only to a small part of the radiation which may fall on it. Radiation generally is produced when a body is energized or heated. Any material, when heated, emits electromagnetic radiation, the quality and the quantity of which follow certain fundamental laws of physics which have been elaborated by Wien and Planck. One of the laws which has been derived is particularly interesting. This states that the product of the wavelength at which the energy is greatest and the temperature of the body in degrees Kelvin[1] is a constant value. It follows from this that as the temperature is raised so the energy distribution moves towards the shorter wavelengths, that is, towards the visible region. For all the radiators which we

[1] Degrees Kelvin = Degrees Centigrade + 273. The Kelvin scale starts at − 273°C.

can make, such as tungsten lamps, the wave-length of maximum output is still in the infra-red, and so most of the radiation is not visible. In the case of tungsten lamps operating at a colour temperature of 3,000° K., over three-quarters of the energy is infra-red, which we feel as warmth, and only 10 per cent in the visible region. The amount in the ultra-violet is negligible. However, the light from the sun contains a considerable proportion of ultra-violet light. Fig. 1.4 shows the relative properties of the energy content of light sources of different colour temperatures (see also § 11).

The glasses generally employed in the construction of optical instruments transmit the ultra-violet down to about 350 mμ. The limit extends further to about 320 mμ in the case of certain special glasses. Thanks to the absorption of our atmosphere, the solar spectrum ends at about 300 mμ, which fact protects us from the very dangerous physiological effects of the shortest wavelength radiations. These can be produced by arcs between metal electrodes or by certain gas discharges (mercury vapour lamps) and are transmitted by certain crystalline materials such as quartz, fused silica and the fluorides of the alkali and alkaline earth metals down to about 200 mμ, which is also approximately the limit of transparency of gelatine. By means of suitable apparatus (reflection gratings

in vacuum), and by using sensitive emulsions without gelatine, it has been possible to study photographically the ultra-violet region down to about 10 mμ, where it joins the X-rays.

Quartz and fluoride lenses, used with filters which transmit only ultra-violet, are employed in certain special applications of photography. A filter suitable for this purpose is a thin film of silver. In photographs obtained with these radiations alone, glass objects appear completely opaque; certain white flowers and pigments are indistinguishable from pure blacks, and, further, no background and no shadows appear in a landscape photographed in bright sunshine. The photograph looks as if it were taken in a dense fog (R. W. Wood, 1910).

A much more widespread application of ultra-violet radiation in photography stems from its ability to cause certain substances to emit visible light by fluorescence. This fluorescence is characteristic of the material concerned and can serve for its identification. As however only the visible emission is photographed, fluorescence photography requires no ultra-violet transmitting optical systems; in fact an ultra-violet absorbing filter is used in front of the camera lens to transmit only the visible light.

The infra-red, which extends the visible spectrum beyond red, was of no photographic interest for a long time, its effects being chiefly thermal. Since the discovery of sensitizers for infra-red which are sufficiently easy to handle (E. Q. Adams and H. L. Haller, 1919; H. T. Clarke, 1925,) it has been possible to place on the market plates and films for infra-red photography up to 1 to 1·3μ. Such infra-red sensitive emulsions need special care in handling; they are usually stored refrigerated and must be protected against all forms of radiant heat. Their keeping quality is comparatively poor.

Infra-red rays are scattered much less by the atmosphere than shorter wavelengths of light. By holding back all wavelengths below 700 mμ (with suitable filters) it is thus possible to take extremely clear long-distance views—a technique which is widely employed in aerial and satellite photography. Infra-red photographs of ordinary landscapes reproduce green foliage as white as snow, owing to the high reflectivity of foliage for infra-red rays. When visible light is filtered out, the blue sky of a landscape is rendered as black, and such views taken in sunshine with a clear sky give an impression similar to that of a photograph taken by moonlight.

The reflectivity of various pigments to infra-

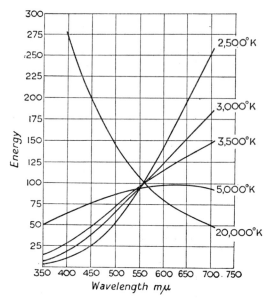

FIG. 1.4. SPECTRAL ENERGY CURVES OF BLACK-BODY RADIATORS OF DIFFERENT TEMPERATURES

red radiation also differs appreciably from their reflectivity to visible light. In this way it is possible to distinguish between visually similar pigments and materials by infra-red photography; such techniques are widely used in forensic photography.

6. Colours in Nature. So far we have considered only light and the colour of light given out by incandescent bodies. But by far the largest part of our knowledge of the world about us results from our seeing of objects which are not self-luminous. With few exceptions we see things by the light which they reflect, although the light in the first instance is emitted by an incandescent source.

The manner in which the surfaces of any object reflect the incident light decides the appearance of that object. The surface may vary from highly polished to absolutely matt; when highly polished, the light is reflected directly, as in a mirror, with a matt surface the incident light is diffused by the broken surface structure. The amount of the incident light which is reflected decides the surface brightness of the object. A light-toned surface reflects a large proportion of the light falling on it, a dark surface only a little, the remainder being absorbed. The absorption capacity of a surface depends not only on the nature of the surface, but in most cases varies with different wavelengths. Principally this is what decides the apparent colour of any object we see. The colour of non-luminous objects is the result of a subtraction process. A piece of red paper looks red because it predominantly absorbs the blue and green parts of the light falling on it, and reflects only the red. Similarly a green surface appears green because it absorbs blue and red.

However, the colours of the world around us are never monochromatic, for they always consist of reflections of broad bands of the spectrum. In general the brighter the surface appears the wider the spectral band it is reflecting. The yellow region of a spectrum is a very narrow band at the overlap of the red and green at wavelengths around 600 mμ. But if a yellow-coloured object were reflecting only this narrow band it would be very dark, since most of the incident light would be absorbed. Yellow pigments reflect most of the red and green regions too. Yellow is the result of stimulation of both red and green receptors in the eye.

The table given below shows the absorption and reflection characteristics of some common artists' colours.

Colours	Spectrum Regions Absorbed	Spectrum Regions Reflected
Ultramarine	Green and Red	Blue
Peacock Blue	Red	Blue and Green
Emerald Green	Red and Blue	Green
Cadmium Yellow	Blue	Red and Green
Vermilion	Blue and Green	Red
Carmines and Purples	Green	Red and Blue

The table shows the existence of colours which do not appear in the spectrum. Since the red and blue wavelengths appear at opposite ends there is no point at which the two overlap. Consequently mixtures of red and blue are never seen in a spectrum.

7. The Accurate Description of the Colours of Objects. For simplicity the colours in the table in the above section have been described by division of the spectrum into three and indicating only reflection or no reflection (absorption). For scientific work (and this includes colour photography) a more precise method of describing the composition of a colour is needed. By measuring the amount of reflectance of a colour for *all* wavelengths throughout the spectrum a graph can be plotted which describes a colour more accurately. But the light which shines on the coloured surface must also be considered. To take an extreme case; a red light shining on a yellow surface, would be completely reflected and the surface would look red. The same surface in a green light would look green. In neither case could it appear yellow, since one of the two bands of wavelengths necessary to stimulate both red and green receptors of the eye and show yellow, was absent in each case. In normal circumstances, of course, the light would contain some quantity of all wavelengths, nevertheless the distribution of quantities must be considered.

The International Commission on Illumination in 1931 regularized the situation by setting up international standards of illuminants. These light sources are standardized to give certain quantities of light at all wavelengths throughout the spectrum, i.e. their light is of a specified spectrum energy distribution. The basic light-source is a tungsten lamp operating at 2,848°K. This is called S_A, for "artificial source." The spectral quality of this artificial light source is then modified by passing the light through coloured liquids of high stability. These give three other standard light sources. These are S_B

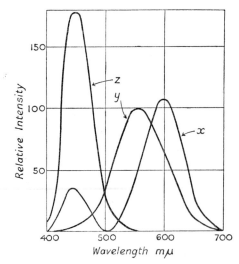

FIG. 1.5. THE RELATIVE STIMULATIONS OF THE THREE RECEPTORS OF THE STANDARD OBSERVER TO LIGHT OF DIFFERENT WAVELENGTHS
(I.C.I. Standards)

(corresponding to British daylight) and S_C and S_D (American daylights). The liquid filters used are called Davis-Gibson filters after their designers Davis and Gibson of the National Bureau of Standards of America.

There is a third factor which must also be taken into account before we can accurately describe the composition of a colour. Since colour is a subjective phenomenon the sensitivity of the eye must be taken into account. This immediately raises the difficulty of the varying response of the human eye. A further part of the work of the International Commission on Illumination in 1931 was the specification of the so-called "standard observer." In the same way as the overall sensitivity curve of § 4 was drawn, three standard curves, representing the sensitivities of the three receptors was calculated. (Fig. 1.5).

Now that all necessary factors are known, they have to be combined and the results shown in the convenient form of a graph.

The graph of the reflectance of the colour at each wavelength is taken and the values for each wavelength are multiplied by the amount of light emitted by the light source at that wavelength, from the spectral energy distribution curve. This value is then multiplied by the relative stimulation of the eye at that wavelength, from the I.C.I. curves. This last operation is carried out for all three receptors of the

eye, and as final results we obtain the relative stimulations of the receptors. We then characterize the integrated stimulations for each receptor by the letters X, Y, and Z for the red, green, and blue. If the sum of these stimulations is divided into the separate stimulations then we obtain values which always add up to 1. These values are represented by x, y, and z. It is therefore only necessary to define two of these values as the third one is always the difference between unity and the sum of the first two. As we need to specify only two we can plot these two graphically. We may, for example, plot x, the red value, along the horizontal axis, with a maximum value of 1, and vertically y, the green value, which again can only have a maximum value of 1. If now all the colours of the spectrum are plotted each separately as if they were the only radiation falling on the eye, as in Fig. 1.6, then we should find that starting with the red end of the spectrum which would give us nearly the maximum value of 1 on the x scale, we should move towards the top end of the y scale as we move towards the green. As we move from the green to the blue so the position of the points on the graph would move towards zero on both scales because neither the green nor red receptors would be very much stimulated by the blue light. We should come to a point where of course the light is no longer visible and no further points can be plotted. By drawing a straight line between the two ends of the curve, the blue end and the red end, we shall obtain

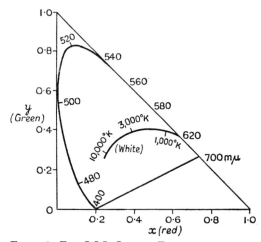

FIG. 1.6. THE I.C.I. COLOUR TRIANGLE SHOWING THE LOCI OF BLACK-BODY RADIATIONS OF DIFFERENT COLOUR TEMPERATURES AND THE SPECTRUM LOCUS

a rough triangle. All the colours are formed by mixtures of the spectrum colours and therefore all colours lie inside this triangle. White light which is a fairly uniform mixture of all the spectrum colours lies in the centre. Any colour can now be plotted on this diagram, and the position on the diagram specifies the colour precisely, except for its brightness.

As the position of the colours or, as they are called, the chromaticity values, move from the white point towards the boundary of the colour region, the proportion of spectrum colour in the mixture increases. We then say that the saturation or purity has increased. This supposes that any colour can be matched by a mixture of white light and a spectrum colour, and so far as the appearance is concerned this is correct. Furthermore, it means that more than one make-up for a colour can be represented by a single point on the colour triangle, because it is only the overall effect of the spectral reflectance curve that is represented by the chromaticity value and not the particular spectral reflectance curve. The spectrum colour which together with white can be used to define the colour under consideration has a determinable wavelength which is known as the dominant wavelength. It follows from the rules and definitions of colorimetry that to obtain the dominant wavelength it is only necessary to draw a straight line through the white point and the colour and to note at what wavelength it intersects the locus of the spectrum colours.

As well as pigmentary colours, the colours of incandescent materials can also be plotted on the diagram. The chromaticities of black-body radiators if plotted in the colour triangle form a smooth curve which extends from the red colours through the white to the blue colours. The common sources of illumination for colorimetry can be located on or near this black-body locus. S_A (a tungsten lamp at 2,848°K) falls on the locus, and the other colours which are defined by the effect of liquid colour filters on the above source fall at points which are slightly off the locus and situated further towards the blue end.

8. Colours by Transmitted Light. In addition to the modification of white light by pigments, we can also observe that transparent media can effect a change. This is a much more easily visualized process, for if we shine a beam of white light through a piece of red glass, for example, we can see that all other parts of the spectrum have been subtracted from the beam

which emerges from the other side. The light is not diffused in its passage through such a material, but parts of the spectrum have been absorbed by the dye which it contains. Dyes can be made which will absorb light in almost any part of the spectrum. The dye chemicals have a certain molecular structure in which electrons are assumed to resonate. Each structure has its natural frequency at which it will absorb a great deal of energy. This leads to an absorption band in the spectrum. By incorporating several dyes it is possible to eliminate parts of the spectrum until selected portions only are transmitted. Such selective absorbers or filters are of great practical importance in photography and are usually made by incorporating dyes in a warm gelatine solution and casting it into thin sheets. Alternatively, the dyes can be incorporated into glass during manufacture, but only a restricted range of colours can be obtained by this method since the temperature at which the colouring matter must be incorporated imposes a great many restrictions.

Even more selective filters can be produced by very thin coatings of transparent media on glass or similar supports. The thickness of such coatings is of the order of the wavelength of light; light waves passing through the coatings are subjected to a phenomenon known as interference. This is connected with the wave nature of light and interference layers can be arranged to absorb or transmit very narrow wavelength bands. Such interference filters are used for certain highly precise scientific applications.

A given light-filter absorbs a constant proportion of the wavelengths which fall on it, irrespective of the intensity. The characteristics of a filter are generally shown graphically. The absorption is plotted on the vertical axis on a logarithmic scale, against wavelength on the horizontal scale. Fig. 1.7 shows such a graph. Instead of absorption, the transmission of the filter is sometimes shown, but there is no essential difference between the two methods since the absorption density is related to the transmission by the formula $D = 2 - \log_{10} T$, where D is density and T is transmission as a percentage. A density of 0·0 corresponds to a transmission of 100 per cent, a density of 1·0 to a transmission of 10 per cent and so on. If two filters of different colours are together placed in the path of a beam of white light, their combined transmissions are the product of their individual transmissions at each wavelength. On the logarithmic scale of

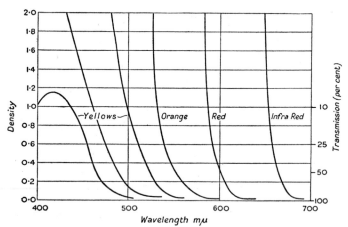

FIG. 1.7. TRANSMISSION CURVES OF A SERIES OF FILTERS

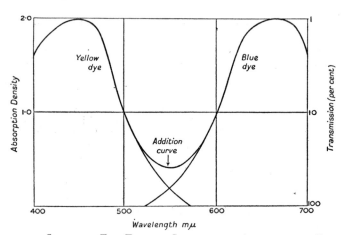

FIG. 1.8. ABSORPTION CURVES OF TWO FILTERS, SHOWING THE ADDITIVITY OF THEIR ABSORPTIONS
WHEN THE TWO FILTERS ARE USED TOGETHER

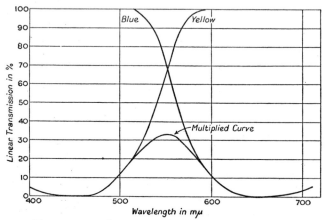

FIG. 1.9. TRANSMISSION CURVES OF TWO FILTERS WHEN USED TOGETHER

absorption density this means that their respective absorptions are added. This is shown graphically in Fig. 1.8. In Fig. 1.9 the same curves are shown plotted as transmission percentages.

From the point of view of colour absorption it is of no importance where in the light-path the filters are placed since a filter is constant in its absorption characteristics. There would be no difference in effect between a filter placed over a light-source and the same filter placed over the camera lens. In practice a filter placed over a camera lens must however be highly precise in other optical respects: in particular it must be absolutely flat and both surfaces parallel so as not to impair the sharpness of the image produced by the lens. In a lamp filter such a degree of optical precision is not necessary.

9. Light Sources: Daylight. One of the most important considerations in photography is the source of light, for the performance of the material and the tone-rendering of the subject depend enormously on the choice of illuminant. The illuminants can be divided into natural and artificial. Daylight which comes from the sun is reasonably constant in its colour quality. There are a number of factors which influence the final conditions and which apparently make daylight variable. Direct daylight or, more precisely, sunlight, is the constant factor and on this is superimposed light which may be scattered by clouds or mist and also blue light which is scattered from the outer atmosphere the of earth. The amount of blue light which is scattered varies with the direction from which it is coming and therefore the resultant effect depends on which part of the sky is most effective in illuminating the subject. In the shadows formed by the sun the light is very blue and has a decided effect on the colour rendering of colour film. These considerations are of importance when we are concerned with accurate colour reproduction in daylight. One way of specifying the colour quality of white light is the colour temperature (§ 11),

10. Artificial Light Sources. Daylight, when available, obviously provides the most universal kind of lighting. Artificial light sources however often have the great advantage of permitting more control over the lighting. They are of course essential when natural daylight is not available for photography. Broadly, artificial light process can be divided into incandescent lamps, combustive sources, arcs and discharge lamps.

The incandescent sources are those which are heated to a high temperature in order to produce their radiation. As the temperature is increased so the amount of light emitted and thus the efficiency increases for photographic purposes. The temperature can be raised until the substance is almost melting in order that the efficiency shall be a maximum. Unfortunately, however, all substances have vapour pressures which increase with the temperature. This implies an increasing rate of evaporation and means that if the source is in the form of a filament it becomes increasingly fragile and finally susceptible to shock or unusual rise in temperature, which causes it to melt or break. That is briefly what happens to (tungsten) metal-filament lamps. The higher the temperature at which the lamp is worked (by the use of higher voltages) the higher the photographic efficiency and the shorter the life.

The evaporation of the tungsten filament can be counteracted to some extent by including a small amount of a halogen (usually iodine or bromine) within the bulb envelope. Such tungsten-halogen lamps can be run at a higher temperature, are more compact and more efficient, but need envelopes of much higher melting glass or of quartz. (They used to be known as quartz-iodine lamps.)

Combustive sources provide light not just by heating matter, but by its burning. The most practical combustive source in general use is the flash bulb where fine aluminium, magnesium or other metal foil or wire burns inside the bulb in an atmosphere of oxygen.

In contrast to incandescent and combustive sources, discharge lamps derive their light from gases made to glow by the passage of a high-voltage current. Originally discharge lamps employed mercury vapour. If a globule of mercury is sealed in a partly exhausted vessel, some mercury vaporizes inside. If a high voltage is applied to two electrodes inside the vessel, it is possible to start a discharge between them through the mercury vapour. The discharge produces heat which in turn vaporizes more mercury and provides a greater discharge of energy. This continues until the optimum conditions of temperature and efficiency are obtained. Unlike the incandescent sources the mercury atoms are disturbed in a definite manner which depends on the atomic structure (see § 3). The light from discharge sources is thus in the form of spectrum lines or emission spectra.

Mercury has two yellow lines very close together at 578 mμ, a green line at 546 mμ, a blue line at 435 mμ, and a violet line at 405 mμ. It has no infra-red, but numerous ultra-violet lines, the two best known being at 365 mμ in the near ultra-violet and the resonance line at 254 mμ, which accounts for a considerable proportion of the energy radiated. As temperature and pressure are increased, the efficiency increases and more of the light is radiated in the visible than in the ultra-violet wavelengths. To compensate for the lack of red in the mercury arc, modern mercury vapour lamps incorporate cadmium metal which has a very strong spectral line in the red band, as well as lines in the blue and blue-green. Such mercury-cadmium lamps have been produced in very high wattages and efficiencies.

If the inside of a tube in which there is a mercury arc is coated with a fluorescent powder, the ultra-violet radiation is absorbed by the powder which then re-emits the radiation as visible light. The efficiency of this process is very high if a low pressure arc is used in which the majority of energy is radiated in the ultra-violet. Usually three powders are used in the fluorescent tubes, to produce either cold daylight or warm white light, which are comparable to true daylight and artificial light respectively. These lamps are very often used to supplement daylight in places like art galleries, for photographic reproduction purposes, or for illuminating transparencies. X-ray illuminators and colour-film viewers also use fluorescent lamps, as they are more economical than tungsten lamps.

Other gases and vapours can also be used in discharge lamps. Some, like neon and sodium, emit light in comparatively few spectral lines. Almost the only type of photographic interest is the xenon discharge. This also has a line spectrum, but at sufficiently high current loading and high gas pressures it emits a continuous spectrum of light as well. Under these conditions xenon arc lamps can be produced with a very small discharge path giving a compact light source of very great intensity. Such xenon arcs are often used in spotlights and cine projectors replacing even high-pressure mercury arcs which used to be available in similar form.

The second use of the xenon discharge lamp is in electronic flash. Here the discharge takes place as a very brief but intense pulse which can be used even in amateur photography for the same purposes as a flash bulb. The electronic flash has however the advantage that one flash tube can yield many thousands of flashes.

The carbon arc, fomerly a widely used light source, is partly a discharge and partly incandescent. Carbon conducts electricity, and the arc is produced by placing two carbon electrodes in contact and passing a current through them. An arc is formed when the carbons are separated, the current being carried by a stream of electrons and ions which bombard the carbons. The latter slowly burn away, mostly from the cathode. The cathode becomes very hot and radiates light, so combining its incandescence with what is effectively a discharge through air. The light from a carbon arc is much richer in blue than in red radiation; to compensate for the lack of red, salts of various metals (strontium, calcium etc.) may be introduced into the core of the carbon rod. Such a lamp is described as a flame arc. The metals burn in the flame of the arc and emit their characterisitc spectral light.

Carbon arcs had the advantage of being for a long time the most intense artificial light source available, but require bulky and expensive control gear to feed the carbons (they have to remain at the same separation even though they are burnt away) and very powerful direct current supplies. For this reason carbon arc lamps are used only in professional film studios and for standard motion picture projection. Even there carbon arcs are increasingly being displaced by the much more convenient and almost equally intense xenon arcs.

One of the most modern sources, and a somewhat unusual one, is the laser. The name itself is an acronym (*l*ight *a*mplification by *s*timulated *e*mission of *r*adiation); it was postulated theoretically by Schawlow and Townes in 1959 and realised experimentally by Maiman in 1960. It involves a special way of light emission by changes in energy levels of atoms; this emission is stimulated by "pumping" energy into the laser system to raise atoms to a so-called metastable state. On returning from their metastable to a basic state the atoms then emit radiation of a single specified wavelength depending on the laser material employed. The light may be emitted in pulses or as continuous radiation (in fact a very rapid succession of short pulses) and has one other significant property; it is coherent. That means that the light waves from a laser are in phase, rather like radio waves. Such coherent light can be used photographically for certain specialized purposes, in particular for recording images in terms of interference wave patterns rather than by projection through lenses or similar optical systems (holography—§41).

11. Colour Temperature. We have seen (§5) that the colour quality of the light emitted by a source radiating a continuous spectrum (such as an incandescent lamp) depends on its temperature. As the temperature rises, the spectral energy curve (see Fig. 1.4) shifts in accordance with the greater proportion of the shorter wave-lengths and reduced proportion of the longer wavelengths emitted. This increasing "white-ness" or decreasing "redness" can be specified by relating it to the temperature of a so-called black body radiator—i.e. one which only emits but does not reflect light. Postulated by Planck, such a theoretical black body can be reproduced app-roximately in a laboratory and its temperature as well as the spectral energy distribution of the light measured. The temperature of the radiator producing light of a given colour quality is called the colour temperature of that light. With sources like filament lamps the colour tempera-ture is not very far removed from the actual operating temperature of the filament.

Colour temperatures can strictly be used only to specify light sources of continuous spectral emission and of spectral energy curves similar to those shown in Fig. 1.4. This concept does not therefore apply to sources of discontinuous or line spectra such as arc or discharge lamps. Where however these contain emission lines fairly well spaced throughout the spectrum, they can often be assigned a kind of equivalent colour temperature by comparison with a continuous radiator. This is based on the reasonably justified assumption that such a source would affect a film—and the eye—in the same way as the equivalent continuous spectral source.

Colour temperatures are given in °K, i.e. absolute temperatures. For instance average day-light has a colour temperature of about 5,500 to 5,900°K, photographic high-power studio lamps are about 3,200°K, while household tungsten lamps may range from 2,400 to 2,800°K. The sensitivity of the eye in distinguishing light of different colour temperatures depends on the colour temperature itself; the minimum detect-able change at around 3,000°K is about 100 to 150°K. At 9,000°K an increase of nearly 1,000°K would be necessary to be noticeable while at 2,400°K a rise or drop of as little as 50°K is visible.

A second way of specifying colour temperature is by so-called micro-reciprocal degrees, or mireds

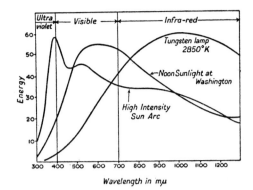

FIG. 1.10. SPECTRAL ENERGY DISTRIBUTION CURVES OF VARIOUS LIGHT SOURCES, ALL OF WHICH, ON THEIR OWN, APPEAR TO PRODUCE WHITE LIGHT

for short. The mired value is the colour tem-perature in °K divided into 1 million. Thus 5,000°K is 200 mireds, 4,000°K is 250 mireds and so on. One feature of the mired scale is that the limit of perceptible colour temperature difference is uniform throughout the scale; it is about 10 mireds. This uniformity of effect, irrespective of the actual colour temperature level, also extends to filters—a matter of some importance when controlling the response of a colour film in colour photography.

Though useful for many purposes, colour temperature is not a precise way of specifying the colour of a light source. The spectral energy curve (for instance Fig. 1.10) gives much more definite information when a closer specification is required. If two sources have the same spectral energy distribution, they will also affect the eye and photographic materials in exactly the same way.

In any consideration on spectral sensitivity as, for example, of a photographic emulsion or of the eye use is made of the "equal energy spectrum." This is the spectrum of an imaginary light source which emits equal amounts of energy into any one band of wavelengths. Spectral sensitivity curves, as referred to an equal energy spectrum, are easily prepared if the spectral emission curve of the source of light is known.

CHAPTER II

QUANTITY OF LIGHT: PHOTOMETRIC UNITS

12. Intensity and brightness—light units—light flux. 13. Illumination—light intensity on a surface—inverse square law. 14. Total light output. 15. Luminance of a reflecting surface—specular and diffuse reflection—luminance units. 16. Reflection factor and its measurement—luminosity—simultaneous contrast. 17. Transmission, opacity and density—light absorption—additivity of logarithmic densities. 18. Specular and diffuse density—Callier coefficient. 19. Reflection density.

12. Intensity and Brightness. The luminous or candle power of a source of light is measured in terms of *candelas* (cd) and its brightness in candelas per sq. cm. This figure is determined by comparing the lamp visually (i.e. in a photometer) with the standard candle, an internationally agreed light source which emits a fixed amount of light when operated under strictly specified standard conditions.

All photometry is based on the daylight-adapted eye (photopic vision, see Fig. 1.2). Where measurements are made by physical instruments, their spectral sensitivity has to match that of the *standard observer* or has to be corrected to yield data corresponding to that standard. It is important to realize this, since the spectral sensitivity of photographic materials does not, as a rule match that of the human eye. An alternative to photometry based on human spectral sensitivity is to determine *energy* at various wavelengths; a third possibility is to describe light by the number of *quanta* or *photons* per unit area, unit time and unit band of wavelength.

All internationally agreed light units are based on the metre or centimetre as units lengths. In Great Britain (and the U.S.A.) units based on the inch or the foot are however still in use. In the following discussions the metric units will be given preference.

The standard candle was first agreed upon as an international unit in 1909, when the light-sources available worked at rather lower colour temperatures than they do to-day. In 1937, a new system of units was agreed upon, which takes as standard the brightness of a black body at the temperature of platinum at its melting point (2,041·3°K). This source has a brightness of 60 candles per square centimetre. The relation between the old standard candle and the new is simple: 1 new standard candle = 0·98 old standard candles.

While the candela and the candela per unit area measures the power and brightness of a source respectively, the radiation or luminous *flux* coming from it is measured in *lumens* (lm). This is the amount of light in candelas per unit solid angle, i.e. a surface of unit area at a unit distance from a point source. As all points of the surface have to be at the same distance from the source, the surface itself postulated for this unit is in fact a curved one. The surface receives a flux of the one lumen when the point source has an intensity of one candela.

13. Illumination. If the light source were a point, without supports, then the luminous flux would be the same in all directions. In fact, owing to the mechanics of electric lamp construction the flux is never uniform in all directions. In some cases special efforts are made by the manufacturers to direct the light in the direction in which it will be most useful, for example, in the case of projector lamps, where all the light which does not fall on the condenser is wasted. The amount of light which falls on a surface depends

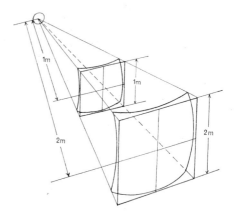

FIG. 2.1. THE FALLING OFF IN ILLUMINATION FROM A POINT SOURCE IN ACCORDANCE WITH THE INVERSE SQUARE LAW

on the distance of the lamp from the surface. For a point source the intensity of illumination of the surface will vary according to the *Inverse Square Law*, that is, the illumination is inversely proportional to the square of the distance. Where the measure of distance is the metre, the measure of illumination of a surface is the metre candle or lux (lx), that is the amount of light the surface will receive from a source of one candlepower at a distance of one metre. If the one-candlepower source is moved to a distance of two metres, the illumination will fall in accordance with the inverse square law (C/D^2, where C is the power of the source and D the distance) to $\frac{1}{4}$ lux. This calculation is only strictly true for a point source. However, in practice the law can be applied with sufficient accuracy in all cases where the dimensions of the source are only a small fraction of the distance from the source to the illuminated surface.

The same considerations apply naturally when distances are measured in feet, the illumination of the surface then being expressed in foot-candles. In both cases the luminous flux falling on the surface is expressed in lumens per sq. metre or lumens per sq. foot respectively. The foot candle is a larger unit than the metre candle, since the intensity of illumination of a surface at 1 foot from the source is greater than of the same surface 1 metre away. Applying immediately the inverse square law, and taking 1 metre as equal to 3.28 feet, 1 foot candle is 10·76 (3·26²) metre-candles. A larger metric unit is the centimetre candle or lumens per sq. cm. This is also known as the *phot*, and is equal to 10,000 (100²) lux. Sometimes the *milliphot* is also used, being 10 lux. 1 foot candle is equal to 1·076 milliphots.

The above calculations have been based on the assumption that the surface receiving light from the source is at right angles to the line joining the two. When this is not true the angle by which the surface deviates from the normal must be taken into account. If the angle (measured from the normal) is α then the intensity of illumination will be $(C/D^2) \cos \alpha$.

When the light source is not small enough to be considered a point, then the inverse square law no longer applies. The most striking example we can consider, is the illumination from a fluorescent tube. A few inches away from the lamp the illumination is constant over quite a variation of distance. At a distance of a foot or two the illumination is proportional to C/D, and from a few feet onwards the illumination obeys the C/D^2 law, because at that distance the

size of the lamp and the angle which it subtends are becoming relatively unimportant.

Whenever there is any form of optical system such as mirrors or lenses, which direct the flux from the lamp, then again the inverse square law does not apply. For instance, the output of projectors is quoted as a flux, and the output of searchlights as *beam intensity* (e.g. beam candle power).

For practical photographic purposes the difference between a light source of small size and a large area source is seen in the quality of the lighting. A small source of high brightness will form sharp shadows and small reflections of high brightness, i.e. highlights. For equal intensity a low-brightness source of large surface area gives a more diffused light and produces less sharply defined shadows.

14. Total Light Output of a Lamp. To measure the total amount of light given out by a light source we must consider the radiation all round the source. If we imagine a sphere totally enclosing a source of one candlepower, the total area of the inside surface of the sphere will be $4\pi r$, where π is the constant 3·14 and r is the radius of the sphere. Whatever unit is used to measure the distance from the source to the surface of the sphere (r), the surface area will always be 12·56 (4 × 3·14) units. The total light flux from a source of one candlepower is therefore (assuming a theoretical source, without supports) 12·56 *lumens*, in either the metric system or the foot-candle system. Since the light is not always being radiated continuously the time of radiation must also be considered to calculate the total light output. The total quantity of light given out by a source of one candlepower in one second is 12·56 lumen-seconds.

This method of specifying the light output of a lamp is commonly used for flash-bulbs and electronic flash units, where the life of the lamp is short, but the intensity of the source during that short time is very high. The smallest flash bulbs have a total light output of about 7,500 lumen seconds with a peak output of nearly $\frac{1}{4}$ million lumens; for the largest bulbs the values are around 100,000 lumen seconds and 4 to 5 million lumens respectively.

15. The Luminance of Reflecting Surfaces. So far we have considered only the quantity of light given out by a light source. When the light falls on a surface it is in part reflected and the surface becomes in some degree a source of light itself, and it can be assigned a luminance. The amount of light reflected depends on the actual surface of the material, which may vary from glossy to matt, and the underlying tone which may vary from white to black.

A highly glossy surface will reflect principally in one direction, in a manner similar to a mirror, and obeying the same laws. Reflections of this sort are sometimes called specular reflections. A completely matt surface will give diffuse reflection, in which the light is scattered and reflected at all angles. In practice, of course, the types of surface vary between these two extremes, and to gain an accurate picture of the reflectance of a particular surface the reflected light must be measured at all angles and a polar reflection curve plotted.

The majority of objects which we see by reflected light, are the result of diffuse reflection, although specular reflections are sometimes seen and indeed are of some importance since they provide highlights which give the eye a clue to the modelling and surface texture.

The luminance or brightness of a completely diffusing surface is measured by taking the intensity for a given direction, and dividing this by the area of the surface as seen from this direction. The unit of brightness is then—as for a primary light source—the *candle per unit area*. In the metric system this unit area is of course the sq. metre and 1 *nit* represents 1 candela per sq. metre. (If a sq. foot is taken, the brightness would be 1 candela per sq. foot.) An obsolete unit for 1 candela per sq. cm is the *stilb*.

The brightness can also be specified again in terms of light flux. In this case 1 *lambert* is the brightness of a perfectly diffusing surface reflecting 1 lumen per sq. cm. (1 foot-*lambert* is similarly the brightness of such a surface reflecting 1 lumen per sq. foot.) A smaller metric unit is the *apostilb*, which is the brightness (strictly, luminance) of a diffusing surface reflecting 1 lumen per sq. metre.

In international use the terms lumens per sq. cm (lm/cm^2) and lumens per sq. metre (lm/m^2) are preferred to lamberts or apostilb.

16. Reflection Factor. Any reflecting surface can be assigned a *reflection factor*, which is the ratio of the flux reflected by the surface to the flux incident upon it. This will of course depend on the surface, whether it is glossy or matt and the tone, but it will also depend on the angle of the incident light and the angle at which the reflected light is collected for measurement. This factor becomes especially noticeable as the surface approaches the perfect specular reflector.

For measurements the practice is to illuminate a surface from a direction perpendicular to it and to measure the reflected light at an angle of 45°. The same results are obtained if these angles of illumination and measurement are interchanged. For special needs these two angles may be varied. The following are a few values of extremes of reflectance values—

Black velvet	. 0·004
Chinese Black on paper . .	. 0·01
Photographic paper, black glossy .	. 0·02
Photographic paper, black matt . .	. 0·06
Black printing ink on paper .	. 0·10
White paper, ordinary . .	. 0·60
White paper, baryta-coated .	. 0·80
Magnesium oxide deposit . .	. 0·90

For a truly diffusing surface the brightness of the surface is equal to the product of the illumination times the reflection factor, divided by π (3·14).

Luminosity is the psycho-physiological correlate to luminance: it is a measure of the visual impression of brightness and depends not only on the luminance of an area in the field of view, but also on the state of adaptation on the eye. This involves thus the surroundings and, in particular, the luminosity of neighbouring areas. An area of a given luminosity may appear bright if surrounded by a dark field, and dark in a light field. This phenomenon is known as *simultaneous contrast*, and plays an important part in the visual assessment of photographs. Simultaneous contrast also plays a part in the visual effect of colours. For example a white patch surrounded by a coloured field will appear to have a colour complementary to the surroundings.

17. Transmission, Opacity and Density. When light passes through any transparent or translucent medium a proportion of the incident light is absorbed and lost, and the remainder emerges. We are dependent on this fact for the production of prints from negatives, for photographic negatives consist of varying quantities of black silver suspended in transparent gelatine. The amount of light which a negative transmits at any one point depends on the quantity of silver at that point. The light transmission of any such semi-transparent material is the ratio between the incident and the emergent light.

Transmission percentage

$$= \frac{\text{Emergent light}}{\text{Incident light}} \times 100$$

In addition to the light lost by absorption, the silver of a negative also diffuses the light. This, if not taken into account, would make the figure for emergent light incorrect, since this would depend on the acceptance angle of the receiver. In practice the transparency of a negative is measured by placing the negative in contact with an evenly illuminated opal glass diffuser. This ensures that the value obtained does not differ seriously from the effective value.

It is more common to indicate the transmission of negatives or positives by their density. This is derived from the reciprocal of the transmission (the opacity):

$$\text{Density} = \log \frac{\text{Incident light}}{\text{Emergent light}}$$

The ratio (incident light/emergent light) is the opacity or light stopping power of the transparent medium. Like the transparency, it depends not only on the denseness (in a general sense) of the medium but also on the thickness of the medium (for instance a light filter). If a given thickness of the medium would absorb 90 per cent of the light (i.e. transmit 1/10 or 10 per cent), then twice the thickness would transmit only 1/100 (1/10 × 1/10) i.e. 1 per cent.

Such additions or combinations become much simpler when working with the logarithmic density units. When combining two densities or placing together two pieces of partly transmitting material, the resulting density is the sum of the individual densities. In the above example, a 10 per cent transmission (opacity 10) corresponds to a density of 1·0 ($\log_{10} 10$; logarithmic values in photography are nearly always to the base 10). Adding two densities of 1·0 gives a density of 2·0. This corresponds in fact to an opacity of 100 or a 1 per cent transmission. This principle of the additivity of density is very important whenever we have to deal with partially light absorbing items or materials in photography. We have already met it with filters (§ 8) but

additivity of density plays a vital part also in assessing the effect of exposure on a photographic material and in printing negatives to produce positives.

The table (bottom of opposite column) gives a few values of density with their approximate corresponding values of opacity and transmission.

18. **Specular and Diffuse Density.** According to the conditions of measurement or use, the values of density for a given piece of material may differ widely. The differences depend in fact on how much of the light coming through the sample of the material can actually be measured. The limiting conditions are *diffuse* (or contact printing) density—where all the light is measured—and *specular* density where only light parallel to the incident beam is measured. For diffuse density measurements the receptor must take in the light emerging from the sample in all directions, for example in a plane *d–d* (Fig. 2.2). For specular density the receptor must be so placed that it takes in only direct light and not scattered light, such as the surface *s–s*.

While for specular density all incident and transmitted light should be parallel, this condition can be approximately realized only in projection systems, such as condenser enlargers, where the value of specular density applies fairly exactly. Specular density is always higher than diffuse density in which all the light transmitted is measured, and which applies in contact printing.

It is possible to determine diffuse density quite precisely; this is laid down in internationally agreed standards. These provide that incident light should be parallel (such as a collimated beam) and that all transmitted light must be measured, for example by determining the luminosity of a piece of opal glass in contact with the test piece. The reverse arrangement—diffuse incident light and parallel take-off—will give the same result.

Density	Opacity	Transmission (percentage)
0·00	1·00	100
0·05	1·10	89
0·1	1·26	79
0·2	1·6	63
0·3	2	50
0·6	4	25
0·9	8	12·5
1·0	10	10
1·3	20	5
1·6	40	2·5
1·9	80	1·25
2·0	100	1·00
3·0	1000	0·1
4·0	10000	0·01

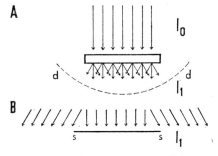

FIG. 2.2. DIFFUSE (A) AND SPECULAR (B) DENSITY

The ratio of specular to diffuse density is the *Callier coefficient*: $C = D_s/D_d$. For silver images in general-purpose black-and-white negative materials this is of the order of $C = 1.4$.

19. Reflection Density. In the case of images on an opaque support it is necessary to measure the reflection density. This is the logarithm of the reciprocal of the reflection factor (§ 16). But it must be noted that for papers with peculiar surface structures, grained or embossed, the reflection values depend to a certain extent on the orientation of the paper with respect to the direction of the incident light. The usual measuring conditions are those described on § 16.

CHAPTER III

LIMITS OF LUMINANCE IN PHOTOGRAPHIC SUBJECTS

20. Luminance range and brightness range in daylight scenes—maximum and minimum reflection factors of objects—atmospheric haze. 21. Sensitivity of the eye—adaptation—control of the pupil—the scanning action of the eye—contrast sensitivity. 22. Perception of details of brightness—sensitivity of discrimination and the factors affecting it. 23. Colour adaptation—colour contrast sensitivity.

20. Luminance Range in some Common Cases. The extent of the luminance range of everyday objects is not generally known and as a result there is a tendency to assume that the ranges are very large, whereas in fact the majority of these are moderate although not necessarily within the tone-range of the photographic material, Measurements which have been carried out either indirectly by means of photographic plates (Hurter and Driffield, 1890) or by direct (visual) photometric tests of points on a subject (Mees, 1914; Goldberg, 1919, 1941; L. A. Jones, 1938), have allowed us to assign numerical luminance values to the brightness of various parts of photographic subjects, such as a landscape, an interior scene, a portrait, etc.

While *luminance range* is the correct scientific term when considering quantitatively the brightness of different reflecting surfaces, *brightness range* is still in wide popular use. Strictly, this is correct—and still rather vague—only when we consider both reflecting and self-luminous objects, for instance a scene which includes light sources (such as a night scene in town) and surfaces illuminated by them.

In a sunlit landscape, without any dense shadows in the foreground, the luminance of the sky (comparable to that of a white paper receiving an illumination of about 17,000 lux—§ 13) is not more than about 25 to 30 times that of the deepest shadows. The following table indicates approximate ratios of extreme luminance values for certain subjects.

The relatively low values of these ratios are due to two facts: firstly, that absolute blacks do not exist in Nature, and, secondly, that, with the exception of polished objects, even the whitest ones reflect only a part of the light which they receive. The only way to get a near approximation of an absolute black is to view through a relatively small hole into a large box, completely lined inside with black velvet, or, failing this, with a coating of lamp black and dextrine.

Subject	Extreme luminance range
Landscape, with sun in the field of view .	2,000,000 : 1
Interior, with windows showing a sunlit landscape	1,000 : 1
Portrait, artificial light, white clothes .	100 : 1
Landscape with white sunlit areas and dense shadows in foreground . .	60 : 1
Lampblack on white paper . . .	20 : 1
Landscape in diffused light, with dark foreground	15 : 1
Interior, no windows or reflections in field of view	10 : 1
The earth, viewed from above: balloon, aeroplane (vertical view) . .	4 : 1
Landscape in misty weather . . .	2 : 1

The most highly reflecting material is magnesium oxide which is deposited on a polished silver plate by burning magnesium; it has a reflection factor of about 98 per cent. Good white papers have reflection factors of about 90 per cent and whitewashed ceilings of about 80 per cent. The lowest reflection factors apply to special surface structures which tend to trap the light, such as brushed velvet and black paper having a fibrous pile. These may have reflections of less than 1 per cent. Photographic blacks on paper, even on glossy paper, reflect never less than 2 per cent and as much as 4 or 5 per cent on matt papers. The tone range of landscapes is considerably reduced by removing the shadows. This is effected by an overcast sky. In this condition the reflection factors of individual objects still hold but reflection factors in landscapes are limited to a very small range. The resultant picture is not usually attractive and is only relieved when the sun comes out again and casts its shadows to brighten up the scene by increasing the tone-range.

In a landscape, the ratio of the extreme luminance values is less for more distant objects. If the distant parts of a landscape are examined with a telescope (or even with a cardboard tube, so as to isolate part of the field of view), no heavy shadow can be observed; diffused light from the atmosphere due to dust and water-droplets in suspension is superposed on the direct light from the object observed. At the farthest distance which can be seen in the direction of the horizon, no detail can be observed, all objects having the same luminance as the sky, and becoming indistinguishable in a kind of bluish mist: the *atmospheric haze*. Painters and draughtsmen make use of this fact (known to them as *aerial perspective*) when they wish to convey the impression of extreme distance.

21. Sensitivity of the Eye. The eye is really part of the brain. Over a very wide range of lighting conditions both eye and brain operate quite happily. There is a range of tone values which the eye can appreciate in its field of view. This range is reasonably constant over quite a wide range of average luminances. That is to say the tone range of the eye is the same on a sunny day as on a dark winter's day. This ability is known as the adaptation power of the eye.

This adaptation is in part physical and in part psychological, i.e. determined by a mental awareness of stimuli related to the overall stimulus level. One purely physical aspect is an automatic regulation introduced by the reflex action of the pupil of the eye. Under daylight conditions the pupil tends to operate at a diameter of about 2 mm; if the illumination changes rapidly, the pupil of the eye tends to close down or open up to compensate for the change. If the illumination is reduced, the pupil can open up to almost 8 mm, giving a substantial increase in the luminosity of the image. As the illumination increases, the pupil closes down again. This is a protective mechanism; in very bright light we tend to supplement this by half closing the eyes as well to reduce the excessive luminosity of the retinal image. At low levels of illumination the pupil always remains fully dilated.

Some of this adaptation takes place even when the eye scans over the scene from brighter to darker areas or vice versa. The scanning action is in fact an essential part of the mechanism of seeing and takes place continuously at a fairly rapid rate even when the eye is apparently focused on a fixed point. In addition to the normal scanning movements the eyeball also oscillates at around 200 cycles per second (Ditchburn, 1959).

In good lighting the eye is capable of distinguishing between two adjacent patches if their luminance differs by 1 or 2 per cent (P. G. Nutting, 1914; E. Goldberg, 1919). As with hearing. our visual sense does not respond to luminosity differences but to ratios; this implies that a scene will have the same appearance regardless of the level of illumination, as daily experience confirms to be true. For this reason the eye is a very poor judge of absolute illumination levels or luminances. These facts characterise the *contrast sensitivity* of the eye. If the illumination is too bright we have glare and the contrast sensitivity decreases. The luminance difference between the two patches has to be considerably larger if they are separated or if in any way slightly non-uniform. This is again due to the rapid adaptation of the eye as it scans from one patch to the other.

The contrast sensitivity decreases at lower levels of illumination; under weak artificial lighting the minimum detectable luminance difference rises to 5 to 10 per cent or even more. The photopic daylight vision mechanism of the eye operates smoothly from 10,000 lux (bright sun) to 100 lux (dull winter day). Below this level night (scotopic) vision begins to be effective and takes over increasingly from photopic vision over a luminance range from 0·2 lux (moonlight from a full moon) down to 0·01 lux (new moon)— with a rapid loss of colour vision. Shadow detail at these levels is completely obscured. Below 0·01 lux photopic vision has completely ceased to operate, but scotopic (night) vision remains effective through the starlight region down to 0·00001 lux.

ILLUMINATIONS IN LUX

Open air, fine weather	Interiors, day time	Interiors, night time, artificial lighting	Streets at night time, artificial lighting
5,000	500	50	5

22. Perception of Details of Brightness. Over a range of 10 to 1 in illumination the eye has much the same acuity and contrast sensitivity. Above and below this range the eye finds it increasingly difficult to operate: at the high levels because the photochemicals supplied to the retina of the eye are rapidly bleached out; and at the lower end merely because there is insufficient light. It can be seen from this that the best conditions are those in which the object to be viewed is at the same level of illumination as that to which the eye is adapted. Therefore to see well it is not necessary to have plenty of light but it is necessary that the light should be in the right balance. Contrast sensitivity, is constant over a range of 10 to 10,000 lux, which can be obtained by bright artificial light and sunlight. If, however, the object to be viewed is dark then it is necessary to increase the level of illumination in order to compensate for the low reflection factor. For instance if black cloth is being stitched on a sewing-machine and the work necessitates some precision it is necessary for the level of illumination to be some 30 times as much as one would need for white cloth. R. J. Lythgoe (1932), has laid down the basis of the practical aspects of lighting and visual acuity.

So far the contrast sensitivity has been considered to remain constant over a wide range of illumination but the sensitivity of discrimination also depends on the way in which the luminances are presented to the observer. In optical instruments it is usual to present them as two adjacent patches having an extremely sharp dividing line, so sharp that when the patches are equal in brightness they appear as a single patch without trace of the separation line. As the sharpness of the line is reduced the sensitivity gradually decreases to several per cent. As the patches are separated the sensitivity drops to a very low value, depending on the surrounding brightness. If the patches are not uniform in brightness, but, for example, of grainy appearance, the sensitivity is lessened. A more practical application to photography is that in which the brightness varies gradually over an area. It is not possible to lay down definite rules as to what is visible and what is not, but it is safe to say that differences as great as 50 per cent in luminance are not noticeable if the variation is smooth. For this reason the fall-off in illumination across the image plane of cameras, enlarger, and projectors is tolerable.

Small differences of brightness can sometimes be confused with small differences in colour. This becomes very noticeable when judgments are being passed on the accuracy of matching of colours in colour processes; in fact by an association of ideas it is usual to tie up difference of colour with difference of brightness.

Our "visual memory" is responsible for quite a number of other errors of perception, too. In general we tend to interpret visual stimuli as much in terms of previous experience as by the exact magnitudes of the stimuli themselves. In brief, we tend to see what we think we ought to see and so are open to a great deal of visual deception.

In black-and-white photography it is sometimes difficult to know beforehand how a scene will be rendered in the various tones of the grey scale. It helps to view the scene through a monochromatic yellow filter which apparently reduces the whole of the scene to a very restricted range of yellows and browns of different brightnesses. The only disadvantage or inaccuracy in this method is that the blues and reds tend to be rendered lower in brightness than they actually are.

23. Colour Adaptation. The adaptation phenomena of the eye to brightness have their parallels in the adaptation to colour. Thus we are aware of colour differences more than of absolute colour tone. In this sense the eye is less discriminating than hearing, since a person with a trained ear can recognize or assign tones of specific frequencies. The eye cannot judge a single colour on its own with any degree of accuracy. In fact, in the presence of illumination of a predominant colour the eye tends to become less sensitive to that colour and accept it as neutral against which it then judges other colours. That is mainly why we tend not to notice the difference in "whiteness" (colour temperature) between daylight and artificial light, unless we can directly compare the two. This colour adaptation can cover considerably differences in predominant light colour, as is evidenced by the fact that we very quickly get used to looking at a scene even through greenish (or purplish) sun glasses.

Analogous to luminance contrast sensitivity there is also a colour contrast sensitivity. This is subject to both physical and physiological factors. The most important physical factor is the level of illumination; this must be high enough to stimulate fully the daylight (photopic) vision. Hence at lower levels of illumination, where the scotopic vision begins to be effective, our ability of colour discernment also drops even though we can still recognize major colour differences.

On the psychological side the visual memory again plays its part—we tend to see colours as we think they ought to be and to ignore actual colour variations. On the other hand, colour contrasts can enhance the perception of certain colours so that we see differences where in fact there are none. Thus a red against a blue-green background appears much more vivid (saturated) than against, say, orange surroundings; it also appears more saturated against a pastel background than against a vivid coloured one.

Finally a physiological factor also enters because different people vary in their ability to perceive and differentiate colours. This is due to differences in the relative sensitivities of the colour receptors in the eyes of different people. If the colour vision is abnormal, we have various degrees of coloured blindness which in extreme cases may make a person unable to distinguish colours at all except by their relative luminosity.

CHAPTER IV

PHOTOGRAPHIC PICTURES: THE AESTHETIC PICTURE; THE IDEAL SCIENTIFIC PICTURE

24. Negative and positive. 25. Range of extreme luminosities in a positive. 26. The ideal scientific reproduction. 27. The aesthetic picture—how we see brightnesses of objects in their surroundings. 28. Objective tone reproduction. 29. Subjective tone reproduction—lighting key—the need for tone distortion—highlight and shadow lighting in a subject.

24. Negative and Positive. The image obtained by the usual photographic processes is a *negative* (Fig. 4.1) in which the brightest parts of the subject are reproduced as dark or dense areas (highlights) and the darker subject portions (shadows) as light to transparent. This is the result of the way in which light acts on the sensitive material: the amount of light reaching the film or plate—e.g. in an image projected by the lens—determines the amount of black silver formed in each region after development.

If this negative is projected optically onto another sensitive layer (for example during enlarging or by rephotographing) the process is reversed and we obtain a positive (Fig. 4.2) which once more reproduces the subject brightnesses in more or less their original form. (A positive can also be obtained by placing the negative in contact with another photographic emulsion and shining light through the negative.)

If the positive is on a transparent support it is usually called a positive transparency, but if it is on an opaque base, such as paper, it is called a print.

25. Range of Extreme Luminosities in a Positive. The following table indicates the ratio of the extreme luminosities in images on paper, obtained by different processes and viewed under normal conditions.

Typographical impression . .	from 10 : 1 to 35 : 1
Black tone photographs, matt surface	from 15 : 1 to 20 : 1
Intaglio print (photogravure) .	less than 35 : 1
Black tone photographs, best quality glossy surface . . .	50 : 1
Colour prints	up to 10 : 1

These values should be considered as the maxima, corresponding with materials of the best quality and with perfect technique. They vary with the conditions under which prints are viewed; an image in which the whites are more glossy than the blacks appears more contrasty when it is viewed in the open air by diffused light than in the light from a source which is almost a point. It appears still more contrasty when it is illuminated under good conditions near a window (Nutting, 1914).

26. The Ideal Scientific Reproduction. In a photograph which reproduces a subject with absolute fidelity, there ought to be equality between each of the luminosities of the picture and the luminosity of the subject at the corresponding point. Obviously this equality is only possible for a certain value of the illumination of the picture and for all other values reduces to a proportionality.

Even supposing that the photographic processes were able to reproduce the subject faithfully over the limited range of luminosities which can be obtained with different papers, it can be seen that reproduction under **exact** conditions is impossible with an image viewed by reflection, since the range of extreme luminosities of the subject would be limited to 20 : 1 in the case of matt prints, or 50 : 1 in the case of glossy prints. There is no such narrow limit to this interval in the case of images viewed as transparencies (diapositives). Note that this advantage is to some extent lost if such an image is examined by reflection from its projection on to an opaque screen, instead of being examined directly. It may be stated as a general rule that for normal subjects, the image on paper should, in order to give natural sensations, differentiate, in the different regions, between luminances of which the ratios should be respectively—

Highlights, 5 per cent; medium tones, 10 per cent; deep shadows, 25 per cent.

For purely record purposes, papers with glossy surfaces are superior, since they not only allow details to be read under considerable magnification (which cannot be done with a print the surface of which has a more or less coarse structure), but also permit of a more correct representation of an extended range of luminances.

Nevertheless, one is often led deliberately to depart from the ideal proportionality between the luminances of the image and those of the subject, and to "compress" the scale luminosities of the image in such a way as to bring it between the limits which are available in practice.

27. The Aesthetic Picture. It would obviously be correct to reproduce strictly the various tones which occur in a dark cave if the photograph obtained was going to be used to ornament the walls of this cave, or of any other place of the same illumination. Since, however, photographs are usually intended to be looked at in a well-lit room, they ought to render the physiological relations of the different luminances of the object, and not their physical values.

The apparent relative brightnesses, i.e. the luminosities, of any scene or object change to a more or less marked degree when the intensity of the illumination in which it is examined is modified, just as if the intensity scale were transposed into a new key (F. F. Renwick, 1918).

A lump of coal illuminated by direct sunshine can send back more light than a lump of chalk in the shade, and yet within its surroundings we see the coal as black and the chalk as white. This physiological interpretation does not always operate when we look at a photograph in which we may take the image of a black object for that of a white one, or conversely, according to their relative luminosities (H. Arens, 1932).

A finished photograph should give an impression of the original scene, but to say that the camera cannot lie is possibly the most misleading statement ever made.

Photographic tone reproduction can be divided into two parts: the objective part, which merely depends upon the luminance values and tone-range of original and reproduction, and the subjective part which depends upon the observer's sensory mechanisms.

28. The Objective Phase. Experiments were carried out by L. A. Jones (1921), in which he laid down a photographic technique which enables true reproduction to be achieved within the limitation of the process. Starting off with a typical emulsion a number of negatives with varying exposure were prepared and from these paper prints were made at different contrasts and exposures. These prints were assessed by large numbers of observers and the statistical results analysed to indicate the most acceptable results. Jones's work on this subject indicated the acceptability of average prints.

29. The Subjective Phase. There are other considerations in the presentation of a print in addition to the fidelity of a reproduction of brightness. R. G. Hopkinson (1937), attempting to reproduce exactly the result of a street-lighting installation on a paper print, has developed a technique which fulfils the subjective part of presentation. This work aimed at setting the observer's mind, through his visual mechanism, to a state in which his subjective mechanism works under the same conditions as when the original is viewed. High-key and low-key effects are well known as a means of suggesting to the observer that the lighting arrangements are very bright or very dark. Hopkinson went still further with this idea and produced prints and viewing conditions which interpreted the original lighting conditions to such an extent that it was possible to judge the results of street-lighting installations on a photographic set-up and thus avoid the necessity for a visit to the scene with all the difficulties of judging whether any improvement had been effected by lighting changes.

Work of great importance in this field is that by R. M. Evans and Miss J. Klute (1944). They considered more closely the subjective side of tone reproduction and attempted to show the various stages that a professional or studio photographer goes through when making his lighting arrangements, which he finds necessary by experience, to produce a pleasing impression of the original. The basis of Evans's work is the psychological indifference to variations of brightness, which are due to different intensities of illumination. For instance, normally nobody is in the least worried to see a person's face in shadow, or that light sources throw shadows of noses in two directions. The reason for this acceptance is that the subject is live and moving and that one's attention is not centred on these aspects but on other things. At any rate it is obvious that the shadows are shadows and that the skin is uniform in tone. The photographic reproduction, however, both projects the solid object on to a plane, and freezes the live subject in movement, and with black-and-white photography one must decide what was colour and what was brightness. And so it is necessary to distort deliberately the exact

FIG. 4.2. THE POSITIVE IMAGE

FIG. 4.1. THE NEGATIVE IMAGE

physical tone reproduction in order to convey the impression required. To do this it is necessary to restrict severely the brightness range of the subject. The densities on the print must indicate not only the reflection characteristics of the original, that is, whether it is a white, a grey, or a black surface, but also whether it is dimly or brightly lit. The final lighting arrangement differs considerably from the conditions one would choose for direct inspection and is usually very near almost perfectly uniform illumination. From this it follows that all unrelated background must be independently lit to a level comparable to that of the main objects in the picture. Shadow portions must be increased in luminosity. The gradation of shadows must be decreased, often by the use of auxiliary lighting. Finally, the brightness of the print must be adjusted (by exposure, and perhaps development), so that the main object seems to indicate the true reflection factor; it must be the true reflection factor if the surround of the picture is white, and if there are in the print no large areas of black or white to form a contrast.

If, however, there is the need or the wish to suggest extraordinary lighting conditions, then it is necessary to over- or under-expose the whole of the print and also to arrange the mount to be of suitable reflectivity in order to suggest the necessary high- or low-key effect.

Other aspects of image presentation, for example the effect of surroundings etc., have been dealt with in papers by C. J. Bartleson (1966 to 1968, some with E. J. Breneman).

CHAPTER V

PERSPECTIVE: MONOCULAR AND BINOCULAR VISION

30. Geometrical Perspective. Although the word *perspective* (from the Latin: to see through) is often used loosely, it is capable of strict definition. If straight lines are drawn from all the points of an object or group of objects to a fixed point (the *viewpoint* or *centre of projection*) and if those lines pass through a certain surface (the *surface of projection*), the image traced out on that surface is the perspective of the object or group of objects. This surface is generally a plane, but is sometimes a cylindrical surface (panoramas), or a segment of a sphere (cupolas), or, more rarely, some other surface.

Practically, according to Leonardo da Vinci, the perspective may be defined as the trace which would be obtained on a transparent surface (glass, or gauze stretched on a frame in the case of a plane perspective), when one eye is kept in a fixed position determined by a

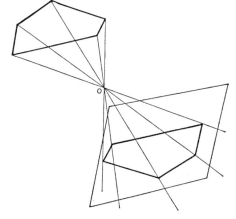

FIG. 5.2. PERSPECTIVE PROJECTION THROUGH A POINT ON TO A SURFACE BEYOND THE VIEWPOINT (OPTICAL IMAGE FORMATION)

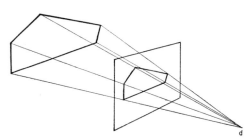

FIG. 5.1. PERSPECTIVE PROJECTION THROUGH A POINT ON TO A SURFACE BETWEEN THE VIEWPOINT AND THE OBJECT

sighthole, and the other is closed, in such a way that each of the points or outlines of this trace exactly masks the point or the corresponding outline in the subject to be represented.

The projection surface can be between the object and the viewpoint or projection centre (Fig. 5.1); it can also be located on the opposite side of the projection centre (Fig. 5.2). The first is direct geometric projection and is easiest to demonstrate and to visualize; the projection has the same orientation (upright and left-to-right) as the object. When the projection surface is beyond

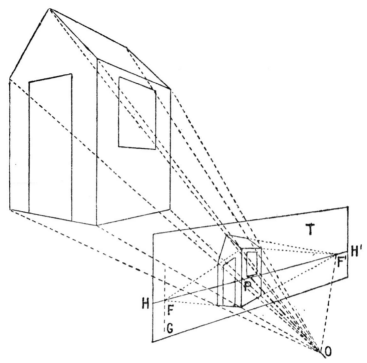

FIG. 5.3. ELEMENTS IN GEOMETRICAL PERSPECTIVE

the centre of projection or viewpoint, the pro-jected image is inverted and reversed left to right; this is analogous to image formation by a lens in a camera. Therefore for the sake of clarity, direct projection constructions will be used in the following description; the two types of projection through a centre are however strictly equivalent in all respects.

Another type of perspective to be considered later (§ 40) involves no point of projection; all projection lines are parallel. This is orthogonal perspective. For the moment we shall however concern ourselves mainly with the perspective of images obtained by projection through a point.

The perspective of anything of which all the parts, whether real or imaginary, have known dimensions and occupy known positions can be obtained by relatively simple geometrical constructions. Conversely, if a perspective contains the images of certain known objects, it is possible to deduce from it the dimensions and the relative positions of other unknown objects whose images figure in that perspective.

Such a perspective regarded by one eye only

from exactly the position of the viewpoint would appear to us, at least as far as the forms are concerned (without considering colours and brightness), just as the object represented would appear when viewed from the corresponding point, the same outlines being seen in the same relative positions.

In conformity with this definition, the surface of a projection plane only plays the rôle of an open window through which appears the land-scape or the scene which was represented.

31. Principal Point and Principal Distance. If we consider a fairly simple object (Fig. 5.3), a viewpoint O, and a vertical plane T, then the perpendicular OP dropped to the plane from the viewpoint meets the plane at a point P (called the *principal point*), the distance OP being the *principal distance* of the perspective obtained.

Any group of straight lines parallel to one another and to the plane of projection will be reproduced in the perspective by straight lines parallel to those considered. In particular, all vertical lines in the subject will be represented by vertical lines in the perspective.

Any groups of parallel straight lines which are not parallel to the projection plane will be represented in the perspective by a group of straight lines converging to the same *vanishing point*, which is defined by the intersection of the projection plane with a straight line dropped from the viewpoint parallel to the direction in question in the subject.

The vanishing points of all the horizontal lines are situated on the *principal horizontal HH'*, the intersection of the projection plane with the horizontal plane through the viewpoint and also (in this case of a vertical projection plane) through the principal point *P*.

In particular, all the horizontals contained in the façade of the shed (Fig. 5.3), or parallel to this façade, are represented by straight lines which converge to the vanishing point *F*, defined by the intersection of the plane of projection with the straight line *OF* dropped from the viewpoint parallel to the straight lines being considered in the subject. All other groups of lines parallel to the façade of the shed will have their vanishing points on the vertical line *FG*.

Once the *position* of the viewpoint and the *direction* of the projection plane have been determined, the perspective obtained is to a close degree independent of the principal distance. The perspectives obtained from a single viewpoint but on several parallel planes are geometrically similar; any one can be changed into any other merely by proportional amplification or reduction; for example, by means of a pantograph. The principal distance only affects the *scale* of the images, which all vary proportionally.

32. Deformations due to Displacement of the Viewpoint. When a perspective is looked at from a point other than its viewpoint, the different parts of the image are no longer seen at the same angles as the corresponding parts of the subject. The representation in this case is falsified, and one no longer appears to see the object but only a more or less distorted form of it.

If we suppose at first that the eye with which the perspective is observed remains at a distance from it equal to the principal distance, but without being placed at the viewpoint, the object undergoes a twist. For example, if the eye is in a position higher than the viewpoint, all the horizontals of the subject appear to slope down from the observer to the horizon; their vanishing points become in fact lower than the eye, and the apparent slope of each horizontal

will be that of a straight line joining the eye to the corresponding vanishing point.

Next, suppose that the eye, while remaining at a distance from the projection plane equal to the principal distance, is displaced laterally. To make this clear, suppose it is placed opposite the vanishing point *F* (Fig. 5.3). This point, being now substituted for the principal point, would be on a perspective examined under correct conditions, the vanishing point of the straight lines of the subject perpendicular to the projection plane. Under the actual conditions of examination one is thus led to consider the façade of the shed as perpendicular to the plane of projection, which is not the case.

Every combination of the two displacements of the eye, the effects of which we have just considered separately, will result in a double twist of the object. Notably, the straight lines, which in the object were perpendicular to the plane of projection, will appear always pointing towards the eye, whatever may be its position relative to the projection plane. Consider the case of an image of a rifle which is aimed directly at the viewpoint. From whatever position the eye views the image the rifle always appears to point directly at the observer, which is not surprising since the profile of the rifle cannot be seen.

Now suppose that the eye, whilst being kept on the perpendicular from the projection plane to the principal point, is displaced along the length of this line. The object will appear *drawn out* in depth or *compressed*, according as the distance of observation is greater or less than the the principal distance, the deformation being in every case proportional to the ratio of these two distances. Imagine two objects at *A* and *B* in the horizontal plane (Fig. 5.4). In the perspective traced from the viewpoint *O* on the projection plane *T*, the images of these two points are at *a* and *b* If, instead of observing this perspective from its viewpoint, the eye is moved to *O'*, at double the distance, obviously the objects cannot be considered as hanging freely in the air, but must be resting on the plane shown. One is, therefore, compelled to assign to these points the positions *A'* and *B'*, the object thus being drawn out in the ratio of 1 to 2. If the distance *AB* is more or less fixed (the case of a man lying down to whom cannot reasonably be attributed double the normal stature), the details of the object situated at *A'*, which we intuitively consider as being at *A''*, will be on an exaggerated scale for the position that we

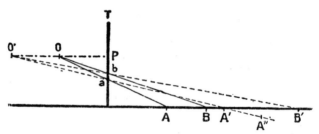

FIG. 5.4. DISTANCE AND PERSPECTIVE

attribute to them in the object. The front planes are expanded relatively to the back planes. Obviously, these deformations may occur in addition to those due to the displacement of the observer upwards or across.

In photography the distance of the principal point from the viewpoint (OP in Fig. 5.4) corresponds to the distance from the camera lens to the image plane or film, since it is immaterial from a geometrical point of view whether the object and the image plane are at the same side of the viewpoint or at opposite sides (compare Figs. 5.1 and 5.2). For a correct perspective impression the picture obtained would have to be viewed again from a distance equal to the focal length of the lens with which it was taken. The above mentioned deformations occur when the viewing distance is either greater or smaller than the focal length of the camera lens. So if the lens used has a short focal length and we view the picture from a distance greater than this focal length the object again appears drawn out in depth and the perspective exaggerated. On the other hand if the camera lens has a long focal length and we view the picture from a closer distance than this focal length, the perspective appears compressed. This is often the case with telephoto views since these are generally taken with long focus lenses to obtain an image on a large scale.

In practice the unnatural perspective resulting in either case is due to the difference between the angles which object points subtend at the viewpoint (the lens) and the angles which corresponding image points subtend at the eye when viewing the picture.

We shall come back to that in more detail in § 36. In the meantime one practical point must still be made. When we observe photographs, they are generally enlargements of the negative. So when considering viewing distances we must also take into account the degree of magnification of the print relative to the negative. Thus the perspective of a print magnified 5 × (linear) from a negative with a camera lens of 50 mm focal length will correspond in image scale and perspective to a contact (same-size) print made from a negative taken with a lens of 250 mm focal length. It is this 250 mm which we must then match as viewing distance when looking at the print. We can term this product of printing magnification and focal length as an *equivalent principal distance.*

Similar considerations apply when viewing a projected image on a screen—whether this is in a cinema, slide projection at home or a television screen. The equivalent principal distance is again the linear magnification of the projected image multiplied by the focal length of the camera lens (*not* the projection lens) which produced it. If we are too near to the screen the reduced viewing distance compresses the apparent depth of objects; if we are too far away the opposite perspective distorion occurs. The former tends to be more disturbing, especially when the observer's viewpoint is appreciably away from the projection axis to produce a twist in the object as well. That such non-ideal conditions are often still considered acceptable is evidenced by the fact that the cheapest cinema seats at the front of the auditorium still sell.

33. Normal Distance of Vision and Angle of Visual Field. A normal-sighted person generally chooses a distance of 10 or 12 in. as the distance from his eyes at which to examine such objects as printed matter, etc. This distance is usually known as the *normal distance of vision.* The smallest distance of distinct vision at which things can be seen without any abnormal effort is rarely less than 6 or 8 in.; a normal eye can often see distinctly an object only from 4 to 6 in. away, but in such cases fatigue sets in so rapidly that this can only be done for a few seconds.

The angular field of the eye is around 45 to 50°. To perceive simultaneously all the objects in a picture the latter should fall within this angle of vision. When looking at a picture we tend therefore to place our eyes at a distance not less than the diagonal of the print. To examine a perspective without the distortions described earlier, it is thus most convenient to have a picture which can be viewed from a principal distance equal to the normal distance of vision. This implies a photograph taken (see above) either with a lens of about 10 to 12 inches (250 to 300 mm) focal length or—if taken with a lens of shorter focus—an enlarged print to achieve this equivalent principal distance. If the actual viewing conditions depart appreciably from these stipulations, the perspective will not be seen correctly.

There are however certain tolerances. In the first place a smaller picture can be examined by means of a magnifying glass which allows it to be brought nearer to the eye. When the image is observed through such a glass under conditions such that the image is at infinity (a condition instinctively fulfilled by an observer of normal vision) the image appears as it would be if the centre of rotation of the eye coincided with the optical centre of the glass. To examine under perfect conditions a perspective with a principal distance less than the distance of normal vision, the magnifying glass should have a focal length equal to this principal distance. While magnifying glasses are not normally marked in focal lengths, the latter—in millimetres—can be obtained by dividing 4 times the indicated magnification into 1000. Thus a glass with a magnification of $2\times$ has a focal length of $1,000/(4 \times 2)$ $= 125$ mm. (This is based on a convention of expressing the magnification as one-quarter of the converging power in dioptres.)

The stipulation of keeping a picture within the visual field of $50°$ is also more of a convention than an absolute rule. The $50°$ angle is a geometric value, but not a physiological one. On the one hand the total horizontal field of vision of the two eyes together is around $140°$; on the other, the eye explores its field of view dynamically by scanning and not statically. It can however take in reasonably quickly images within the $50°$ angle. Yet when the field of vision presented to the eye in a picture greatly exceeds this, it is often possible to convey a greater degree of realism by obliging the eye to go through the same scanning process as it would have done when viewing the original scene. This is the justification of various wide screen systems of cinematography, especially when these are presented in panoramic perspective (§ 39).

The tolerances in the position of the eye during the examination of a picture become greater the greater the principal distance.

In particular, if the principal distance is at least equal to 10 times the mean separation of the eyes, there will no longer be a very marked difference between the objects as received individually by each of the eyes, and the binocular view of the picture will no longer cause any inconvenience.

34. **Anomalies of an Exact Perspective.** A perspective, traced directly on glass or resulting from correct graphical construction or optical projection, is exact in the geometrical sense, but aesthetically it may be *picturesque* or *defective*, according to the value chosen for the principal distance and the included angle. If the eye can be placed at the viewpoint, it will obviously see an object identical with the object seen from the same viewpoint, but as soon as one moves from the normal position (and this will necessarily be the case if the principal distance is very short, or if the included angle exceeds the angle of the visual field) serious distortions will appear, especially towards the limits of the field. These distortions are due again to the fact that the eye takes in a view by scanning over it, and in doing so swings its optical axis from one end of the field to the other. The resulting impression is equivalent to an image projected on a spherical surface, a very different case from a plane perspective.

From whatever angle we may look at a sphere its outline always appears exactly circular. On the contrary, the plane perspective of a sphere is an ellipse, except in the case where the centre of the sphere is on the perpendicular from the viewpoint to the projection plane. As the visual ray to the centre of the sphere makes an increasing angle with this perpendicular, so the distortion also becomes greater.

Nevertheless, if one stands in front of a colonnade, all the columns appear the same diameter. If there is a difference, the columns farthest away appear somewhat smaller. In the perspective of a colonnade seen from the front, the images of the columns become larger as one moves farther away from the principal point.

Fig. 5.5 (from an old paper by Moëssard), shows in elevation, in plan, and in perspective a series of identical vertical cylinders, each being surmounted by a sphere. This is an example of anamorphosis (i.e. a perspective which is displeasing, although correct), due to the fact that an excessive angle has been included. (By means of the angular graduations given, the

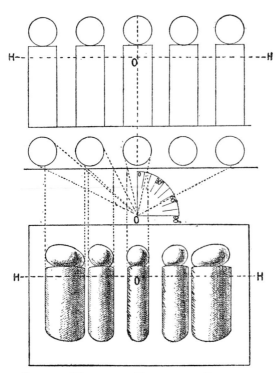

FIG. 5.5. WIDE-ANGLE PERSPECTIVE DISTORTION
OF SOLID OBJECTS

scan across the view and hence swing its axis of vision instead of taking in the whole image at once. For at the right viewing distance—which would correspond to the equivalent principal distance (focal length of the camera lens multiplied by enlarging magnification)—we have a deformation due to displacement of the viewpoint (§ 32) which exactly compensates the wide-angle perspective distortion. In Fig. 5.7 HH represents the plane of the same image as shown in the lower part of Fig. 5.5. From a viewpoint O the eye can only take in the centre portion A while looking with its optical axis at right angles to the plane HH. To take in B and C the observer has to turn his eye (and possibly even his head), so that the images B' and C' are formed at right angles to the newly aligned optical axis; hence A', B' and C' are similar in width, even though in the flat image plane HH B and C are progressively spread out compared with A.

The artist, painter, engraver, or draughtsman always modifies the strict laws of geometrical perspective by means of certain tricks of which the greatest masters have given examples. He generally limits the included angle to between 15° and 20° by choosing a principal distance somewhere between twice and three times the greatest dimension of the image. Further, even if he respects the laws of perspective whilst tracing the principal lines, he departs from them for the details, each object being represented almost as if it were seen from the front. It can almost be said that the painter only adopts the plane perspective for the placing of the different elements, the tracing of these resulting from the drawing on the plane of their spherical perspectives.

obliquities corresponding with different deformations may be seen.) Distortion similar to that of the spheres represented in Fig. 5.5 is often noticed in the faces of people photographed in the foreground of a view taken with a camera lens covering a relatively large angle (photographs of crowds, banquets etc.). Similar distortions occur in wide-angle interior views.

This specific wide-angle distortion is however limited to images of solid objects. A row of windows in the front of a building—situated for all intents and purposes in a flat plane—will all appear of the same size in a true geometric projection, whatever the angle taken in. This is because the oblique projection of the windows near the edge of the field is compressed in the opposite way in which the image would be expanded in the image plane (Fig. 5.6, where the angles a, b, c, get progressively narrower, but as long as A, B and C, are the same so will their images A', B' and C' remain equally wide).

A second relevant point is that a distorted perspective rendering as in Fig. 5.5 appears visually correct again if we look at it from a sufficiently close viewpoint to oblige the eye to

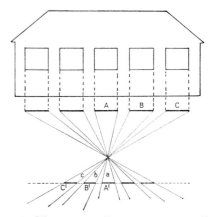

FIG. 5.6. WIDE-ANGLE PROJECTION OF A FLAT
OBJECT

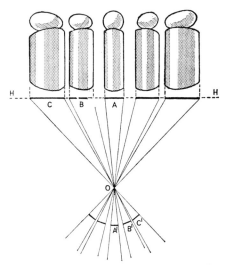

FIG. 5.7. COMPENSATION OF WIDE-ANGLE PERS-
PECTIVE DISTORTION BY DEFORMATION DUE TO
DISPLACEMENT OF THE VIEWPOINT

Notice, however, that the observer who can only see with one eye and who cannot move, though provided for by the theorists of perspective, is not found amongst Nature artists, who always judge their effects with both eyes open, and frequently move about so as to look at their picture from points far removed from the actual viewpoint; by doing this they can correct the anomalies which would show to badly-placed spectators. This explains why pictures in museums can be examined from very different positions, and often even abnormal positions, without appearing displeasing. Unfortunately, this wide tolerance is not found in the examination of a perspective, unless its principal distance is very great and the included angle very small (see § 40).

35. **Influence of Choice of Viewpoint.** The choice of viewpoint affects the aspect of the image of each of the different objects and at the same time the ratio of the respective sizes of the images of objects situated at different distances.

Consider the case of a sphere (Fig. 5.8), and

let us determine the perspectives from the two viewpoints O and O'. It will be realized at once that, seen from very near, the sphere will show only a small fraction of the surface which can be seen from a farther distance away; all the shaded zone will be seen from O and not from O'. It can be seen that if we substitute for the sphere a human face seen from the front, then from the viewpoint O' the ears will be hidden, and the mouth (the size of which is about one-quarter of that of the whole face) will occupy a third of the apparent diameter and seem to be enormous.

Now consider the case of two objects of the same dimensions situated at different distances from the viewpoint, in the same direction. If the nearer of the two objects is at a distance from the viewpoint equal to n times the distance between the objects, the respective scales of their images will be in the ratio $n/(n + 1)$. Thus the images will be less different as n becomes greater, as is shown in the following table, where the values of $n/(n + 1)$ are given for different values of n.

n	1	2	3	4	5	10	20	100
$n/(n + 1)$	0·50	0·66	0·75	0·80	0·83	0·90	0·95	0·99

Thus it can be seen that if the distance of two equal objects is equal to the distance of the nearer of them from the viewpoint, one of the objects will be represented twice the size of the other. If we multiply by ten the distance to the first of the objects, and compensate for this increase of distance by extending the principal distance until an image of the nearer object is obtained which is the same as previously, the more distant object will not differ from it more than 10 per cent. An example of this may be seen in telephoto pictures, particularly of cricket matches, where the two batsmen are about 20 yards apart and the viewpoint may be 200 yards away.

Returning now to the case of the front view of a portrait, and bearing in mind that the point of the nose is about five inches in front of the

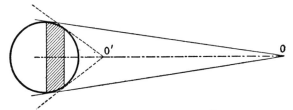

FIG. 5.8. EFFECT OF VIEWPOINT ON PERSPECTIVE

back outline of the ears, it can be calculated that in a portrait taken at about four feet from the sitter, a rigorous application of the laws of perspective would result in the nose being represented on a scale greater by 10 per cent than the scale of the ears. A painter, when sketching a portrait, is always at least 10 or 15 ft from his model.

Let us take the case of a house, and consider its perspective at a distance of about 300 yd. At this distance the house is in correct relation with the distant landscape. If now we approach to within 20 yd of it, whilst keeping the same principal distance, the image of the house will be magnified 15 times, but the distance will be practically the same size as before, and will thus be on a much smaller scale.

Similarly, a painter, when prevented from going back far enough to see properly, would design the background on a magnified scale in order to correct this effect, which, though it would be scarcely noticeable in the examination of a landscape itself, because our brain corrects the sensations which our eyes transmit to it, might be displeasing in the case of a plane image.

36. Perspective and Image Scale. The interdependence of viewpoint and perspective of an object scene gives us one visual clue of its actual distance. A second clue is the apparent scale in terms of the angle the object subtends at the viewpoint. A perspective appears unnatural when these two clues are contradictory. Thus the perspective seen from a viewpoint O' in Fig. 5.8 must be associated with a large image of the head so that it fills our field of view; the perspective from viewpoint O is associated with a smaller image of the head. If we consider photographs taken from the two viewpoints, that from O' would not look too disturbingly unnatural if the face really fills the image field and the picture is viewed from the correct equivalent principal distance—we are simply dealing with a very close view of a face, and its perspective is in accordance with what we would expect such a close view to look like. If however the same image is viewed from considerably further away so that it subtends an angle at the eye more appropriate to the viewpoint O in Fig. 5.8, the perspective appears violently exaggerated, because the image scale is no longer appropriate to a near viewpoint, even if the perspective is.

Conversely, the shallower perspective seen rom O is associated with a small image scale— where the head occupies only a small part of our eld of view. So when viewing such a picture

from a principal distance corresponding to the viewpoint O', the perspective appears compressed as if we are looking not at a face but at a flat image.

It is this discrepancy between image scale and perspective which becomes disturbing in photographs viewed from the wrong distance. Fig. 5.9 shows the misleading perspective impression arising from this. From a near viewpoint the two cars A and B at different distances from the observer appear appreciably different in size as in C. They are however also comparatively large in the image field. From a more distant viewpoint their size difference in the image is much less marked (see the table above) and the cars also seem comparatively small in the field of view, as in D. Both C and D appear correct, as the perspective and the image scale clues are consistent—for a near viewpoint in C, and a distant viewpoint in D. When however picture C is viewed from too far away so that the apparent scale of the cars in this field of view becomes more like in E, the size difference (perspective) of the cars contradicts their visual scale. That is when the perspective appears distorted by being too drawn out. Conversely, if the image D is viewed from too near, its visual scale becomes more like F. The perspective becomes flattened (a typical telephoto perspective) because with that visual scale we are accustomed to associate a perspective as shown in C.

The discrepancy between perspective and image scale becomes more noticeable in perspectives (and photographs) from a near viewpoint because here both perspective and scale alter more rapidly with a change of principal distance. Hence here the choice of the correct viewing distance is more critical than for a perspective associated with a more distant viewpoint.

37. Binocular Vision. Even with the clues of perspective and scale only a rough idea of the relative distances of objects can be obtained by monocular vision (using one eye only). One knows how difficult it is to place a finger in the neck of a bottle placed by someone else at the height of the observer's eyes, when one eye is shut. The factors to be appreciated are the variation of the apparent dimensions of an object of known size, the changes in the relative position of the objects when the observer moves transversely, the aerial perspective (§ 20), and the variations in the effort necessary to accommodate the eye (*focusing* the eye) according to the distance of the object. Chromatic aberration of the eye also plays an appreciable

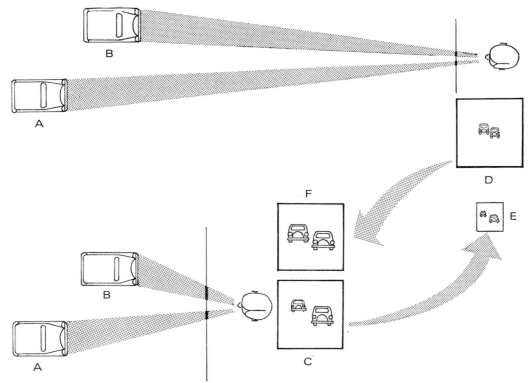

FIG. 5.9. PERSPECTIVE AND IMAGE SCALE

part in the estimation of distances, images being bordered with a red or blue fringe according to whether the corresponding objects are nearer or farther than the plane on which the eye is focused.

The causes which give rise to the sense of relief in *binocular vision* (using two eyes) are, on the one hand, the dissimilarity of the two retinal images, each eye seeing a single near point projected on two different points of the background, and on the other hand, the effort of convergence of the ocular axes towards the fixed point, this effort becoming greater as the point becomes nearer. These two factors are important only for relatively near objects; when viewed from the air from only a few thousand feet, objects on the ground lose their relief.

Consider two perspectives of a single subject, each perspective having the same principal distance, on two parts of the same plane, from two viewpoints the separation between which is equal to the mean separation of the eyes (about 65 mm). If the centres of rotation of one's eyes be placed at the viewpoints, each eye only seeing the perspective of its own viewpoint, the same sensation of relief will be experienced as in direct observation of the object with the two eyes (the variations of the accommodation no longer obtain in this case). This relief may be so striking that an observer who did not already know would scarcely believe that the solid image which he could see was actually the result of two plane images.

This fact forms the basis of *stereoscopy*. Stereoscopic vision implicitly assumes that the observer has two equal and symmetrical eyes.

38. Perspective on a Non-vertical Plane. If from the viewpoint O (Fig. 5.10) the perspective of a solid body S be drawn on the non-vertical plane T, the images of all the vertical lines of the solid will converge to the vanishing point V, where V is the intersection of the plane T with the vertical dropped from the viewpoint.

In presenting this plane under the same obliquity to an observer whose eye, placed at O, would be forced to look in the direction of the principal point P, especially in the absence of external marks which would indicate to him the obliquity of the plane on which was the perspective, he might have the illusion of the

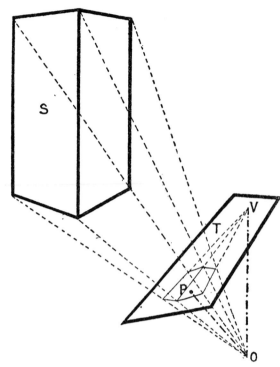

FIG. 5.10. PERSPECTIVE ON AN INCLINED PLANE

object represented. But an observer who did not know, examining such a perspective under the same conditions as he would regard a normal one, would be led to conclude that the solid object represented was not a parallelepiped, but a truncated pyramid. He might, not unnaturally, conclude that the solid figure was represented as in the act of falling. (We are not envisaging here the case of views intentionally taken looking downwards or upwards for documentary purposes or in order to achieve some special effect.)

A vertical plane of projection is the essential condition for the reproduction of vertical lines as verticals in the perspective.

Experience shows that once the perspective has been drawn under these conditions, the projection image can then be shown obliquely without appearing displeasing. This is the case with pictures hung rather high in such a way that their viewpoint is at the height of the observer's eyes when standing.

Even when we realize this condition of obliqueness, we still tend to reject the representation of an object on an inclined surface, even when viewing it under its normal inclination. This is however once

more a case of seeing what we think we ought to see and of comparing the picture with other visual clues present in the surroundings, such as the vertical walls of the room in which it is hanging. In the absence of external clues there is no difference between looking squarely at a projection (e.g. a photograph) on a non-vertical plane i.e. which was inclined relative to the main plane of the object—and looking obliquely at a perspective projected on a plane parallel to the object plane. This fact can indeed give rise to numerous optical illusions and artificial perspectives obtained by appropriate manipulation (R. M. Evans, 1959).

Even on the more practical level of commercial photography it is often desirable and possible to control the perspective in terms of convergence of vertical (and also horizontal) lines. Technical cameras therefore include provisions for tilting the image plane in different directions without moving the point of projection (the lens), and also for displacing the lens without moving the image plane. These adjustments are known as the *camera movements*, and will be discussed when we come to deal with camera design.

39. Panoramic Perspective. In cylindrical perspective, known as panorama, the viewpoint is situated on the axis of the cylinder of revolution (vertical cylinder), which constitutes the projection surface. In this system of perspective, verticals are represented by verticals, the horizon line by a meridian circle, and all other straight lines by ellipses. When the projection surface is maintained in its cylindrical form and looked at from the viewpoint, what is seen is identical with the subject, but if the

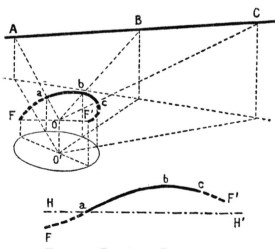

FIG. 5.11. PANORAMIC PERSPECTIVE

projection surface is now unrolled and becomes a plane, all the straight lines of the subject, with the exception of the verticals and the horizon line, are represented by curves. Thus it is, for example, that the straight line *ABC* (Fig. 5.11) is represented in the panoramic perspective, after this has been flattened out to a plane, by the curve *abc*, with vanishing points at *F* and *F'*, which are common to the perspectives of all other straight lines parallel to that considered.

Such deformations are obviously a drawback in cases where it is desired to represent subjects containing numerous straight lines other than the verticals, such as architectural works or views of towns having straight streets. But the suppression of all deformations due to excessive obliquity of the visual rays relatively to the projection of plane perspectives (§ 34, Fig. 5.5) gives to panoramic photographs, often limited to a fraction of the complete horizon, a special interest in such cases as the representation of a very extensive landscape, for example high mountainous country, or of a large number of people.

Due to its being unfolded to give a plane surface, such an image no longer permits of *one* viewpoint only, but of an *infinite number* of them, arranged on a straight line parallel to the horizon line, at a distance from the image equal to the principal distance. Such a projection should be considered as the combination of a great number of projections each formed from a straight vertical band, each to be examined from its particular viewpoint. The observer moving in front of the projection should thus only look at the details of the image which he sees exactly opposite to him.

Alternatively, the panorama can be reconstituted in its correct perspective by rolling up the photograph again into a cylinder which surrounds the observer. For a correct perspective impression the radius of this cylinder must be equal to the principal distance of the original projection multiplied by the original magnification if the picture was enlarged. Such reconstructions are approximated in practice in panoramic wide screen motion picture processes where the image is projected on a curved screen. The panoramic view, by extending to the limits of the horizontal field of vision of both eyes (about 140°) simulates a greater degree of realism (see § 33). However, the placement of the observer in front of such a panoramic projection screen to see the line ABC in Fig. 5.11 as a

straight line, is quite critical. From any viewpoint other than in the axis of *OO'* in Fig. 5.11 the line would appear curved either inwards or outwards according to whether the viewpoint is too far from, or too near to, the screen.

In practice panoramic photographs often used to be taken with a camera whose lens axis swung from one end of the view to the other while projecting the image onto a flat or a curved film plane. One modern application is in aerial photography, where the lens swings about a centre axis pointing vertically downwards at the ground, covering the view from one horizon to the other. The resulting image also shows the same curvature of all lines parallel with the direction of the lens movement from *A* to *B* (Fig. 5.12), except for the centre line *CD* in the plane of this movement. If the parameters of the optical projection—the height of the projection point (aircraft height) from the object plane, the distance of the projection point from the image plane (focal length of the lens) and the angle of movement— are known, the image can be rectified, i.e. brought back to its correct proportions. This may be done either mechanically during printing or by computer controlled re-projection.

40. Orthographic Perspective. All aspects of geometric perspective discussed so far were based on projection through a point, the projection centre or viewpoint. A three-dimensional object can however also be reduced to a two-dimensional plane by projection with parallel rays. This leads to a so-called parallel perspective, since all lines which were parallel in the object are also parallel

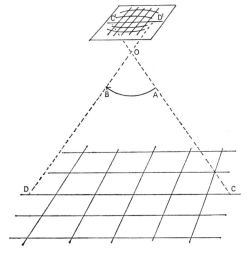

FIG. 5.12. PANORAMIC AERIAL PROJECTION

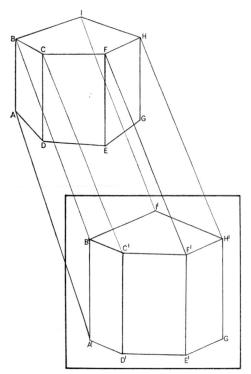

FIG. 5.13. ORTHOGRAPHIC OR PARALLEL PROJECTION

of such surfaces are similarly altered in a uniform manner.

(e) The foreshortening is also influenced by the angle at which the projection rays reach the projection surface; under suitable conditions object dimensions can be lengthened as well as shortened in the projection plane.

The main advantage of parallel projection is that the exact dimensions and proportions of the object can be established comparatively easily from the projection image: we must know only the angle of the object plane relative to the projection surface and the angle at which the projection rays reach that surface. This ease of exact scaling makes orthographic projection sufficiently attractive for attempts at reproducing its conditions as closely as possible by photographic means.

Such an approximation is obtained by geometric projection through a point, if this point is sufficiently far away from the object. Under those conditions perspective depth virtually disappears in terms of diminishing scale with increasing distance; this is thus the extreme case of telephoto perspective (§ 36). When a telephoto or long focus lens is used to obtain a reasonably

in the plane of projection. If we regard central projection or projection through a point as analogous to image formation in a camera, then the corresponding analogy of parallel projection is the formation of a shadow.

In Fig. 5.13 the lines joining the points A, B, C, D, E, F, G H, I of the object (itself drawn in geometric perspective for the illustration) with the corresponding points A', B', C', D' etc. in the projected plane are all parallel. The resulting perspective then has the following features:

(a) It is independent of the distance between the object and the projection plane;

(b) All angles and proportions in an object plane parallel to the projection plane are rendered unchanged. This is also the case in projection through a point, but in parallel projection all surfaces and dimensions in a plane parallel to the projection plane are also always of the same size as in the object.

(c) All lines which are parallel in the object— in whatever plane—are also parallel in the projection surface.

(d) Lines in planes inclined to the projection surface are all foreshortened to the same degree, depending on the angle of inclination. All angles

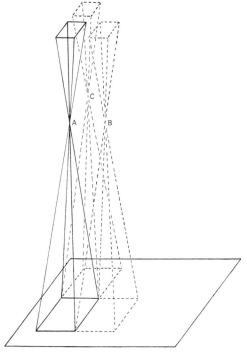

FIG. 5.14. APPROXIMATE ORTHOGRAPHIC PROJECTION BY THE ASSEMBLY OF A MOSAIC

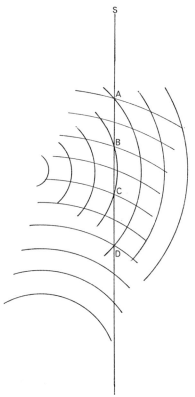

FIG. 5.15. WAVE INTERFERENCE

coherent, i.e. of one wavelength and in a continuous wavefront, this interference forms a regular pattern which can become visible on a screen (for example S in Fig. 5.15), with the interference points showing up as alternate light and dark fringes (A, B, C, D).

If one of the wavefronts is modified by reflection from, or passing through, a solid or transparent object respectively, different parts of this wavefront are retarded or deflected in different ways and the interference pattern produced becomes irregular. The irregularity then directly represents the topography or structure of the object. The interference pattern can be recorded on a photographic plate placed in any plane such as S (Fig. 5.15) where the interfering wavefronts meet.

If the plate with its wavefront interference image is processed and then illuminated by a light source of a single and coherent wavelength, the illuminating waves are diffracted by the interference pattern recorded on the plate, and the original object which gave rise to the distortion of the interference pattern becomes visible. The principle (Gabor, 1948) became feasible for practical application (Leith & Upatnieks, 1962) once a sufficiently coherent light source became available with the laser (§ 10). With ordinary light which is non-coherent, interacting wavefronts are too irregular to produce diffraction patterns.

The most basic set-up for holography involves directing a laser beam so that it partly hits a mirror M (Fig. 5.16) and partly the object O to be recorded. The light reflected from the object interferes with the light reflected from the mirror, forming an interference pattern characteristic of the object O in the plane of the hologram H. The hologram image has no recognisable form and needs reconstruction by being

large image under these conditions, the angle of field covered is very restricted.

To take in a field of any size with this simulated orthographic perspective we must therefore take a large number of separate photographs from viewpoints progressively displaced within a plane. In Fig. 5.14 these viewpoints A, B, C are in a plane parallel to the projection plane of the required orthographic representation. The individual images obtained in this way are then assembled as a mosaic to cover the full object field. This is the principle of aerial mapping and can also be applied to the photography of building models to obtain reasonably orthographic images suitable for preparing plan drawings.

41. Holography. A rather special case of image formation which relies neither on projection through a point nor on parallel projection is *holography*. It depends on the fact that when two trains of waves or wavefronts meet, they *interfere*—that is, they reinforce each other where their crests meet and cancel (extinguish) each other where the crest of one wave meets the trough of another. If both waves are pure and

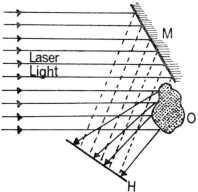

FIG. 5.16. HOLOGRAM FORMATION

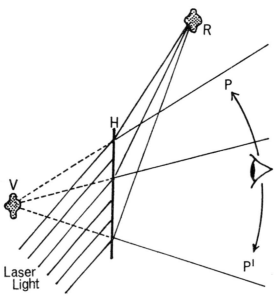

FIG. 5.17. HOLOGRAM RECONSTRUCTION

illuminated by a laser beam (Fig. 5.17). Under these conditions the diffraction of the light by the hologram produces both a virtual image V and a real image R. The real image has all the characteristics of a perspective projection through a point and can be made visible by placing a projection surace in the position where this image is formed. The virtual image is visible by direct observation through the hologram.

Holography has numerous rapidly growing applications including recording and reproducing colours. Significant for our discussion on perspective is the depth of the image. This is literally a three-dimensional one, and movement of the eye along PP' (and similar directions at right angles to the plane of Fig. 5.17) reveals different views in stereoscopic relief, as if the original object and not just image were situated at V. The equivalent principal distance for the perspective scene is the mean distance from O to H in Fig. 5.16; the eye has to be at a fairly specified distance from the hologram H in Fig. 5.17 to see the image. Movement of the eye involves in effect movement of the projection point, in contrast to a normal geometrically formed image where the projection point is fixed and displacement of the observation point from the projection point leads to the deformations already mentioned.

42. Sharpness of Vision. Sharpness of vision, or visual acuity, which varies from individual to individual and with the lighting conditions, is measured by the distance from centre to centre of black parallel lines of equal width, separated by white spaces of the same width, this distance being expressed as a fraction of the greatest distance at which the lines can still be separately seen when viewed closely, i.e. when their images are formed on the most sensitive part of the retina. A good eye can distinguish two lines the distance apart of which measured from centre to centre corresponds to an angle of 1 minute. This would be given by a distance of 1/250 in. at 12 in. Practically, the sharpness of an eye is considered to be about the average when it can separate lines 1/250 in. apart at a distance of 8 in., corresponding with an angle of 1/2,000 radian.

Visual acuity has its counterpart in the resolving power both of optical systems as lenses and of the sensitive material, i.e. the film emulsion. Resolving power will be discussed in more detail in the context of these two items.

43. Depth of Field of the Eye. When the eye is accommodated for regarding an object at a certain distance with maximum sharpness, objects nearer and farther away do not give sharp images on the retina. There exists, however, a certain zone within which all objects appear to the eye with the same sharpness. The depth of this zone is known as the *depth of field*, which becomes greater as the object viewed is farther away.

In fact, in looking at a scene of which the different elements are at very different distances from the observer, the accommodation varies constantly as the eye concentrates on the various points. Thus, in the average sensation which results, the most important points are seen more sharply than those of only secondary interest, which are, as it were, only seen accidentally.

Depth of field is also involved in the image formation by lenses.

CHAPTER VI

PRINCIPLES OF COLOUR PHOTOGRAPHY

44. Colour Analysis. We have seen in Chapter I that while we can specify a colour physically by the wavelengths of light it contains or reflects, colour impressions are produced in the observer's brain. In normal humans at least, the whole appreciation of colour is based on a system of three stimuli. The accuracy of colour appreciation of people with normal vision is extraordinarily high. Indeed few physical instruments can measure colour more closely than the human eye can match sample colours held side-by-side.

Since colour vision is dependent on only three colour stimuli it is theoretically possible to reproduce any visible colour by a mixture of suitable red, green, and blue lights (Maxwell 1860) and it is upon this principle that nearly all practical processes of colour photography depend.

The first step in colour reproduction is thus the analysis of the colours of the subject in terms of the relative stimuli or intensities in the three primary spectral bands. A colour photographic process therefore has to imitate the selective sensitivities of the three receptors in the eye to produce three separate colour "signals" determined by the hue of every image point. These signals are usually three separate images either produced in three individual sensitive layers, or interlaced in one layer.

The second step is synthesis: the component images have to be combined again with coloured light in such a way that each gives rise to a separate colour stimulation of the intensity required to reconstitute the hue of every image point.

Two points are significant here. Firstly, the link between analysis and synthesis is not actual colour but information about colour. This information is in itself not coloured at all—it may just as well be (and in principle often is) a series of monochrome images or even electromagnetic signals. The process of colour analysis is in turn controlled by media of specific colour transmission (filters) or sensitivity (emulsions) which are not related to the colours of the original image.

Secondly, the colour at the synthesis stage is again produced by a new set of colouring agents (filters, pigments or dyes) whose contribution is controlled by the signals or images produced at the analysis stage. These colouring agents have the job of reproducing the original colour stimuli but not necessarily the original colours.

Colour reproduction is thus an indirect process and can be accurate only if:

(a) The means (filters and/or film sensitivities) can separate and distinguish every possible colour signal;

(b) The dyes, pigments or other means of recreating colours during synthesis can between them produce every individual colour value; and

(c) The characteristics of (a) and (b) are so

matched that this individuality is not lost in transmission, i.e. between analysis and synthesis.

In other words, like colours in the original must not produce unlike colours in the reproduction, and unlike colours in the original must not produce like colours in the reproduction. In practice no filters, films or colouring agents can truly meet these requirements, so that photographic colour reproduction is rather a compromise. It is acceptable mainly because absolutely faithful colour reproduction is very rarely needed. Direct comparisons between original and reproduction are not often made and few people have a good memory for colour.

There are certain colour processes which rely on diffraction rather than on colouring agents, and these will be considered separately (§ 58). For the moment let us however see how the principles of colour analysis and synthesis outlined above work out in practice.

45. Additive Colour Systems. In 1860 Clark Maxwell gave the first practical demonstration of a process of colour photography. His method was to photograph a coloured object three times, once through each of three filters, red, green, and blue, passing bands of wavelengths approximating to the sensitivity bands of the receptors in the eye. From the three negatives (nowadays known as a "separation set") he made three lantern slides (positive transparencies) which were projected by three magic lanterns so that the three images on the screen fell in superimposition. Over the lenses of the lanterns, the three taking-filters were positioned, the red filter for the lantern projecting the slide from the red-filter negative, and so on.

Maxwell thus showed that the principle was correct but he was hampered by lack of colour-sensitive plates. Colour photography had to wait for the invention of panchromatic plates before the perfectly sound early theoretical work of Maxwell, Cros, du Hauron, and others could be put to proper practical test.

The theory of Maxwell's system is simple. The separation negatives are records of the amounts of red, green, and blue light being reflected from the original subject (or transmitted in the case of such a subject as a stained glass window). Thus in the negative exposed through the red filter all red image areas become dark; the more red light the corresponding objects reflect, the darker they become. For the red filter transmits preferentially red light; by the same token green and blue imgae components record little or not at all on the negative which in those

areas remains transparent (Fig. 6.1). Similarly the negative exposed through the green filter in front of the camera lens permits only green image portions to record on the negative, in proportion to the green reflectivity of the appropriate subject areas. The blue-separation negative finally records the blue components of the image. This is thus the basic process of colour analysis which leads, as already indicated, to three different black-and-white (and not colour) records.

For the synthesis the positive transparencies made from the negatives are in turn most transparent in the areas corresponding to the highest red, green and blue reflectivity respectively of the original. Thus the positive from the red-separation negative is clear in the areas corresponding to red in the original. The positives from the green- and blue-separation negatives are dense in these red areas since the negatives were there clear. So when the three images are projected in superimposition on the screen, light can pass through areas corresponding to red image portions only in the first transparency. As this is projected through a red filter, only red light reaches the screen in those areas: they therefore appear red on the screen. In the same way green elements of the picture are contributed by clear or thin areas in the second transparency projected through the green filter, and blue areas by the third transparency projected through the blue filter.

Whites in the original become high densities in all three negatives and are thus clear or nearly clear areas on all three positives. So a large amount of red, green and blue light reaches the screen in such areas; the addition of the three light colours produces white. Colours other than the primary red, green and blue are also formed by combinations; thus yellow areas are clear on the red-filter and the green-filter transparency, red and green light in combination giving yellow. Blue and red in equal parts gives a purplish colour (magenta), blue and green gives a blue-green also known as cyan. Unequal proportions of two colours give various intermediate shades; the addition of all three light colours in different proportions produces unsaturated or pastel hues.

Because the processes involve the addition of light colours (and hence stimuli) this system is known as additive colour synthesis. This term applies however only to the method of projecting these three images in register on a screen; the first step of producing the three separation negative images is common—in one form or another—to most other colour systems as well.

Of course, the accuracy of the reproduction

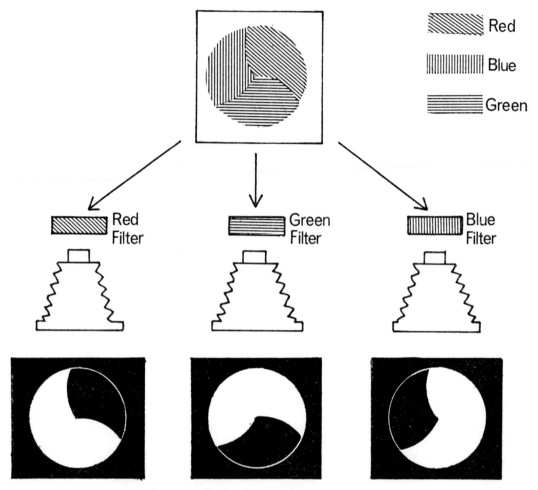

FIG. 6.1. COLOUR ANALYSIS BY SEPARATION

depends on the accuracy of the filters, accuracy of exposure and development of the negatives and positives, and proper balance of illumination in the lanterns. In order to get the correct spectral transmission in a blue filter, for example, it is necessary to make it rather dark so that not only would the exposure required for the blue-filter negative probably be long compared with the others but also more light would be required in the blue-filter lantern to bring the final reproduction into balance. There are, of course, limitations to the brightness range of the original subject which can be correctly recorded at the same contrast, just as there are in monochrome photography and for the same reasons. However, providing that these limitations are borne in mind when the photograph is taken, the accuracy attainable by this system is very high indeed.

The fact that Maxwell's demonstration worked at all is all the more surprising, since his plates were only blue-sensitive. What helped him was the—not fully appreciated—fact that the reds in his subject also reflected some blue violet and that his red filter was sufficiently transparent to this (Evans 1961).

46. Practical Additive Projection Systems. Obviously the three-lantern system is hopelessly clumsy for normal use and attention was turned to the possibility of achieving the same result in a neater way. F. E. Ives invented an instrument which he called a Kromoscope. In this instrument the three monochrome transparencies were illuminated by a single

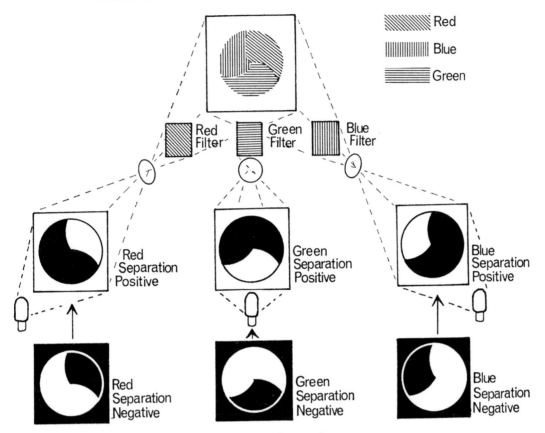

FIG. 6.2. ADDITIVE COLOUR SYNTHESIS

light source and were reflected by a system of semi-transparent mirrors so that the three images could be seen fused together on a ground glass screen. The colour filters were placed in suitable positions in the optical system. Again, good colour reproduction was attainable but the special piece of optical apparatus was required for viewing.

Derivations of the multi-lantern principle have however been used in a number of experimental systems of cinematography. Mostly these involved producing red, green and blue separation negatives in successive positions of the same film strip or even contained next to each other within one film frame. The taking camera uses an optical beam splitter or a similar system with three colour filters to create the three separation negatives; the positive film is projected again through a similar system—also with three filters —to superimpose red, green and blue images on the screen.

The advantage of such processes was that they used only black-and-white film materials; the problems of designing suitable equipment and of keeping the three images in register (accurately superimposed) on the screen were however considerable. Hence such additive methods of colour cinematography could not compete with the far simpler operation of current subtractive colour processes (see § 53).

47. Mosaic Processes. An alternative to combining three separately located images in an additive system—whether by projection or by viewing systems—is to interlace them in one image plane. This is the method of the first practical colour films and plates—which were marketed in various forms from the turn of the century until the early 1950s.

The basis of the mosaic process is a screen or mosaic of microscopic filter elements on a transparent support, arranged in a regular pattern. Any area of the screen carries an equal number

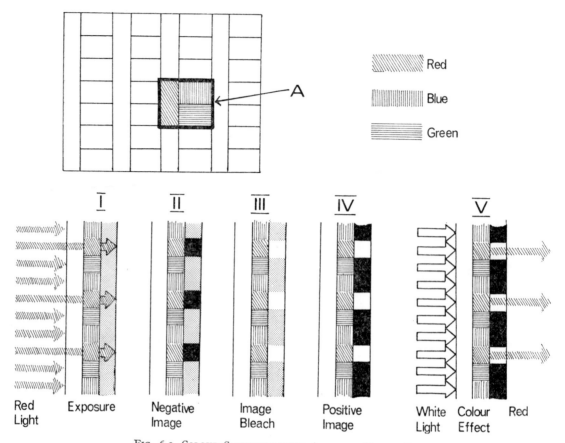

Red

Blue

Green

I   II   III   IV   V

Red   Exposure   Negative   Image   Positive   White   Colour   Red
Light   Image   Bleach   Image   Light   Effect

FIG. 6.3. COLOUR SYNTHESIS WITH ADDITIVE MOSAIC FILM

of red, green and blue filter elements, too small to be individually discernible by the eye. They were produced by various methods, for instance by printing interlaced lines of dye on the screen support. In contact with this screen is a panchromatic (i.e. fully colour sensitive) negative emulsion. This is then exposed in the camera through the filter screen, so that the light has to pass through the filters to reach the emulsion.

In red image portions light passes only through the red filter elements, producing a negative screen pattern corresponding to these elements—a little like the half-tone screen in a photomechanical reproduction. In green image areas light similarly forms a negative image behind the green elements and in blue areas behind the blue elements (Fig. 6.3). After reversal processing (bleaching the negative image and development of the remaining silver salts to a positive image—steps III and IV in Fig. 6.3) red image areas now let light through the red filter elements, while the portions behind the blue and the green filter elements are blocked by the positive image. On viewing the resulting positive transparency, the eye sees those areas as red, green or blue respectively, and—since the filter elements are too small to be visible by the naked eye—we see them as continuous areas. Colours like yellow are produced by areas where light passes through the red and the green filter elements and white where light passes through red, green and blue elements.

In effect the colour separations are thus interlaced within the area of image instead of being located on separate supports. Again, because the individual elements are small enough, the eye sees combinations of them additively. Similarly a combination of varying densities blocking off the three differently coloured elements reproduces all the various colours in the original subject.

The first mosaic colour plates (Lumiere Auto-chrome—1907) did not use a regular raster at all, but an irregular one made up of starch grains dyed red, green, and blue to make tiny colour filters. Equal quantities of the three colours of grain were thoroughly mixed and sifted on to a glass plate which had been prepared with an adhesive to retain them. This resulted in a glass plate covered all over with a random distribution of tiny three-colour filters, and the interstices between the grains were filled with an opaque medium. On top of the filter layer or "réseau" as it was called, was coated a panchromatic emulsion. The original Agfacolor process (1912) was similar but used dyed gum globules instead of starch.

The main drawback of the random grain mosaic however was that the laws of statistical distribution made it impossible to avoid clumps of grains of like colour. So although the individual grains were very small (of the order of 0·01 mm), the texture of the colour image appeared considerably coarser than that. A mechanically printed geometric raster screen is in fact the only way of obtaining a completely regular distribution of the red, green and blue filter elements. The limit of detail resolution is determined not by the size of individual elements but by the area of the smallest filter "unit" comprising an equal red, green and blue area (the area A in Fig. 6.3).

For reversal colour transparencies such screen plates and films with the emulsion coated on the same support as the filter raster were the most convenient method. Another variation of the system which enjoyed popularity for a long time made use of separate ruled screens for taking and viewing. The taking screens were used in contact with the emulsion of a standard panchromatic plate and could be used over and over again. The exposed plate was developed to a negative and a positive transparency was made from it by contact. The positive was bound in register with a screen, rather similar to the taking screen, to give the final colour transparency. This system had the advantages that only successful pictures had to be bound with a screen so that failures involved only the cost of a panchromatic plate, and that as many duplicate colour transparencies as required could be made from each negative without loss in quality.

48. Negative–Positive Mosaic Process. While additive screen processes were mostly associated with colour transparencies, they could in principle also be applied to negative–positive reproduction, and one process (Dufaycolor) was used in that way for colour cinematography. This means essentially that the stages of negative and positive image formation takes place in two separate films instead of in the same emulsion. This results as the first step in a colour negative in which not only the tones are reversed but also the colours. Let us briefly see what this implies.

The first stage of red light falling on an area of the screen film results in black silver being formed (after negative development) behind the red filter elements of the screen. The blue and green filter elements remain clear, so that by transmitted light the colour of the image of an originally red subject is made up of blue and green, giving by addition a bluish green. Similarly, originally green portions in the colour negative transmit red and blue and so appear magenta and originally blue subject details transmit, in the colour negative image, red and green light—thus producing the impression of yellow. The negative image is thus in complementary colours (§ 52).

In producing a positive from such a negative, the screen would not strictly speaking be necessary if the negative raster image can be superimposed precisely with the colour mosaic of the positive film—as is the case in the screen plate system (§ 47). This is however not practical for motion picture film printing, so the actual colour of the negative image has to influence the generation of positive colours. This involves projecting the colour negative on a positive screen film in such a way that the light from every individual negative filter element (red, green and blue) reaches a complete unit (like the unit A in Fig. 6.3) of the positive screen. It calls for a somewhat special lighting set-up and leads to a slight loss of definition in the positive, but it can be done.

The positive colour image formation is now a reversal of the way in which the negative colours were produced. Thus the blue-green light from blue and green elements in the negative produces a black silver deposit behind the blue and green elements of the positive, leaving only the red filter elements clear. So the positive image there appears red; as the blue-green areas in a negative corresponded to red in the original, we have regained the colour we had in the first place. The blue and red (magenta) negative areas in the same way recreate the original green in the positive, and the yellow negative areas (red plus green) again yield blue in the positive. The process works equally with complex colours; yellow in the original affected the emulsion behind both the green and the red filters elements in a negative, leaving only blue clear. This blue image in the negative affects the emulsion behind the blue filter elements in the positive, which then transmits red and green light to reconstitute the original yellow.

Although the use of negative-positive colour reproduction was employed for only a very short time with mosaic type additive films, very similar considerations apply in negative-positive colour reproduction with present day subtractive colour materials (§ 56).

49. Drawbacks of Additive Colour Synthesis. The mosaic type additive colour transparency has two serious shortcomings.

The first is the limited light transmission of the transparency. A mosaic material reproduces red by blocking out the green and blue elements entirely and similarly for other colours. Thus, only one-third of any given area of an additive transparency is transmitting light and additive transparencies are always rather dense.

A second obvious limitation is the restricted image resolution imposed by the finite size of the filter elements. These must be appreciably greater than the grain size of the film or plate emulsion to give silver deposits behind each filter element, which are a reasonably faithful measure of the light intensity transmitted by that filter element. The best mosaic type colour films still had filter elements about 0·02 mm in diameter and the raster pattern does become very noticeable on projection. Further drawbacks arise from these two limitations. The red, green, and blue filter elements must appear equally bright in order to give the correct colour balance. This involves some sacrifice of ideal taking-filter characteristics and the accuracy of colour reproduction is reduced. Since the individual réseau elements are very small, irradiation in the emulsion causes the image behind one element to spread slightly behind adjoining elements. This reduces the colour saturation

of the final transparency. Edge effects in development also cause de-saturation.

The problem of the light transmission in practice also restricts the additive process to transparencies which can be viewed or projected by transmitted light. An additive print, with a similar réseau on a white opaque support, would (unless very desaturated primary colours were used) be impossibly dark because its brightness depends on the light reflected from the support. Also, a colour positive on an opaque support would need to have the emulsion layer between the support and the mosaic screen to permit exposure through the latter. That in turn would raise serious difficulties for processing.

For all these reasons additive colour systems have been completely displaced by subtractive methods for general photography.

50. Additive Colour Television. The one field where additive colour synthesis has successfully survived is in television. This is mainly because here additive signals are easier to handle in encoding and transmission and because two major drawbacks of mosaic screen photographic processes disappear. The television image is viewed in natural size on the screen, so there is no question of loss of resolution in enlarging. Also the colour elements are self-luminous and thus do not depend on the absorption of at least two thirds of an incident beam of white light.

The colour analysis takes place in the television camera where beam splitters A and C (Fig. 6.4) divert part of the image forming light via mirrors D and E into three television camera tubes R_1, G_1 and B_1. By using appropriate filters or colour discriminating beam splitters, each tube thus registers the signal corresponding to one colour. The three signals are suitably encoded and combined for transmission via F; on reception at H they are decoded and fed to three electron guns R_2, G_2 and B_2 in the television

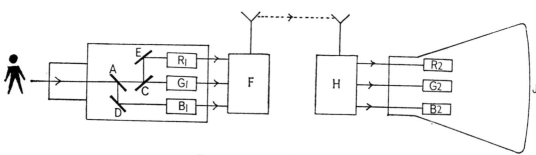

Fig. 6.4. Colour TV System

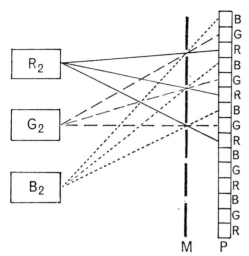

FIG. 6.5. COLOUR TV TUBE

receiver tube. The three beams produce a colour image on a special screen.

The colour synthesis depends on the structure of the receiver tube itself. The essential elements are shown in section in Fig. 6.5. The phosphor screen surface P of the tube is made up of innumerable regularly arranged elements of blue, green and red phosphorescence. Each type of spot thus emits only light of one colour when struck by an electron beam from the electron guns. Between the electron source and the screen is arranged a so-called shadow mask M, in effect an opaque screen with a large number of regularly spaced holes. These are so arranged that for instance the electron gun R_2 which receives the red signal can reach only the red phosphorescent spots of the tube screen. Every time this electron beam reaches a hole in the shadow mask, a red phosphorescent spot in front of this mask (as seen from outside the receiver tube) lights up; the spaces between the holes prevent the electron beam from activating green and blue fluorescent elements. Similarly the green signal electron gun G_2 is so positioned that it can only reach green phosphorescent screen elements through the shadow mask while the blue signal gun similarly reaches only blue fluorescent spots.

The three electron beams scanning the screen thus act similarly to the three lanterns described in § 45 projecting on one screen—while the colour impression is produced in the same way as with a mosaic type transparency (§ 47), namely by the close neighbourhood of separate minute colour elements. The intensity of the electron beams during scanning determines the relative intensity of each colour element and hence the actual colour hue produced.

51. Lenticular Processes. The shadow mask system in colour television is distantly related to one other process of additive colour photography: the lenticular process typified by the Keller-Dorian system marketed as Kodacolor 16 mm colour cine film in 1928 (not to be confused with the present-day Kodacolor process which will be dealt with later). This also uses an optical aid to locate the colour elements correctly in the image.

The lenticular process involves the use of a film coated with a normal panchromatic emulsion on one side and embossed with a pattern of cylindrical lenticules or minute lenses on the other side. A filter consisting of bands of red, green, and blue is placed over the taking lens. The film is exposed through the base side and each of the tiny lenses on the base images the banded filter onto the emulsion. In an area corresponding to a red in the original subject a minute image of the red band of the filter will be formed but no light will reach the emulsion from the blue and green bands. The film is processed by the reversal method to give a direct positive so that there will be minute clear areas corresponding to the tiny red images of the filter band and there will be opaque areas corresponding to the images of the blue and green bands.

The positive is projected on to a screen while the taking-filter is placed over the projector lens with the coloured bands orientated in the same way as they were on the camera lens. White light passes through the tiny clear spaces in the positive and is directed by the little embossed lenses so that it passes through the red band of the filter over the lens and gives rise to a red area on the screen. Similarly, in an area corresponding to a yellow area in the original subject, tiny images of the red and green bands are focused on the emulsion so that when the film is reversal-processed, there will be clear areas corresponding to the images of the red and green bands and an opaque area corresponding to the image of the blue band. Then, when the film is projected, white light passes through the clear areas and is directed through the red and green bands to be thrown on the screen as a yellow area. This process was capable of giving good results but one outstanding difficulty was distortion of the film base during processing and drying. Obviously if the spacing or curvature of the embossed lenses

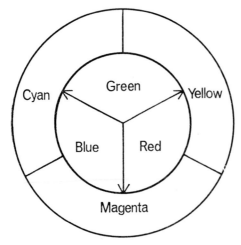

FIG. 6.6. PRIMARY (INNER CIRCLE) AND COMPLE-
MENTARY (OUTER CIRCLE) COLOURS

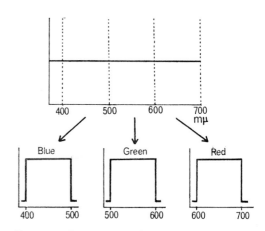

FIG. 6.7. DIVISION OF SPECTRUM INTO THREE
(THEORETICAL) PRIMARY COLOURS

changes between exposing and projecting, the light will no longer pass exactly through the correct filter bands when the film is projected and the colour accuracy will suffer.

52. Primary and Complementary Colours. In discussing the way the spectrum is split up into three fairly equal colour bands, we have encountered two types of three-colour group. The main one is the triad of red, green and blue, each corresponding to approximately one-third of the spectral range. These are known as the additive primaries, or just the primary colours (Fig. 6.6).

Ideally these primary colours should be the three equal parts into which an equal energy spectrum can be divided (Fig. 6.7). In fact there are no light sources with emissions corresponding to the three curves of Fig. 6.7—

nor filters with such transmission curves or photographic emulsions (or other light receptors) whose sensitivity curves correspond to this ideal. The practical sensitivity curves of the three receptors in the eye have the approximate shape shown in Fig. 6.8 (which is similar to Fig. 1.5)—vastly different from the three spectral "chunks" of Fig. 6.7. The transmission curves of red, green and blue filters on the other hand are appreciably different again; Fig. 6.9 indicates typical filter curves that may be used for colour analysis.

Where coloured lights are concerned, one criterion of the division of the spectrum into three equal bands is that the blue, green and red lights (more precisely the stimuli to the eye) should together produce white. This can be satisfied in various ways, ranging from three

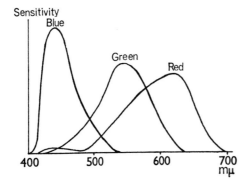

FIG. 6.8. APPROXIMATE SENSITIVITY CURVES OF
THE COLOUR RECEPTORS IN THE HUMAN EYE

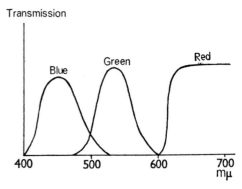

FIG. 6.9. APPROXIMATE TRANSMISSION CURVES OF
FILTERS FOR ADDITIVE COLOUR ANALYSIS

broad spectral sections down to separate mono-chromatic stimuli of almost single wavelengths (Fig. 6.10). The narrow bands in Fig. 6.10 are also red, green and blue respectively; because they are so narrow their stimulations must be correspondingly more intense than the light of the continuous spectrum—here approximately daylight (after R. W. G. Hunt, 1957). Such a set of stimuli as in the lower part of Fig. 6.10 is called metameric with respect to the continuous spectrum of the upper part of the diagram.

We have briefly encountered another trio of colours in connection with colour negatives: cyan, magenta and yellow. As defined, their characteristic is that they cover additively two thirds instead of one third of the full spectrum: cyan covers blue plus green, magenta covers blue plus red and yellow covers red plus green. These are the complementary colours, also known as subtractive primaries—because they consist of the total spectrum, in each case with one primary third missing (Fig. 6.11). Each of these is complementary to one of the primaries in the sense that the combination produces (ideally) white: cyan is complementary to red, magenta complementary to green and yellow complementary to blue. (The arrows in Fig. 6.6 point in each case to the colour complementary to the one at the tail of the arrow.) Two of the colours—cyan and yellow—also have a spectral equivalent; the stimulus of blue-green light of around 520 mμ is similar to that of cyan, and spectral yellow at around 580 mμ looks similar

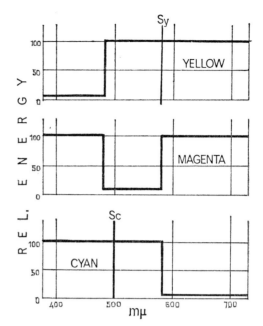

FIG. 6.11. COMPLEMENTARY COLOURS (SUBTRACTIVE PRIMARIES)

to complementary yellow. Magenta however is a mixture of bands from opposite ends of the spectrum and has no metameric spectral equivalent. Like the spectral equivalent S_y and S_c (Fig. 6.11) the broad-band cyan and yellow stimulate two of the eyes receptors each (green and red, and blue and green respectively); magenta stimulates both red and blue receptor cells.

Again the idealized spectral characteristics corresponding to the curves in Fig. 6.11 do not exist in practice. The cyans, magentas and yellows used in colour photography are derived from dyes whose transmission curves (solid in Fig. 6.12) depart appreciably from their ideal shape (dotted in Fig. 6.12). Thus cyan dyes which should fully transmit in the blue and green bands in fact absorb some green and blue light as well as the red which they should absorb. Magenta absorbs well in the green band, but also too much in both the blue and the red. Yellow dyes absorb a little in the green band (which they shouldn't) and usually transmit a little blue—which they should absorb. These deficiencies of dyes are responsible for some of the shortcomings in faithful colour reproduction in processes using such dyes.

Two other terminologies for complementary

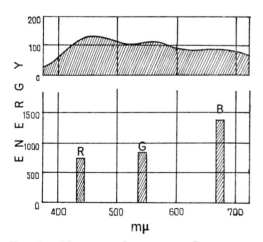

FIG. 6.10. METAMERIC STIMULI OF A CONTINUOUS SPECTRUM WHITE (TOP) AND NARROW WAVE-LENGTH BANDS

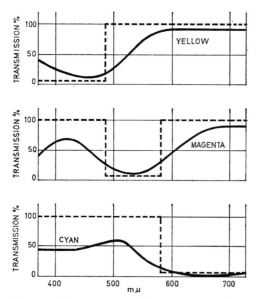

FIG. 6.12. TRANSMISSION OF COMPLEMENTARY DYES

colours should be mentioned. They are sometimes described as "minus colours" by the band they absorb: cyan is also known as minus red, magenta as minus green and yellow as minus blue. The second convention relates mainly to graphic arts use: photo-engravers and printers frequently refer to the set of subtractive primaries as blue, red and yellow. To avoid confusion with primary blue and red, it is preferable to call these complementaries cyan and magenta.

53. Subtractive Colour Synthesis. Most present-day systems of colour photography use dyes to control the amounts of red, green and blue light reaching the eye. These dyes are the complementary colours cyan, magenta and yellow (§ 52) and they act by holding back or subtracting the corresponding primary colours red, green and blue from white light—hence the designation *subtractive*.

The first step in subtractive colour reproduction is the same as in additive reproduction, namely colour analysis to produce three negative images which by their densities record the red, green and blue components of every part of the original (R_n, G_n and B_n in Fig. 6.13). Positive images R_p, G_p and B_p are obtained from these negatives and converted into complementary coloured dye or pigment images. Thus the red filter positive becomes a cyan image, the green filter positive a magenta

image and the blue filter positive a yellow image.

The three dye images have the same function of controlling the light passing through the individual positives as the silver images had in the three lanterns (projectors) of Maxwell's set-up (§ 45). There are however two important differences: (1) because they are transparent dyes, the images can be superimposed and (2) at the same time any two images provide what in effect is equivalent to the colour filter of the lantern of the third image. The reconstruction of the full colour picture therefore needs only one light source to illuminate it, namely white light. In addition the white light need not be projected through the colour images on to a screen, but can equally be reflected directly from a white support onto which the images are placed. We then have a colour print on paper instead of a colour transparency. This is how it works in practice.

A red image area which recorded as a silver deposit in the red separation negative R_n (Fig. 6.14) therefore appears clear in the corresponding positive R_p and also in the cyan dye positive derived from it. The same area, which was clear in the green and blue separation negatives G_n and B_n has a silver deposit in the corresponding green and blue separation positives G_p and B_p—and hence in the corresponding magenta positive M_p and yellow positive Y_p. The clear area of the cyan positive corresponds to the transparent area in the black silver image of the red filter positive which allowed red light to reach the screen in the red projection lantern of the additive synthesis set-up (Fig. 6.2). This red light is however now provided by white light shining through the magenta and the yellow dye images *superimposed on the cyan image*. For the magenta dye transmits red and blue while the yellow dye transmits red and green. On superimposition the magenta dye holds back green and the yellow dye holds back blue, so that only red is transmitted.

It is this mutual subtractive action of the other two dyes—i.e. from the images which do not record the red component of the original, which is significant. The amount of redness depends on the cyan image; a weaker or darker red would record as a less dense silver deposit in the red separation negative R_n and hence produce some density in the red separation positive R_p, and some cyan in the cyan positive C_p. This would then hold back some red as well —like a medium density in the red filter

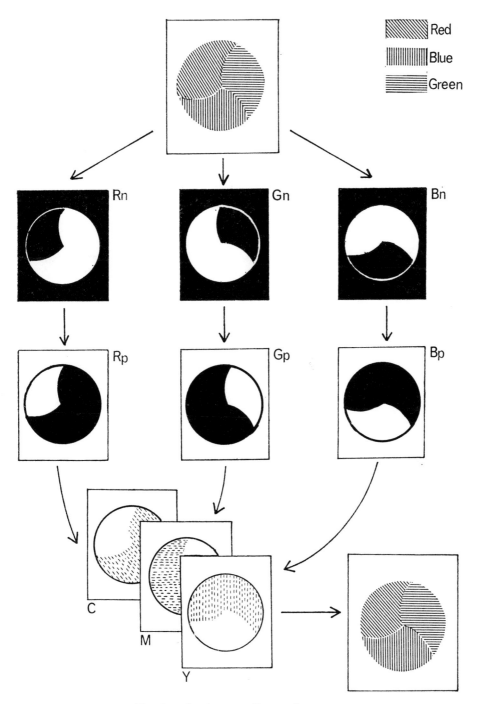

FIG. 6.13. SUBTRACTIVE COLOUR SYNTHESIS

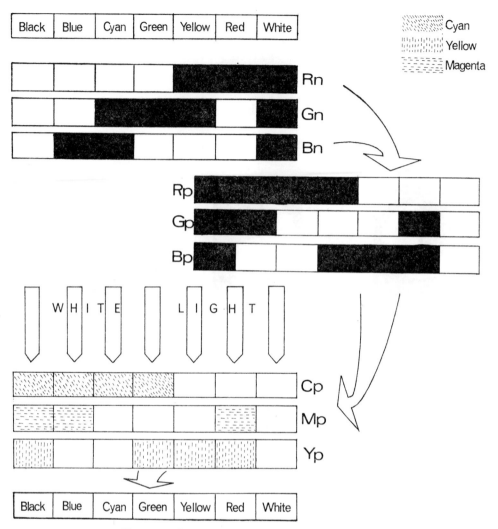

FIG. 6.14. SUBTRACTIVE COLOUR REPRODUCTION

positive of the red lantern, leading to a reduced brightness of red in the combined image. So the cyan positive controls the amount of red in the picture. At the same time the other two superimposed dye images do not interfere with this function of the cyan image because ideally both the magenta and the yellow images fully transmit red light.

By a similar step-by-step deduction we can show that a green object area records a density in the green separation negative G_n in Fig. 6.14 but no density in the red separation and blue separation negatives. So this leads eventually to a clear area in the magenta positive and cyan

and yellow deposits in the cyan and yellow separation positives respectively. As these are again superimposed, they absorb both the red and the blue component of white light passing through, leaving only green. Again the cyan and the yellow images do not interfere with the green-controlling function of magenta since (ideally) they both transmit green. In the same way the yellow image controls the amount of blueness in the final picture, the actual blue light passing through the clear areas of the yellow separation positive being provided by the red-absorbing cyan and the green-absorbing magenta dye images in superimposition.

An area which records in both the red and the green separation negatives—i.e. yellow—yields a clear image portion in both the cyan and the magenta separation positives C_p and M_p respectively. So only the blue component of white light is held back by the yellow dye image, producing yellow in the picture. A more orange hue would record more strongly in the red-separation negative image and less so in the green-separation negative. Hence the magenta positive would also have some density so subduing the green component of yellow to some extent—i.e. the hue shifts towards reddish (i.e. orange). Cyan, magenta and indeed all other colour mixtures are produced in an analogous way; the effect in every case depends on the relative subtractive action of the three superimposed dyes.

It is perhaps unfortunate that the sharp distinction made in the past between additive and subtractive synthesis has tended to obscure the fact that both systems have the same aim of controlling the amounts of red, green and blue light through the three separation positives. This relationship between the additive and subtractive systems may become clearer with an ingenious illustration first given by E. R. Davies. Imagine three lanterns set up to project in register monochrome positive transparencies made from a set of separation negatives and with the appropriate red, green, and blue filters over the lenses (i.e. the classical Maxwell additive set-up). The picture on the screen should be a good colour-reproduction of the scene originally photographed. Now imagine it were possible to take the transparency from the "red" lantern and slide it down the beam until it laid in the plane of the screen. Clearly, the monochrome transparency would spoil the image on the screen but it would still be possible for it to fulfil its function of modulating the red light from the red lantern without interfering with the picture if its image were altered from black to cyan. The picture on the screen would now be as it was when the transparency was in the lantern. Similarly, the transparency from the "green" lantern could be placed on the screen if it were changed to magenta colour and lastly, the transparency from the "blue" lantern could be placed on the screen if its colour were changed to yellow. All three positives would now be on the screen and illuminated by unmodulated red, green, and blue light from the three lanterns. However, the three lanterns could now be switched off

and a white light switched on, still without changing the picture. This shows clearly that the fundamentals of the additive and subtractive systems are the same.

54. Colour Analysis Methods. From what has been said, it follows that subtractive processes depend on making photographic images cyan, magenta and yellow in colour. There are many ways of doing this, but all depend on making colour separation negatives in one form or another. These may be literally separate negatives (§ 55) or they may be produced in individual layers of a film coated on the same support. The positives can similarly be separate dye images made individually from the separation negatives and then superimposed; or they may be formed in the same layers as the already superimposed negative images and the latter then removed. Alternatively, the positive dye images may be formed by a further stage of colour analysis from a set of superimposed negative dye images (§ 56).

55. Separation Negatives. The most straightforward—and earliest—way of producing separate separation negatives is to make three exposures, one after the other, in an ordinary camera using a red, a green and a blue filter in turn in front of the lens. As the three images must differ in nothing but the tone rendering of the colours, this method is suitable only for inanimate objects and for set-ups where the camera remains absolutely immovable between the exposures. This is obviously a highly cumbersome procedure which began to be superseded over half a century ago by more flexible methods to speed up the operating sequence. Thus repeating backs were made for some time which carried three plates and three filters, moving them mechanically or even automatically into position one after the other in the image plane of the camera.

For moving and action subjects simultaneous exposure of all three separation images was essential. Various methods to achieve this evolved, of which the one-shot colour cameras were the most sophisticated. Made mainly in the 1920s and 1930s, they consisted of a beam splitter arrangement of one or more semi-reflecting mirrors or pellicules to divert part of the image-forming rays from the lens to two additional image planes. Hence geometrically similar images were formed on three separate plates behind a red, green and blue filter (Fig. 6.15). The plates A, B and C then formed the colour separation set. A multitude of designs

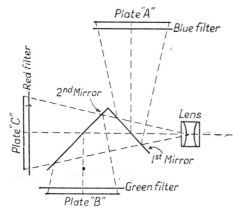

FIG. 6.15 SCHEMATIC LAYOUT OF A TYPICAL
ONE-SHOT CAMERA

and beam splitting arrangements existed, but all became obsolete with the appearance and growing popularity of reversal and negative colour films which could be handled in ordinary cameras in the same way as black-and-white materials.

The preparation of colour separation negatives remains the essential for all colour printing processes where pigment or dye images are assembled mechanically. This includes certain commercial colour print processes and above all it includes all the methods of photomechanical colour printing for which colour plates are prepared from separation negatives. In practically all these cases the original for colour separation is however nowadays a normally photographed colour transparency of the subject and not the subject itself.

Colour separation positives may also be prepared directly from colour negatives (§ 56), using the same principle of colour separation. The fact that the colours in a negative are reversed (§ 48 and 56) does not affect the validity of the procedure. Such separation positives can be superimposed directly or used as matrices for producing assembly colour print images.

56. Integral Tripacks. The most elegant way of producing the three colour separation records simultaneously is to have the three negative emulsions superimposed in the camera at the time of the exposure and keep them together during the subsequent stages of the colour process. Proposed in principle by Du Hauron over a century ago, this became practical only when ways were perfected of coating three individual emulsion layers on a single film support. Apart from coating technique,

the main problems which had to be solved were adjusting the response of the emulsions (by means of their colour sensitivity and the use of filter layers) so that each recorded only light of one primary band of the spectrum. Further, a process was needed for converting the silver image in each layer to an appropriate dye image complementary to the response of the layer, without interfering with the images in the other layers.

The first colour materials to satisfy these requirements were 16 mm. Kodachrome cine film (1935) and New Agfacolor (1936). The two differed somewhat in their chemical basis but not in their principle on which practically all modern colour films are based. Both were reversal colour films in which the process of image formation went through the same stages as the scheme of Fig. 6.14. The three separation images remain however permanently superimposed and the silver negatives, silver positives and dye positives are formed by successive stages of chemical treatment. The practical aspects of this are discussed later on when we come to deal with colour film processing. Having the emulsion layers coated on the same support incidentally also solves all problems of registration in assembling and superimposing separate colour images.

The result of such a reversal colour film is usually colour transparency for viewing by transmitted light or by projection. Colour prints can also be made from transparencies by what amounts essentially to rephotographing the colour transparency on another colour reversal material. Such duplication however tends to enhance the imperfections in the colour reproduction which are unavoidable with practically every process of colour photography.

An integral tripack material can also yield colour negatives by simply converting the negative images directly into dye images. Such a colour negative again shows reversed colours as well as reversed tones (§ 48), the colour hues being complementary to those of the original subject. This negative is then printed on another tripack colour material to yield a positive which re-reverses the negative colours to their original values (Fig. 6.16).

Thus a blue subject detail produces an image in the blue recording layer of the negative material; this image is yellow. The yellow negative image in turn produces its images in the green-recording and the red-recording layers of the positive material; these images are magenta

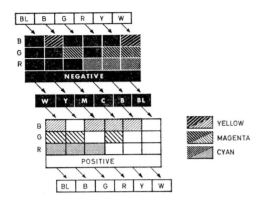

FIG. 6.16. NEGATIVE-POSITIVE COLOUR REPRODUCTION

YELLOW

MAGENTA

CYAN

and cyan respectively which in superimposition yields blue again. Analogous transformations take place with all other subject colours.

The positive image can be either on a film or a paper base to yield transparencies or prints respectively. As with black-and-white negative-positive systems, the colour negative is an intermediate for producing any number of positives —whereas the reversal colour transparency is a final product and unique.

The fact that the negative and positive stages are separate in the reproduction chain also permits the introduction of various colour correcting systems at the printing stage. Nor need the negative be a faithful complementary record of the subject colours; deliberate departures from true complementary correspondence can often improve the final quality of reproduction. Even the matching of emulsion responses and complementary image colours does not have to be rigid—many other combinations are possible. (For example the blue-recording layer can yield a magenta image, the green-recording layer a cyan image and the red recording layer a yellow image, provided that sensitivities and colour images produced are adjusted accordingly in the positive material.)

57. Luminance Range and Colour Range. In viewing a coloured scene, the vividness of a colour depends on the relative intensity of stimulation of the eye's three colour receptors. We can regard this as the ratio of luminances of the broad-band primary components of that colour. In scenes where the luminance range is restricted, the ratio of luminance values of the primary colour components is similarly limited. At reasonably high lighting levels—i.e. sufficiently high to stimulate all three colour receptors of the eye for photopic vision—a limited luminance range means that colours as seen contain not only the dominant primary stimulation but a proportion also of the other two—in effect an admixture of white light. So the colours appear desaturated. This is a simple (though somewhat approximate) explanation why the colours in a scene look more vivid in direct sunlight than in more diffused light conditions.

At low lighting levels the luminances of one or two of the primary components of a colour may fall below the full photopic vision level of the eye. Scotopic vision can here be regarded as contributing an element of black to the colour as seen, which thus becomes degraded. Hence we may see colours different in hue in poor light even before we have ceased to be aware of the colour impression as such. As one (or possibly even two) of the primary colour stimuli drop out due to too low intensity, a shift of the hue perceived may also occur. The emulsions used for colour analysis in colour photography will, with appropriate exposure conditions, not react in this same way. This is one reason why dark shadow areas in a colour photograph often record in appreciably different colour values from those of the original.

The luminance range of a colour subject is relevant also to the faithfulness with which it can be reproduced in a colour photograph. This becomes especially important when we consider both colour transparencies (a form of presentation much more common in colour than in black-and-white photography) and colour prints. When a colour transparency is viewed by transmitted light, the luminance range it can present is limited only by the reproduction characteristics of the film and in practice covers the ratios of luminance values of the vast majority of subjects likely to be photographed. A colour transparency projected on a screen presents a luminance ratio almost as great. Any loss of contrast is negligible under favourable projection conditions (for instance with a highly reflective and directional screen viewed from near the projection axis). Indeed it is possible to raise the luminance level of a transparency in projection so that the shadow luminosity is greater than the luminosity of the original scene as observed. Under these conditions the colours in the shadows can become more saturated— simply because we can see them better.

The situation is greatly different with colour prints on paper. Owing to the reflectance limit of a paper surface—which is appreciably reduced in a colour print compared with a black-and-white print (see § 25)—the range of subject luminances which can be satisfactorily reproduced by the luminosities in a colour print is very much more restricted. For acceptable colour reproduction it is thus important to control the ratio of luminance values in the subject by ensuring that the shadows are not too dark and the highlights not too light.

58. Diffraction Colour Systems. A prism is the usual way of splitting white light into its spectral components. An alternative method is to employ a diffraction grating, i.e. a grid of regularly spaced lines ruled into for instance the surface of a glass plate, or a series of regularly spaced layers within the depth of a film emulsion. If the spacing is of the order of the wavelength of light, interference effects result in the reflection of light of specific wavelengths when white light is directed at this diffracting arrangement. This action is analogous to the selective colour transmission of interference filters (§ 8). The colour seen depends on the exact spacing of the grating lines or planes. If such planes can be formed of silver deposits in an emulsion, we could have a system of colour reproduction involving only diffracted light and no dyes.

The earliest colour photographic process to use this idea was the Lippmann process. It was carried out by exposing a panchromatic plate, the emulsion of which was almost transparent, with its emulsion surface in contact with a metallic mirror. This was achieved by building special dark slides which allowed mercury to be run in behind the plates in order to ensure optical contact between the emulsion and metallic reflecting surface. Light passed through the emulsion and was reflected back by the mercury surface, but the light on the return passage through the emulsion layer was out of phase with that on the first passage. Thus an interference was set up and this resulted in the emulsion layer being rendered developable where the peaks of the waves coincided. The distribution of the image through the thickness of the emulsion layer when the plate was developed, was therefore dependent on the wavelength of the exposing light at every point on the picture. The developed negative was backed up with a mirror and viewed by reflected light. When the plate was illuminated and viewed at the correct angle the picture was seen in full colour. At every point in the picture light of all wavelengths, other than those

which gave rise to the image, was absorbed. Those wavelengths which could go through the image and, after reflection, come back through the image, gave the correct colour sensation. From a scientific point of view this is an extremely elegant process but in practice it is not very useful. Not only are the taking and viewing conditions critical but emulsions of sufficient transparency are very slow.

A more modern (though still experimental) application of a similar principle is used in thermoplastic recording (W. E. Glenn, 1959). Here an electrostatic latent image is produced in a thermoplastic layer on a suitable film support. When the thermoplastic layer is briefly heated to its softening point, the electric charge image forms microscopic surface reticulations in the softened layer, which freeze again on cooling. As such an image is all transparent, it has to be viewed under conditions where the light scatter produced by this pattern becomes noticeable.

The significant aspect from the point of view of colour reproduction is that colour information can be fed into the electron signal producing the electrostatic image in such a way, that a diffraction grating is in effect superimposed on the image. The spacing of this grating depends on the colour involved. Original colours can become visible again if the thermoplastic film is projected under suitable conditions.

59. Colour Holography. The holographic process (§ 41) is also capable of recording and reproducing images in colour. The system is again additive in the sense already discussed (§ 45): it relies on the combination of simultaneous colour stimuli in the three primary colours. For this purpose a normal holographic set-up is used, but with three laser sources of different colours, with wavelengths in each of the three main spectral bands. The laser beams are combined to form a single beam. This is in turn split into an object beam shining on the object and a reference beam shining on the photographic plate. The hologram pattern formed by the object beam interfering with the reference beam then contains not only dimensional but also colour information of the object.

Under suitable experimental conditions this information can reconstitute the original colours when ordinary white light shines on the hologram. In effect three individual hologram reconstructions take place, in the colours of the original laser beams. As these reconstructions are superimposed optically, the original colours result by additive combination.

SECTION II
THE OPTICAL IMAGE
BEFORE PHOTOGRAPHIC RECORDING

CHAPTER VII

THE CAMERA OBSCURA AND PINHOLE PHOTOGRAPHY

60. The camera obscura. 61. Identity of the camera obscura image with an exact perspective.
62. Pinhole photography—optimum pinhole sizes and distances—sharpness—effective speed.
63. Making a pinhole—fitting on a camera. 64. Pinhole camera applications.

60. The Camera Obscura. The camera obscura (Fig. 7.1) appears to have been known at a very early date. According to Eder's *Jahrbuch für Photographie*, it was mentioned by Ibn al Haitam in 1038. In one of his undated manuscripts, the celebrated painter, engineer, and philosopher, Leonardo da Vinci, who died in 1519, describes this phenomenon in the following way: "When the images of illuminated objects enter a very dark room through a very small hole and fall on a piece of white paper at some distance from the hole, one sees on the paper all the objects in their own forms and colours. They will be smaller in size and . . . upside down because of the intersection of the rays . . ".

Outside the room each illuminated point, sends through the aperture a beam of light in the form of a narrow cone. This cone has its apex at the object point in question, and its base is that of the aperture. Thus it illuminates the scattering or translucent screen on which it is received by a small spot, which is thus the image of the point object.

Within certain limits, the spot formed by the projection of the aperture on the screen will become smaller, and consequently the whole image sharper, as the aperture itself becomes smaller and as the material in which the aperture is made is thinner. The image will also become sharper as the aperture is moved farther away from the screen. In fact, under these conditions, the sizes of the individual spots increase much less quickly than the dimensions of the image.

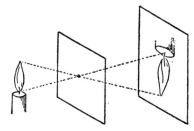

FIG. 7.1. FORMATION OF THE IMAGE IN A PINHOLE CAMERA

Such images sometimes occur unintentionally on photographic plates as parasite images or "doubles," when there happens to be a small hole in the outside wall of the camera.

The camera obscura was much improved in the second part of the sixteenth century by fitting a biconvex lens at the aperture. In the early part of the eighteenth century it was developed into a portable instrument similar to our present-day cameras, and used by artists as a means of making sketches from Nature.

61. Identity of the Camera Obscura Image with an Exact Perspective. In 1568 D. Barbaro recommended the use of the camera obscura for automatically making perspective drawings.

Suppose that a sheet of glass is placed in front of the camera, parallel to the screen, so that the glass plate and screen are equidistant from the aperture. The perspective on the glass plate, with the aperture as viewpoint, will be identical with that on the screen from the same viewpoint (Fig. 7.2).

62. Pinhole Photography. Although nowadays employed only for very specialized applications, pinhole photography can give very useful results in the case of inanimate objects.

In order to obtain an image of sufficient sharpness it is an advantage to use an aperture of the smallest possible diameter in a very thin plate, since a thick plate would restrict the field due to vignetting (cf. § 86) and would decrease the contrast due to reflections from the cylindrical surface of the aperture. A simple experiment, such as forming the image of a luminous filament of an electric lamp, shows that with each distance of the object from the camera there corresponds, for a given diameter of the aperture, a distance from the aperture to the receiving screen (e.g. a matt glass) at which the greatest possible sharpness of the image is obtained. When the distance of the object is large compared with the distance from the aperture to the screen, the diameter of the "disc of confusion" which is formed as an image of each point in the object, is at least equal to the diameter of the pinhole. Because of diffraction by

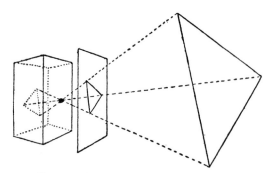

FIG. 7.2. PERSPECTIVE RENDERING BY A
PINHOLE CAMERA

the edges of the aperture, each point in the object is imaged as a diffraction pattern, the size of which decreases as the aperture increases. The first phenomenon is more important when the aperture is large, and the second when the aperture is small. Thus according to the laws of geometrical optics, the diameter D of the image of a point is given by $D = d$ where d is the diameter of the pinhole.

According to physical optics, however, the effective diameter of the image of a point source is given, approximately, by $D = 2f\lambda/d$, where f is the distance from the aperture to the screen, and λ is the wavelength of light. The optimum conditions are found when the diameter as given by geometrical considerations is equal to that given by considerations of physical optics. Thus $d \approx 2f\lambda/d$, whence the optimum distance f is given by $f \approx d^2/2\lambda$.

Taking $\lambda = 0.0005$ mm, $f \approx 1{,}000d^2$; Abney and Dallmeyer both found $f = 625d^2$, and Colston and Coombes both found $f = 1{,}250d^2$.

To photograph very near objects the optimum extension is calculated in just the same way as when using an objective of focal length f under the same conditions (§ 128).

The sharpness of images photographed in this way, when the conditions are properly adjusted, is quite comparable to that of images given by soft-focus lenses. A considerable angle of field can be covered by a pinhole.

The one disadvantage of this process is the relatively long exposure required. The effective relative aperture (§ 102) would on the average be of the order of $f300$. Although this corresponds to a light transmission around 0·01 per cent of a modern lens at a medium large aperture, present-day sensitized materials are fast enough to permit practical exposures.

63. Making a Pinhole. It is not very easy to obtain commercially metal plates having calibrated holes with clean edges suitable for pinhole photography.

In order to make such a circular aperture in a piece of metal foil it is best placed on a strip of soft wood or on a piece of lead, and a needle used as a punch. The needle should be stuck through the centre of a cork along the axis of the latter, cut off flush with one end, and the other end of the needle then cut about 1/25 in. from the other surface of the cork. This projecting end must be in the parallel cylindrical part of the cork. Now rub the protruding end on an oilstone until a plane and polished end with sharp edges is obtained. The hole is then made in the metal foil by giving the top of the cork a sharp blow. The edges of the hole thus made should be examined with a strong magnifying glass, and, if necessary, made perfectly smooth by means of the finest emery paper. The metal foil may now be mounted between two cards.

The aperture made in this way may be fixed to the front of a camera or any light-tight box which can be loaded with a plate or film. The image given by a pinhole is generally so faint that it cannot be easily examined on a ground glass screen. In order to find out the width of field which the pinhole gives, an aperture of about ⅛ in. diameter may be temporarily substituted for it, or, failing this, a spectacle lens of focal length equal to the distance previously ascertained as optimum distance between aperture and screen for photographing distant objects. The principles of the pinhole camera have been discussed by E. W. H. Selwyn.

64. Pinhole Camera Applications. A number of applications of the principles of pinhole photography have been made in different fields.

A small camera with four pairs of pinhole apertures has been used for photographing the internal walls of the stomach (J. Heilpern and F. G. Back, 1928), and a high-speed cine camera (120,000 frames per second), utilizing pinhole apertures has been applied to the study of arcing in industrial circuit-breakers (D. C. Prince and W. R. Rankine, 1939).

A pinhole camera with a 0·3 mm diameter pinhole has also been used for taking pictures inside engine cylinders. With the arrangement employed, the camera covers over 190° of the cylinder bore, a result which would be difficult to achieve with a lens (1960).

CHAPTER VIII

GENERAL PROPERTIES OF OPTICAL SYSTEMS: ABERRATIONS

65. Properties of optical media—transparency—speed of light. 66. Refraction—refractive index—total internal reflection. 67. Prisms—deflection—derivation of lens shape. 68. Dispersion—variable refraction of different wavelengths—Abbé number. 69. Homogeneity—stresses in glass. 70. Lenses—convergent and divergent—optical axis. 71. Images formed by convergent lenses—ideal and actual image quality. 72. Real images—virtual images. 73. Optical centre—nodal points. 74. Foci—focal length. 75. Chromatic aberrations—focal lengths for different wavelengths—location of sharpest image plane—chemical and visual focus—achromatic correction of lenses—infra-red correction—longitudinal and transverse chromatic aberration. 76. Spherical aberration—point of focus of rays from different zones—under- and over-corrected spherical aberration—aspherics. 77. Focus shift—movement of optimum plane of focus at different apertures. 78. Astigmatism—meridional and sagittal sections—shape of image points in successive planes. 79. Tangential and radial images—circle of least confusion—focal surfaces—astigmatism curves—correction. 80. Coma—effect of lens stop position on light distribution of image patch. 81. Curvature of the field—visual and optimum photographic plane of focus with screen focusing cameras—compensation by curved film planes. 82. Distortion—pin cushion and barrel distortion—effect of lens stop position—wide angle distortion—fish-eye lenses. 83. More advanced aberrations—secondary chromatic faults—zonal spherical aberration—oblique spherical aberrations—higher order astigmatism. 84. Influence of temperature. 85. Influence of diaphragm aperture on the different aberrations—chromatic and spherical aberration—astigmatism and curvature of field—coma—distortion—diffraction effects—Airy disc—diffraction-limited lens. 86. Distribution of light in the field—vignetting——natural and artificial light loss—effect of barrel distortion—compensating for the light loss. 87. Field illuminated; field covered—circle of good definition—diagonal and horizontal angles of view. 88. Loss of light in passing through a lens—absorption in glass—absorption at glass-air surfaces. 89. Anti-reflection coatings—surface films—effect of refractive index—optimum absorption wavelength—matching colour transmission of lenses. 90. Effect of internal reflection—ghost images and flare—total internal reflection. 91. Stereoscopic effects. 92. Faults in lenses—lack of homogeneity—air bubbles—centring faults.

65. Properties of Optical Media. An optical medium is any type of matter which allows light to pass through it. If light rays passing through the medium emerge substantially without loss of order, the medium is transparent. If the rays on passing through become disordered by scattering, the medium is translucent. For optical image formation we need transparent media, of which glass is the best known and most widely used. Translucent media may be used to deliberately diffuse light either in illumination or in making an image visible (as on a ground glass screen).

The term "transparency" is also used to indicate the proportion of light transmitted through a medium. It is in that case equivalent to the transmission percentage (§ 17). A medium can be non-selective—when it transmits all wavelengths of light equally—or selective, when it absorbs some wavelengths more than others.

A selective medium is in consequence coloured (§ 8).

We have seen (§ 2) that light waves travel at a speed of approximately 3×10^8 metres per second in a vacuum. When passing through an optical medium, the light is however slowed down. The degree of slowing down depends both on the nature of the medium and on the wavelength of the light. This leads directly to the phenomena of refraction and dispersion (see § 66 and 68).

The light changes speed every time it passes from one medium to another. It slows down on going from an optically less dense to an optically denser medium and speeds up again when going from a denser to a less dense medium.

66. Refraction. When a light ray reaches a boundary between two optical media, the change of speed leads to a deviation of the ray (Fig. 8.1). The ray is bent away from the boundary in

63

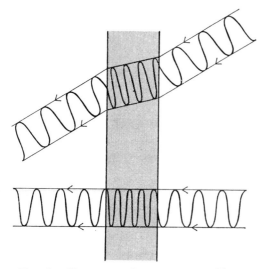

FIG. 8.1 PASSAGE OF LIGHT BETWEEN MEDIA
OF DIFFERENT OPTICAL DENSITIES

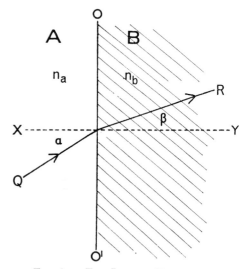

FIG. 8.2. THE LAW OF REFRACTION

the optically denser medium and towards the boundary in the less dense medium (optical density is not of course the same thing as physical density). The deviation depends on the angle of incidence of the light ray on the boundary surface and on the characteristics of the two media. The relationship can be specified (Fig. 8.2) by the equation:

$$n_a \times \sin \alpha = n_b \times \sin \beta$$

where n_a and n_b are characteristic of the media

A and B. The angles α and β are always measured with respect to the vertical XY to the boundary OO'. The values n_a and n_b are called the refractive indices of the media concerned. If A is a vacuum (and near enough if it is air) $n_a = 1$, and the refractive index n_b of the medium B is given by:

$$n_b = \frac{\sin \alpha}{\sin \beta}$$

This applies whether the light ray travels from Q to R in Fig. 8.2 or in the opposite

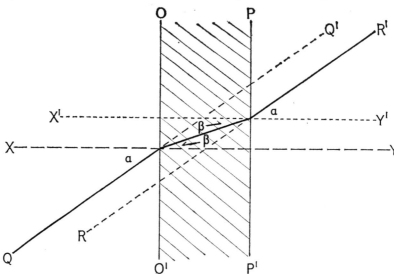

FIG. 8.3. REFRACTION WITH TWO PARALLEL SURFACES

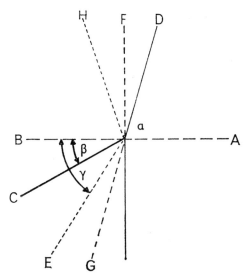

FIG. 8.4 TOTAL INTERNAL REFLECTION

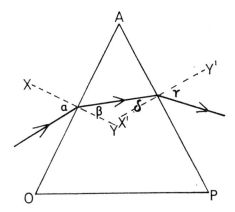

FIG. 8.5. REFRACTION IN A PRISM

direction. When the ray enters and then leaves an optical medium it regains its former direction if the exit boundary (PP') is parallel to the entrance boundary OO' (Fig. 8.3). The ray has however been displaced from its original path QQ' to a new path RR'. This follows from simple geometry.

When the ray passes from the denser to the less dense medium, i.e. the emerging angle α is greater than β, an increasing angle of incidence leads to a point where α becomes 90° and the ray EF in Fig. 8.4 does not emerge any more. As the angle becomes greater still, a ray G is reflected back into the medium along H. This so-called *total internal reflection* is made use of in certain optical systems where a plane glass surface can be used as a reflector to avoid the drawbacks of a silvered mirror.

The refractive index n for most optical media is between 1 and 2, but may in a few cases go beyond (for example about 2·4 for diamond). The exact refractive index and dispersion (§ 68) are the two important specifications of different glass types used in lenses and other optical instruments.

67. Prisms. If the entrance and exit surface of an optical medium are not parallel, as in a prism, the light ray passing through is permanently deviated. In Fig. 8.5 the refraction relationship stated in § 66 still applies:

$$n = \frac{\sin \alpha}{\sin \beta} = \frac{\sin \gamma}{\sin \delta}$$

but the angles α and γ on the one hand and β and δ on the other are now different since the surfaces AO and AP are at an angle. The ray passing through the prism therefore emerges in a new direction as well as along a new path. The amount of deviation produced by the prism depends on the angle OAP in Fig. 8.5 as well as the angle of incidence α. If we imagine a series of prism sections of different angles arranged as in Fig. 8.6, a bundle of parallel rays reaching this arrangement will be made to converge (or diverge if the prisms are arranged as in the right hand part of Fig. 8.6). The cross-section of a lens can in fact be regarded as made up of an infinite number of prism sections of different apex angles (BAC, EDF, etc.).

68. Dispersion. The refractive index n of a medium—which determines the angle of deviation when a light ray passes from one optical medium to another—varies with the wavelength of the light. Light of different wavelengths is therefore refracted to different degrees—blue light most and red least. In a prism with its permanent deviation of light rays passing through

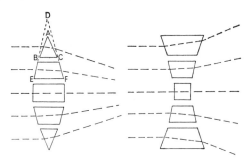

FIG. 8.6. PRISMS AND LENSES

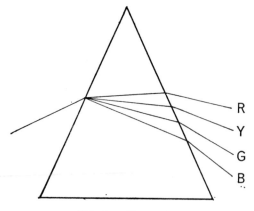

FIG. 8.7. DISPERSION

it, this differential refraction results in a ray of white light being split up into a spectrum. The degree to which the refractive index varies for different wavelengths depends again on the nature of the optical medium concerned and is not necessarily related to the mean refractive index.

A measure of the disperson is the Abbé number ν, given by:

$$\nu = \frac{n - 1}{n_F - n_C}$$

where n is the mean refractive index (for light of a wavelength of 587·6 millimicrons—the D line of the helium spectrum) and n_F and n_C the refractive indices for light of 486·1 and 656·3 millimicrons respectively (the hydrogen F and hydrogen C lines in the spectrum—§ 3). The higher the Abbé number, the lower the dispersion. The Abbé number is thus the second important specification for a glass type which a lens designer must know (§ 137).

69. Homogeneity. One important requirement for glass (or other media) used in optical instruments is that it must be homogeneous throughout its mass—the refractive index must be uniform from point to point. Local variations in the refractive index—usually due to stresses set up in the glass during manufacture—result in light rays reaching different parts of a glass body being refracted to different extents. (A common example is the distorted view obtained on looking through cheap window glass at an angle.) This calls for elaborate precautions and procedures in the manufacture of optical glass which account largely for its cost. Inhomogeneous media are also liable to be anisotropic, i.e. the refractive index (and other properties) may vary directionally. Certain crystalline materials are also anisotropic; here the reason is usually the crystal structure.

Widespread inhomogeneity on a microscopic scale—unevenness of the surface or in the internal structure—leads to light scatter.

70. Lenses. Lenses are masses of glass, bounded (by successive moulding, grinding and polishing operations) by two spherical surfaces or a spherical and a plane surface. Their shape can be regarded as derived from an assembly of innumerable prism sections of different angles, as shown in Fig. 8.6. When a parallel beam of light reaches a lens along its axis, it may either converge after passing through the lens (when the light beam gets progressively narrower) or diverge (when it gets wider—Fig. 8.8). *Convergent* (or *positive*) lenses are thicker at the centre than at the edge (Fig. 8.9, I to III); on the other hand the edges of *divergent* (or *negative*) lenses are thicker than the centre (Fig. 8.9, IV to VI).

Actually, this is true only if lenses of the above mentioned shapes are in air or other medium of lower refractivity than the glass of the lens. If a lens of shape IV to VI in Fig. 8.9 is cemented between two lenses of shapes I to III consisting of a glass of higher refractive index, the middle lens (Fig. 8.10) also acts as a converging one.

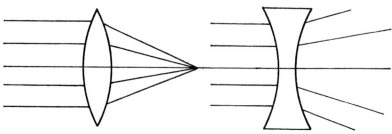

FIG. 8.8. CONVERGING (LEFT) AND DIVERGING (RIGHT) LENS

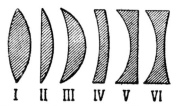

FIG. 8.9. TYPES OF LENS ELEMENTS

I. Biconvex lens
II. Plano-convex lens ⎱ Positive lenses
III. Convergent meniscus ⎰
IV. Divergent meniscus ⎱
V. Plano-concave lens ⎰ Negative lenses
VI. Biconcave lens

(An air space would be even more converging.) This becomes clearer if we consider the assembly of Fig. 8.10 in terms of converging surfaces. A converging surface lens is an interface between two optical media curved towards the medium of higher refractive index. If in Fig. 8.10 the glass of the element B is less strongly refracting than the glass of elements A, then all four surfaces *1, 2, 3* and *4* are converging. (The direction from which the light passes through the lens does not affect this.)

We can thus define a positive or converging lens more generally as a lens bounded by converging surfaces in the sense just stipulated or by converging and diverging surfaces the sum of whose convergences is greater than their divergences (or diverging power). The opposite would hold for a diverging lens.

The *optical* (or *principal*) *axis* of a lens is the straight line joining the centres of the two spherical surfaces, or, in the case of lenses having one surface plane, the perpendicular on to that surface from the centre of curvature of the other. In every combination of lenses the optical axes must coincide; this is known as a *centred system*.

Lenses made for sight-correction often also have toroidal and cylindrical surfaces, and

in recent years photographic and other lenses have been made with paraboloidal, ellipsoidal, and other aspherical surfaces. Many lenses in everyday use (such as some magnifiers, condensers, cheap snapshot cameras and viewfinders etc.) are not ground and polished but are made by moulding the glass in polished moulds.

71. Images Formed by Convergent Lenses. The elementary teaching of optics assumes an ideal simplicity in the instruments studied which is quite artificial (lenses of zero or negligible thickness; rays at small inclination to the axis passing through the lenses close to the axis, etc.). These mathematical fictions can only with difficulty be applied to the complex system of the photographic lens, often working at a very large aperture over a very extended field; it is all the more necessary to call attention to this point, as the application of the rules thus simplified may lead, by mathematical deductions which are strictly logical but ill-founded, to grossly erroneous conclusions.

When a convergent lens is placed at a suitable distance from a luminous object (or more generally any well-lit object, stray light being excluded) it forms an inverted image which can be received sharply on a screen placed at a determined distance from the lens. This screen may, for example, be a piece of white paper viewed by reflected light, or ground glass viewed by transmitted light.

A simple lens (reading-glass of large diameter or condenser lens), when used to project the image of a window on white paper pinned to the opposite wall but placed not exactly opposite to the window, provides an excellent lesson in optics. The image is rather poor, being spoilt by a number of defects or *aberrations* (the only optical instrument that can give perfect images is the plane mirror). The images of the bars will show rainbow colours

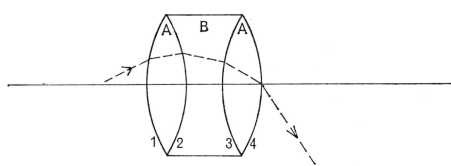

FIG. 8.10. CONVERGING AND DIVERGING LENS SURFACES

(*chromatic* aberration), and even if this aberration is removed by viewing through suitable coloured filters, the image is not sharp (*spherical aberration* due to the spherical form of the lens surfaces). The image can be improved by covering the lens with a opaque paper pierced with a circular hole smaller than the lens (*diaphragm* or *stop*), but is then not so bright. Further, it is seen that the images of the bars are more or less curved (*distortion*), the curvature varying with the position of the diaphragm. The lens requires to be moved towards or away from the paper in order to bring the centre and edges of the image successively into focus (*curvature of the field*). Finally, the image of the vertical bars is not sharp at the same time as that of the horizontal bars, especially at the edge of the image (*astigmatism*).

72. Real Images—Virtual Images. An optical image (such as we have considered in the previous paragraph), capable of being received on a matt screen, is called a *real image*.

When a convergent lens is placed at too short a distance from an object, it is impossible to form a real image of the object at any position of the screen. But on looking through the lens an upright, magnified image of the object is seen. Such an image, visible only through the lens by an observer looking in the direction of the object, is called a *virtual image*. All the observational instruments (telescopes, microscopes, etc.), adjusted for an observer with normal sight, give virtual images.

A divergent lens can give only a virtual, upright, diminished image of a real object, at a position closer to the observer than the object. This property is utilized in the construction of "direct vision" viewfinders.

73. Optical Centre—Nodal Points. The optical centre of a lens is a point on its axis such that any ray within the lens which passes through it, or is directed towards it has its external parts (i.e. the continuations of this ray in the air) parallel to each other. This may be seen in

Figs. 8.11 and 8.12, in which two parallel radii have been drawn, one for each surface. If the tangents are drawn at the point of intersection of each radius with its own surface, these tangents will also be parallel. A ray which joins these two points must have its external parts also parallel to each other.

The ray AB in Figs. 8.11 and 8.12 does not pass through these points of intersection, but is another example of a ray which suffers displacement but not deviation. It will be seen that the optical centre can lie either inside or outside the lens. Note that the lenses drawn in Figs. 8.11 and 8.12 have the same radii of curvature, and the same distance (SS') between centres.

The nodal points N and N' in Figs. 8.11 and 8.12 are the points in which the external parts of the ray would meet the axis if continued. In a perfectly corrected system these points, called the *front* and *rear* nodal points respectively, are fixed, whatever the direction of the rays considered. In other words, any ray which is directed towards the front nodal point appears to emerge from the rear nodal point. Each nodal point can be regarded as the image of the optical centre produced by one of the surfaces of the lens, and each nodal point can be considered as the image of the other nodal point formed by the complete lens.

The intersections PP' of the surfaces with the axis are sometimes called the *poles* or *vertices*.

Where the exterior surfaces of an optical instrument are bounded by the same medium (air in the case of a photographic lens) the nodal points are identical with the *principal* or *Gauss* points. This is not the case with an immersion microscope objective where the outside surface touches a liquid in contact with the preparation.

74. Foci—Focal Length. The image of an infinitely distant point (e.g. a star) towards which the optical axis of a lens is pointed, is the *focus* of that lens. From considerations of symmetry this is necessarily situated on the optical axis. As the lens can be turned with

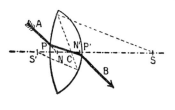

Fig. 8.11. Optical Centre
in Lens

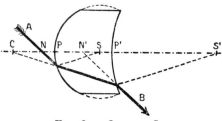

Fig. 8.12. Optical Centre
Outside Lens

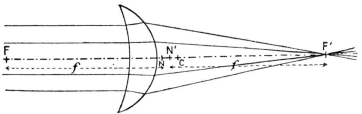

FIG. 8.13. FOCUS AND FOCAL LENGTH

either face to the point-object, it possesses **two** foci F and F' (Fig. 8.13). In the case of a convergent lens the foci are the nearest points to the lens at which a real image can be formed of a real object. The word " focus " (Latin: hearth) recalls the use of " burning glasses," the concentration of rays being a maximum in the neighbourhood of the focus so that tinder or other inflammable material can be ignited there when the lens is directed towards the sun.

When the two surfaces of the lens are in free contact with the air, the distance of each of the foci from the corresponding nodal point is the same; this distance $(NF = N'F')$ is called the *focal distance* or *focal length*. For a rough approximation and where a thin lens is considered, the nodal points can be ignored and the focal length reckoned from the optical centre C. In many normal lenses the optical centre is close to the diaphragm.

The focal length of an optical instrument is one of its essential characteristics.

75. Chromatic Aberrations. As a result of dispersion (§ 68)—in other words the variation of the refractive index with the wavelength of the light—white light traversing a lens forms a series of images of different colours, which do not coincide. The rays which are refracted most, ultra-violet and violet, form their images nearer to the lens than those which are refracted less, orange and red (Fig. 8.14). There is thus an infinite number of images each corresponding to one of the component radiations. In particular the position of the foci (images of infinitely distant points on the axis) and of the nodal points (images of the optical centre) vary with rays of different colours, as does also the focal length.

The difference of focal length $(f' - f'')$ expressed in terms of the mean focal length f, is:

$$f' - f'' = \frac{n_F - n_C}{n - 1} \times f = \frac{f}{\nu}$$

where ν is the Abbé number (§ 68) when we consider the difference between the wavelengths of the hydrogen F and hydrogen C lines.

This expression represents about 0·16 per cent of the focal length for *crown* glasses and 0·25 per cent for *flint* glasses, the general designations of two classes of optical glass. The difference in wavelength of the F and C lines covers for most practical purposes the effective useful range of colour sensitivity of normal photographic emulsions.

The practical result of this is that irrespective of the location of the image plane (the photographic film or a viewing screen) the sharp image corresponding to the apex of one of the cones of light is surrounded by bright rings corresponding to sections of all the other cones. So objects of different colour give rise to images of varying sharpness.

To the eye yellow-green appears brightest, and we therefore tend to focus images visually for the yellow-green band of the spectrum. If this focus setting is used to photograph an image formed predominantly by light of a much shorter or a much longer wavelength—either by using an emulsion sensitive only to blue light or photographing for instance on an infra-red sensitive material through a deep red filter—the phenomenon of chromatic aberration is likely to give rise to an unsharp negative. At a time when emulsions used were predominantly only blue-sensitive (or in fact when such emulsions are used for special purposes such as copying) lenses with chromatic aberration were sometimes referred to as having a *chemical focus* as distinct from the visual focus.

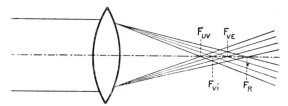

FIG. 8.14. CHROMATIC ABERRATION

The more practical way of overcoming this difficulty is to use a colour-corrected lens. In principle this consists of combinations of components of different refractive index and different dispersion. For instance a positive lens of high refractive index and low dispersion (high Abbé number) may be combined with a negative lens of low refractive index but high dispersion (low Abbé number). If the negative lens is much weaker in diverging power than the positive lens is in its converging power, it is possible to match the actual dispersions of the two so that the images formed by different colours are reunited. (It needs a much weaker lens of the higher dispersive power to compensate the dispersion of the stronger lens of the lower power.) Yet the combination—because of the difference in the refractive indices—still acts as a converging lens.

In practice the refractive index does not vary linearly with the wavelength of the light. So when, say, the blue light and the red light images are made to coincide by such a lens combination, there will still remain a degree of chromatic aberration in the regions in between (*secondary chromatic aberration* or secondary spectrum). Lenses for photography are generally corrected for D (yellow) and G (blue-violet) rays of the solar spectrum, and are then called *achromatic* (from Greek, meaning colourless). For some work, in particular colour photography, such a correction is insufficient, and coincidence of the nodal points and foci for three different colours is aimed at, generally by the employment of at least three glasses. A lens so corrected is called *apochromatic* (as defined by Abbé, an apochromatic objective should also be *aplanatic* —§ 76—for two colours).

Fig. 8.15 shows the position of focus plotted against wavelength for three different types of lens. The mean focal plane is indicated by the line *PP'* and the letters *B, C, D, E, F, G, H* represent the positions of the *Fraunhofer* lines on the wavelength scale.

Achromatic and apochromatic lenses are not usually corrected for infra-red. When photographing with infra-red emulsions it is therefore necessary to rectify the focusing, this correction being made once and for all by methodical trial and error for each lens. As a rule the extension of the camera must be increased, after visual focusing, by 0·3 to 0·4 per cent of its value.

On some modern camera lenses the distance setting scale has a special index mark for infrared focusing. Distances are then set against this

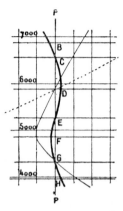

FIG. 8.15. CHROMATIC ERROR OF VARIOUS LENSES
———— Apochromatic
———— Achromatic
··········· Non-achromatic

mark instead of against the normal index mark when using infra-red emulsions. But this is also a mean setting since the focal length varies for different wavelengths in the infra-red—which cover quite a wide range. There are also lenses whose chromatic correction covers both the visible and a good part of the infra-red spectral regions.

In addition to the above correction for *longitudinal chromatic aberration* or *axial chromatism*, some correction is usually also needed for *transverse chromatic aberration* or *lateral chromatism*. This error appears as images of varying size for different colours and is disturbing in colour photography, where the three colour images must all be of exactly the same size.

For the study of other abberations we shall assume that chromatic aberration is eliminated by means of a colour filter.

76. Spherical Aberration. Among the aberrations due to the spherical curvature of the lens surface, the name spherical aberration is usually confined to that shown by light-rays at small inclinations to the axis.

If we suppose a lens divided into zones concentric to the optical axis, which can easily be realized in practice by means of diaphragms with annular apertures (Fig. 8.16) centred on the axis, the focal length of a converging lens diminishes progressively from the central zone to the edge. For any position of the screen or photographic plate between the extreme foci *F* and *F'''* (Fig. 8.17), the image of a luminous point will be a circle, the brightness of which diminishes from the centre to the edge. The

FIG. 8.16. ANNULAR DIAPHRAGM TO SHOW
SPHERICAL ABERRATION

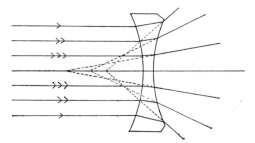

FIG. 8.18. SPHERICAL ABERRATION OF A
DIVERGING LENS

points of intersection of successive pairs of rays determine a surface, the form of which resemble the bell of a trumpet, along which there is a concentration of light. This can be observed, for reflected light, on the surface of liquid in a teacup, and is called the *caustic* of the beam.

This aberration may be reduced by the choice of suitable curvatures for the surfaces. Spherical aberration is at a minimum for a biconvex lens of which the surface on which the light is incident has a radius of curvature $\frac{1}{6}$ that of the surface of emergence (for glass of mean refractive index 1·5). This minimum aberration is only 64 per cent of that of an equiconvex lens of the same focal length. Spherical aberration is at a maximum in the case of a meniscus. A lens shaped for minimum spherical aberration is however liable to show increased *astigmatism* (§ 78). Restricting the lens aperture also reduces spherical aberration—as the outer zones of the lens contribute more to this error—but of course reduces the lens speed (§ 127); moreover, if the diaphragm is not close to the lens, rays of different obliquity passed through different zones of the lens, thus increasing the *curvature of field* (§ 81).

With a converging lens spherical aberration makes marginal rays converge more than axial rays (Fig. 8.17). This is known as *under-corrected* spherical aberration. In a diverging lens the marginal rays diverge more strongly than the axial rays; this is *over-corrected* spherical aberration.

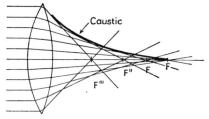

FIG. 8.17. SPHERICAL ABERRATION

These opposite effects of the two lens shapes can be used—as in the case of chromatic aberration—to correct spherical aberration by lens combinations. In practice this means that a converging and a diverging lens may be cemented together (have a common boundary surface) while the curvatures of the outer surfaces are so chosen that the under-corrected spherical aberration of the converging element matches the over-corrected aberration of the diverging element. With an appropriate choice of glass types such a combination may still be in effect a converging or diverging lens unit. In practice it is only possible to make the images produced by two zones of the lens coincide; generally the axial and a marginal zone or one close to it. This correction does not hold for intermediate zones. In order to show the importance of residual aberrations a curve is drawn in the principal section, of which each point is defined (Fig. 8.19) by the intersection of the incident ray with a line drawn perpendicular to the axis through the corresponding focus. It is usual to magnify the scale of the intersection distances for convenient reading.

An optical system rigorously corrected for this aberration is said to be *aplanatic* (Greek = free from error). Owing to the syllable—*plan* this term is often confused with freedom from curvature of field. As a matter of fact, no photographic lens is rigorously aplanatic. It is possible to correct spherical aberration only for certain object distances, which are selected as being those at which the lens will most frequently be used, *according to the purpose for which it is designed*. In practice, the correction is sufficient for most requirements at intermediate distances. We shall see, however, that the residuals of this aberration determine the distortion of the image.

77. Focus Shift. With a lens of comparatively simple correction for spherical aberration as described in § 76, a change in the lens aperture

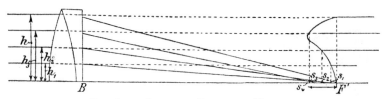

FIG. 8.19. CHART OF SPHERICAL ERROR

(§ 102) can also shift the plane of optimum focus. When the lens is used at its full opening (Fig. 8.20, left) the plane of optimum image sharpness AA' over the whole image plane is some way in front of the focal plane OO'. On stopping down to a smaller opening (Fig. 8.20, right) the contribution of the marginal correction to the image sharpness disappears and the plane of optimum sharpness shifts farther forward of the focal plane OO' to BB'. So strictly speaking, the lens should be refocused (where sharpness is accessed visually) on stopping down. In practice the depth of focus (§ 126) often tends to mask such a focus shift if it is not too serious; on the other hand the focus shift can lead to anomalous depth of field effects (§ 122).

For the same reason the image definition of such a lens with the spherical aberration corrected for two zones is at its best at a certain optimum lens aperture, and falls off both at smaller apertures (where the correcting effect contributed by the marginal rays disappears) and at very large apertures—where the outermost lens zones again introduce further spherical aberration.

One way of almost complete correction of spherical aberration (and of certain other aberrations) is to use aspheric lens surfaces. Here the various points of the surface form not a sphere but a parabola, ellipsoid or a more complex contour which may involve curvatures in two directions in different zones. While the aspheric surfaces required for a given correction can be calculated by computers, the manufacture of such surfaces is comparatively complex

and costly. They are therefore only used in certain special optical systems (see also § 166).

78. Astigmatism. Astigmatism (Greek = absence of point) is an aberration which is seen in oblique rays and arises from the asymmetry of the refraction in different sections of the beam; the most obvious effect is the concentration of light into two distinct foci.

This effect may be understood, at least qualitatively, by studying Fig. 8.21A and 8.21B. Imagine a cylindrical bundle of rays with AA' as axis, striking the lens at an oblique angle. The section of that bundle which lies in the plane of the diagram (*meridian section*) will be refracted as shown in Fig. 8.21A. The section of the bundle which is at right-angles to the plane of Fig. 8.21A encounters surfaces of greater curvature: in fact it encounters a section on $A'B'$, which is shown in Fig. 8.21B and is called the *sagittal section*. The point B, to which the rays of the meridian section converge, is then farther from the lens than the point C, to which the rays in the sagittal section converge.

If a screen (white paper, ground glass, etc.) is held perpendicular to the optical axis and gradually moved away from the lens, the beam emerging from the lens and originating in a single point source will describe on the screen successively the following shapes: a circle (when the screen is in contact with the lens); ellipses, becoming flatter and flatter with their long axes in the meridian plane, which degenerate to a short straight line in that plane; ellipses orientated as before but becoming more and more circular; a circle; ellipses getting flatter and

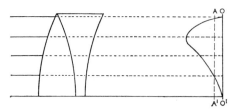 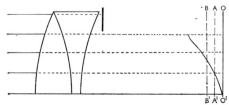

FIG. 8.20. FOCUS SHIFT DUE TO SPHERICAL ABERRATION WHEN STOPPING DOWN FROM
FULL APERTURE (LEFT) TO A SMALL APERTURE (RIGHT)

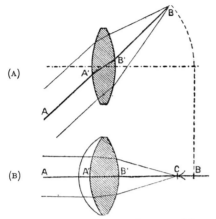

(A)

(B)

FIG. 8.21. ABERRATION OF OBLIQUE (A) AND AXIAL
(B) RAYS

FIG. 8.23. ASTIGMATISM OF CONCENTRIC
CIRCLES

flatter, with their long axes in the sagittal plane;
a short straight line in the sagittal plane;
ellipses again. This experiment can be best
carried out by using one of the elements of a
condenser. Fig. 8.22 represents this succession
of "images" of a point source of light, considerably exaggerated. The focal lines R and T are
called *radial* (or sagittal) and *tangential* (or
meridional) respectively.

79. **Tangential and Radial Images.** If one tries
to form an image of a wheel, the centre of which
lies on the axis of the lens, it is found that it is
impossible, in the presence of astigmatism, to
form a sharp image of the spokes (radial lines) at
the same time as a sharp image of the rim (which
represents an infinite series of small tangential
lines—Fig. 8.23), for at the position of the
radial focal line (Fig. 8.22) only the spokes will
be sharp, and in the position of the tangential
focal line only the rim of the wheel will be sharp.
If the two focal lines are not widely separated
from one another, a more or less sharp image of
all parts of the object will be found at the intermediate position where the pencil gives a circular
patch (*circle of least confusion*, C, Fig. 8.22).

The locus of the radial images of infinitely

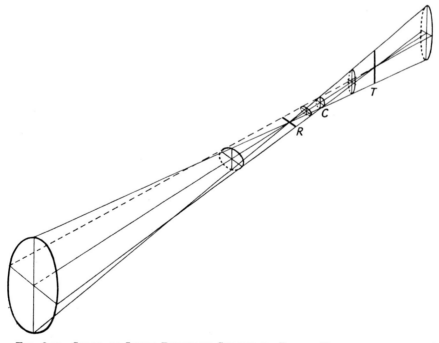

FIG. 8.22. SHAPE OF IMAGE POINTS IN SUCCESSIVE PLANES DUE TO ASTIGMATISM

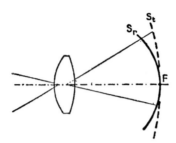

FIG. 8.24 ASTIGMATIC FOCAL PLANES

distant points (e.g. stars) given by a lens is a surface S_r (Fig. 8.24), which (at least in the central region) is generally concave to the lens; the tangential images lie on another surface S_t, generally less curved than S_r. These two surfaces (*focal surfaces*) have a point of contact at the paraxial focus F.

The radial and tangential images of points in any plane perpendicular to the optical axis form analogous surfaces.

In order to represent the astigmatism of a lens, a graphic method is used similar to that already employed for spherical aberration (Fig. 8.19). The displacements of the two focal surfaces (multiplied by four to facilitate reading of the curves) for a lens of 4 in. focal length are plotted on the horizontal scale, while the angle made by the secondary axis with the principal axis is plotted vertically on the scale of 0·1 in. to the

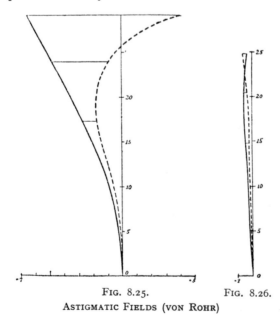

FIG. 8.25.   FIG. 8.26.

ASTIGMATIC FIELDS (VON ROHR)

degree. Figs. 8.25 and 8.26 from von Rohr, show respectively the astigmatism curves for a lens partly corrected for astigmatism (Orthostigmat type II) and for one well-corrected (Planar).

Correction of astigmatism is only possible by the employment of at least three separated lenses, or, if the lenses are to be cemented in groups, at least four lenses of different material. Two at least of the glasses must form what is called an *abnormal pair* in which the refractive index varies in the opposite direction to the dispersion, in other words, a high refractive index associated with a low dispersion and vice versa.

It is impossible to ensure complete correction of astigmatism; all that can be done is to reduce the curvature of field and astigmatism for a given obliquity between the principal and secondary optic axes (for example 20°), the astigmatism being sufficiently small at other obliquities to be relatively unimportant.

A lens corrected for astigmatism is said to be *stigmatic*, or, more usually (in spite of the pleonasm), *anastigmatic* or an *anastigmat*.

80. Coma. Coma is an oblique aberration (i.e. arising—like astigmatism—with rays reaching the lens at an angle to the optical axis). It is due to the fact that different zones of the lens produce images of different scale, each displaced slightly from the position of the secondary axis, giving a comet-like appearance, from which the name of the aberration is derived. When the tail of the comet is directed away from the principal axis, the phenomenon is called "outward coma." The effect of this aberration, except in the case of isolated luminous-point objects (such as stars) is usually noticeable as a general reduction in the contrast of the image.

Fig. 8.27, taken from S. P. Thompson, shows the cross-section of the beam of light by a plane perpendicular to the axis in the neighbourhood of the normal position of the image of a point formed by a plano-convex lens, having a diaphragm like that of Fig. 8.16, but containing several annular apertures.

Coma is often associated with astigmatism, but whilst in the case of a lens incompletely corrected, astigmatism attains a maximum and then decreases as the inclination of the rays to the axis increases, coma steadily increases. Also, being of zonal origin, coma is much more rapidly reduced by the use of a small diaphragm than is astigmatism.

The correction of coma, particularly in high-aperture objectives, is more difficult than that of astigmatism, but it is possible to reduce it by suitable choice of curvatures and refractive indices. For instance, if a biconvex lens giving minimum spherical aberration (§ 76) is compared with a meniscus of the same focal length with its convex surface towards the incident light, it is found that the meniscus, while giving very pronounced spherical aberration, has much less coma at an angle of incidence of 20°.

Coma is also affected by the position of the lens stop or diaphragm. When the stop is in front of the lens, and an oblique beam reaches the lens from below (Fig. 8.28A) it is the upper half of the lens which is primarily responsible for the image formation. If the stop is behind the lens (as in Fig. 8.28B) the light forming the image mainly passes through the lower half of the lens. The light distribution in the coma patch is then reversed. Lens stops are rarely found behind or in front of the complete lens system, since these locations also give rise to distortion (§ 82); usually the stop is located between the components of a multi-element lens. If the two halves of a lens system in front of and behind the stop are the same—i.e. the lens is symmetrical—coma is greatly reduced. If the light paths on the object and the image side of the lens are also symmetrical, in other words the lens used at unit magnification, the image is free from coma.

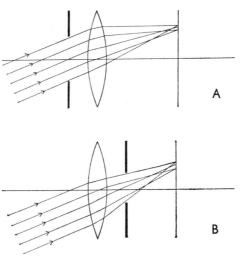

FIG. 8.28. COMA AND THE LENS STOP POSITION

81. Curvature of the Field. For reasons of symmetry, it is easy to see that the images of infinitely distant points given by a sphere of glass would lie on a spherical surface concentric with that of the spherical lens, and of radius equal to the focal length. In these circumstances the image of a near plane would be a surface of still greater curvature.

The focal surface of a lens of old type (achromats, rectilinears, symmetricals) always has a very marked concavity towards the lens, the mean radius of curvature being between 1·5 times and twice the focal length. The condition that must be fulfilled to flatten the field is incompatible with the condition for achromatism, unless an abnormal combination of glasses (§ 79) is used.

In an astigmatic lens system the surface that is to be considered as the locus of the image is neither the radial nor the tangential surface, but an intermediate surface containing the circles of least confusion (C, Fig. 8.22).

The practical consequence of curvature of the field is that, if a plane held perpendicular to the axis is displaced relatively to the lens, the position corresponding with maximum sharpness of the central region of the image is more or less distant from that corresponding with maximum sharpness of the marginal regions of the image. There is (as we shall see) a latitude in the position of the focusing screen or photographic film (depth of focus) in focusing the image sharp. But curvature of the field

FIG. 8.27. COMA
(S. P. Thompson)

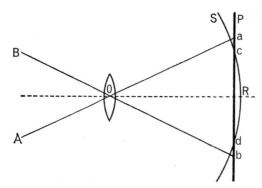

FIG. 8.29. CURVATURE OF FIELD

sets a limit in every case to the useful angle of field of the lens. Fig. 8.29 which is essentially only diagrammatic, shows the impossibility of having on a plane *P* a sharp image formed on the surface *S*. By adjusting the position of *P* to give a sharp focus for the intermediate zone *cd*, the central and marginal (*ab*) parts of the image can be considered *nearly* sharp. The useful field of the lens is then limited to the angle *AOB*.

If the same lens is used with a smaller negative format, and has a smaller field, the plane *P* of main optimum sharpness could be nearer to the focal point *R* in Fig. 8.29 and the overall sharpness better. Alternatively, for lens with a smaller field, the correction of a given degree of curvature can be achieved more simply. Hence it is important to choose a lens system according to the image size for which it is required (§ 134). This applies equally for all other aberrations.

Curvature of field can be particularly disturbing in connection with cameras where the image is focused on a focusing screen—i.e. technical and view cameras on the one hand and single-lens reflexes on the other. (Camera types will be described in detail in the next section.) For screen focusing one tends to adjust the lens for maximum image sharpness in the centre of the field. With most modern single-lens reflex cameras special focusing aids (split-image wedge rangefinders and microprism grids) are located in the centre of the screen. Under these conditions the image plane is set for maximum sharpness at the point *R*, i.e. the apex of the curved surface *S* in Fig. 8.29. This visual focusing therefore does not locate the image plane in the position of main optimum sharpness *P* if the lens has any appreciable degree of curvature of field.

With a scale-focusing or rangefinder focusing camera on the other hand, it is possible to allow for the difference between *R* and the plane *P* by simple calibration. This is still possible even with a single-lens reflex camera whose lens is not interchangeable; it merely needs relocation of the focusing screen by the appropriate amount so that the photographer focuses visually at the point *R* while the film is in the plane *P* in Fig. 8.29. As the difference between the two varies from lens to lens, this solution is not possible where different interchangeable lenses are used, as is the case with many single-lens reflexes and all technical and view cameras.

The curvature of the field of anastigmats is always very much less than that of simple objectives. In the least favourable cases the radius of curvature of the field is at least four times the focal length. For astronomical work of great precision, the plates are bent into a spherical form, of curvature equal to that of the focal surface (which is very small). The glass plate, which is thin, is bent by suction against a concave support of cast iron. An earlier method of compensation was to place a plano-concave lens against the plate to lengthen the focus of the marginal parts of the image (Piazzi Smyth's corrector).

A similar type of solution is adopted in many amateur snapshot cameras: these have a simple lens with little correction beyond being achromatized (§ 75), and shaped to obtain the best compromise for spherical aberration (§ 48), with curvature of field partially corrected by curving the film plane in the direction of the film travel through the camera, which of course is perfectly feasible with any type of roll or strip film.

It is also possible to have a converging lens with a negative curvature of field, where the image plane of maximum sharpness is convex to the lens instead of concave. This is comparatively rare and is usually a residual aberration after the correction of other image faults—rather than a deliberate design measure.

82. Distortion. It has long been known that the image of a square *AAAA* centred on the axis by a meniscus lens will be either a *pincushion* shape *BBBB* (Fig. 8.30) or *barrel* shaped *CCCC*, according to the position of the stop relatively to the lens. The deformation is greater the greater the angle the square subtends at the lens. Fig. 8.31 explains in a simple manner the mechanism of this phenomenon. According to the position of the stop, different portions of

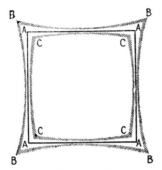

FIG. 8.30. TYPES OF DISTORTION

an oblique beam possessing aberration are used for forming the image, so that the concentration of light occurs at different distances from the axis, whilst for a pencil parallel to the axis the position of the image is independent of the position of the diaphragm. The more or less blurred images *BBBB* and *CCCC* result from the selection by the diaphragm of certain rays which, in its absence, would give an extremely blurred image combining these two partial images.

In a lens incompletely corrected for spherical aberration of oblique pencils, a displacement of the diaphragm in its own plane will produce similar deformation of the image, which will not be symmetrical if the diaphragm is not correctly centred. The same effects may arise with any aperture limiting the beam of light, e.g. the shutter, when this occupies a position other than the normal plane of the stop, or the plane of the focused image.

The distortion is reversed if the stop is placed behind instead of in front, from which the simple conclusion was arrived at that by placing the stop in the plane of symmetry of an objective formed of symmetrical elements the distortion would be zero. Although, in fact, distortion is reduced under these conditions, it will only be zero if such an objective (said to be *rectilinear*) is used symmetrically, i.e. when producing an image of a plane surface the same size. In fact, a symmetrical lens, when used with an angular field of 90° in the photography of distant objects, gives quite distinct pin-cushion distortion. This must not however be confused with wide-angle distortion arising from the geometry of wide-angle perspective (§ 34). The latter is independent of the lens type or design, while pin-cushion or barrel distortion depends entirely on how the lens is designed. Under certain circumstances barrel distortion may counteract the effect of the wide-angle distortion described in § 34; such compensation is however more likely to arise by pure chance, when the objects photographed are at a specific distance and at a specific angular location relative to the lens axis.

Actually, distortion is a very general phenomenon, being present (although to only a small extent) in lenses corrected for astigmatism and curvature of the field, in which case it is due in part to spherical aberration of the nodal points, i.e. to the slight variation in the position of these

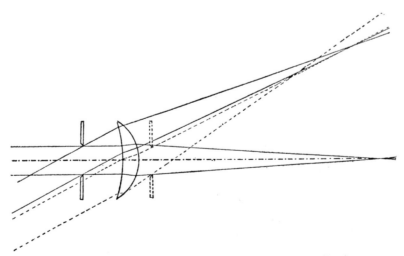

FIG. 8.31. DISTORTION VARYING WITH POSITION OF THE DIAPHRAGM

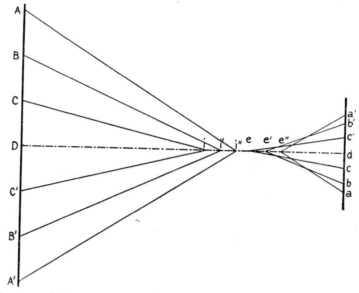

FIG. 8.32. DISTORTION DUE TO SPHERICAL ABERRATION OF NODAL POINTS

points when light traverses different zones of the lens. Fig. 8.32, where the nodal point aberration is considerably exaggerated, shows that in these circumstances the images *abcd* of equidistant points *ABCD* cannot themselves be equidistant, the *scale* of the image (ratio of the object to the image) varying progressively from the centre to the edge. With pin-cushion distortion the scale increases from centre to edges, and the distortion is said to be *positive*; with barrel distortion (*negative*) the scale decreases from the centre of the edge.

In an unsymmetrical objective the lens designer can reduce distortion to negligible proportions for a given object distance. (The name *orthoscopic* has sometimes been given to images free from distortion, but strictly speaking, an image is free from distortion only if the image of a plane object is itself a plane.) For all other object distances, distortion will be present, although it may be so small as to be only detected by laboratory methods.

Distortion, like the other aberrations, can be represented graphically. In Figs. 8.33 and 8.34, drawn respectively for a symmetrical and an unsymmetrical lens (of comparable quality, and of the same aperture), the divisions of the vertical scale correspond to the angles made by the secondary axes with the principal axis, while the horizontal scale indicates percentage variation of scale, positive (+) or negative (−).

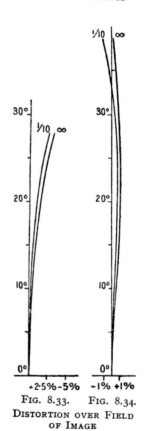

FIG. 8.33.   FIG. 8.34.
DISTORTION OVER FIELD
OF IMAGE

Two curves are shown for each lens, one for objects at infinity (∞) and the other for an object photographed at a reduction of one-tenth (from E. Wandersleb).

Distortion may be introduced deliberately into a lens, as is the case in so called fish-eye systems, a special kind of ultra wide-angle lens (§ 149). As these lenses may cover a subject field of 180° and more, the use of distortion is essential if the image is to be formed in a flat plane of finite area. The amount of barrel distortion introduced rises very rapidly with the angle for which the lens is designed; a fish-eye lens covering 140° on a 24 × 36 mm camera format may easily reach 50 per cent distortion; with greater angles the amount can exceed 90 per cent, and is with such lenses considerably greater than the wide-angle distortion in § 34.

83. More Advanced Aberrations. The lens aberrations described so far are comparatively simple to explain and—from the point of view of the lens designer—to handle. Mostly such a comparatively elementary treatment applies only to lenses if the field covered and the relative lens opening (§ 102) are small. Under these conditions residual more complex aberrations are negligible; but these come into play to a considerable extent with larger lens apertures and fields. Their treatment is correspondingly more complex and involves mathematics which is not only advanced but also exceedingly cumbersome. Here however is a brief summary of what is implied in more advanced aberrations.

We have already noted (§ 75) that secondary chromatic faults remain (secondary spectrum) when images of different colours have been brought to the same size and into the same plane for two (or three) selected wavelengths.

In spherical correction the coincidence of converging rays from the central and from a selected marginal zone of the lens is in fact a selective combination of different orders of spherical aberration. It is this which leads to zonal spherical aberration, since the different orders of aberration are not linear and thus cannot balance each other over all the zones. The higher orders also include oblique spherical aberration arising from light rays going obliquely through the lens. This leads to image points which are no longer circular but may be star shaped, figure-eight shaped and so on. (This is not the same as coma, but the final shape of the light patch—which an image point becomes —may be due to a combination of the two effects.)

A result of higher order astigmatism is that the curves for the astigmatic focal plane (Fig. 8.24) do not remain spherical with an increasing obliqueness of the ray, but may bend back again (as for instance in Fig. 8.25). A high degree of correction for astigmatism in the centre of the field may thus make the marginal definition worse.

84. Influence of Temperature. The constants used in the calculation of lens systems are usually taken for a temperature of 20 °C. When a lens is used at widely varying temperatures, the definition may be seriously affected. In high altitude aerial photography, for instance, cameras may be enclosed in a heated chamber or in heated muffles. A reduction in temperature causes a reduction in refractive index, and a contraction of the lens elements and mounts, that is, a variation in all the quantities (indices, curvatures, thicknesses, and separations) introduced in the computation of the original aberrations and of focal length, the resultant of which may be in a different direction from the change in the size of the camera. The choice of suitable materials for the lens-mounts and the camera body may allow the plane of the film or plate to lie in the plane of best focus, but obviously cannot correct the aberrations introduced by reduced temperature (J. W. Perry, 1943).

With some optical glasses, the ultra-violet transmission increases at low temperatures (W. J. Arrol, 1940), which explains certain effects observed at these low temperatures.

When a lens system is to be used under such circumstances, it is best to test it under similar conditions, and in particular to check the focusing scale.

It may be noted here that when a lens system is not in temperature equilibrium with the surrounding air (which takes some time for large-diameter objectives) the images tend to be unsharp because of local variations of refractive index of the air (E. B. Woodford and R. N. Nierenberg, 1945). At very high altitudes the variation in the refractive index of the air introduces an appreciable change of focus in aerial cameras fitted with long-focus lenses.

85. Influence of Diaphragm Aperture on the Different Aberrations. The employment of diaphragms with smaller apertures (up to a certain limit) improves the definition given by a lens which is incompletely corrected, but the degree of improvement is different for the different aberrations. As a rough guide (for the primary aberrations only) it may be said that chromatic aberration varies almost directly as the diameter of the stop; spherical aberration on the axis varies as a rule almost as the cube of the diameter. Astigmatism and curvature of the field are approximately proportional to the diameter and the square of the slope of the secondary axis to the optic axis; coma is proportional to this slope and to the square of the diameter, approximately. Distortion is independent of aperture, except when due to spherical aberration of the nodal points. These statements are true for small apertures and fields; for a given design the aberrations vary with aperture according to more complex rules.

If we consider chromatic aberration and spherical aberration, the above statements lead one to suppose that the definition on the axis will improve progressively as the aperture is reduced. It was shown in § 62, however, that the diameter of the image given by a pinhole increases as the aperture is reduced, according to physical optics, and therefore the definition **must** deteriorate. This is due to the fact that when aberrations are zero, the image of a point source of light consists of a central bright spot, surrounded by concentric rings of light of lower intensity, and which become progressively weaker from ring to ring. Fig. 8.35 shows how the intensity varies along a line through the centre of this diffraction image. The central disc, which is of more importance than the rings, is called the "Airy disc," after the Astronomer Royal, G. B. Airy (1830). The phenomenon is a consequence of the wave nature of light, the study of which is called physical optics.

In view of this we would expect the size of the image of a point source, situated on the axis, to decrease as the aperture is reduced, to a point where the aberrations may be considered negligible in comparison with the diffraction **due to the wave nature of light.** From this aperture downwards the size of the image point then begins to increase. There is thus an optimum aperture, at which the definition is a maximum. This concept of optimum aperture is not the same as the aperture at which aberrations are best balanced. At all apertures where

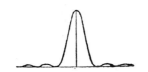

FIG. 8.35. INTENSITY DISTRIBUTION IN DIFFRACTION IMAGE

the diffraction effects become more significant than the residual lens aberration, the lens is said to be *diffraction limited*.

When we consider the remainder of the field the aberrations usually increase as the slope of the secondary axis increases. Thus the aperture at which the aberrations are balanced out by diffraction effects is smaller than the corresponding aperture at which the axial definition reaches a maximum. Since the centre of the field is a geometrical point, it is of no importance in comparison with the remainder of the field, and the optimum aperture, having regard to the whole of the image area, is thus lower than the optimum aperture for the centre of the field.

A suitable measure of definition is the *resolving power*, which is the number of parallel equidistant lines per millimetre, which can be distinguished in the aerial image or in a negative made by the lens. These two resolving powers are quite different because of the difference in action between the receptors of the eye and the photographic emulsion. The resolving power also has two different values for points in the field away from the lens axis, according to whether the lines are directed towards the centre of the field, or are at right-angles to this direction.

The optimum aperture for the aerial image differs from that for the photographic image, so that over a wide range of apertures the aerial resolving power decreases with decreasing aperture, whilst the photographic resolving power increases (E. W. H. Selwyn and J. L. Tearle, 1946).

Though resolving power was for many years regarded as an absolute criterion of lens performance, it is in fact only part of the story. See § 169.

86. Distribution of Light in the Field. No lens can give a uniformly bright image of a uniformly illuminated surface, even if this is of small extent.

This can be explained by comparing the effects of a beam directed along the axis with one in an oblique direction, forming the images P and P' respectively (Fig. 8.36). Viewed from the point P the lens has the appearance of a uniformly illuminated circle, whilst viewed from P' the appearance is an ellipse, the area of which is smaller than that of the circle by an amount which increases with the obliquity. Furthermore, P' is farther from O than P, and, as is well known, the illumination diminishes when the source of light is farther away. Finally, the oblique beam illuminates the screen or sensitive

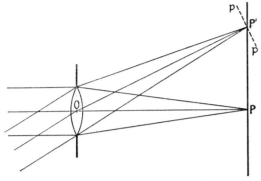

FIG. 8.36. MARGINAL INTENSITY OF IMAGE

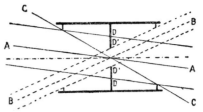

FIG. 8.38. CUT-OFF OF MARGINAL RAYS

surface in the plane PP', perpendicular to the optical axis, less than it would a screen placed at pp, perpendicular to its mean direction.

Combining the effects of these different causes it is possible to calculate the maximum illumination at different angles. Assuming that the Inverse Square Law is applicable, the illumination I at any angle ω to the principal axis is given by $I = I_0 \cos^4\omega$ where I_0 is the intensity of illumination at the centre of the field. This is shown graphically in Fig. 8.37. The angles marked in this graph are half the total angles of coverage of the lens; with for instance an angle of incidence of 30° the angle of the field (across the diagonal of the film or plate) would be 60°.

In practice the reduction in illumination between centre and edge of the field varies

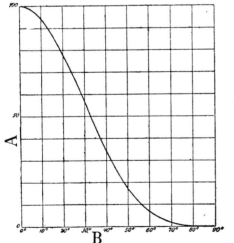

FIG. 8.37. INTENSITY OF ILLUMINATION OF
IMAGE OVER FIELD OF DEFINITION

A = Illumination of image (100 at centre)
B = Angle of incidence of principal ray

according to the construction of the lens. If the total thickness of the lens is large compared with the diameter of the lens, *vignetting* occurs. This is illustrated in Fig. 8.38 which represents a lens mount with the lens elements removed. For a certain aperture of the diaphragm DD, all those rays more oblique than AA would be partially intercepted by the lens cell and the tube. If the diaphragm is replaced by a smaller one $D'D'$, the limit of obliquity for which there is no cutting off is increased, since, in these circumstances, the beam BB passes freely. From this it is seen that reducing the aperture of the stop reduces the variation in brightness across the field. This phenomenon can be observed by moving the eye in the plane of the sharp image formed by the lens. It is then seen (Fig. 8.39) that the aperture of the stop DD is more and more covered by the lens rims L and L' as the eye moves away from the optical axis.

Because of these effects, the intensity of illumination at, say, 25° from the axis may be only 50 per cent of that on the axis, as against the 67 per cent given by the $\cos^4\omega$ formula.

The fall-off in illumination due to the obliqueness of the light rays at the edge of the field is sometimes referred to as the *natural* light loss; the reduction in intensity due to vignetting as the *artificial* light loss.

Often the diameters of the front and rear elements of a lens are just sufficient to cover the stated aperture of the lens for the axial image only, with the result that vignetting occurs for

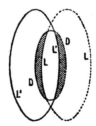

FIG. 8.39. LENS APERTURE FOR OBLIQUE PENCILS

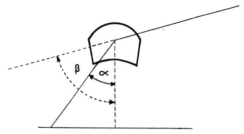

FIG. 8.40 EDGE ILLUMINATION WITH
BARRELL DISTORTION

off-axis images. This assists the lens designer, since troublesome aberrations at the higher obliquities may be reduced by this stopping down of the aperture. Lenses are sometimes claimed to have "extra marginal illumination" when the designer has provided sufficiently large external elements to maintain the $\cos^4\omega$ law as far as possible.

With some model wide-angle lens designs especially the inverted telephoto type (§ 156) the exit pupil of the lens may appear unchanged in size—in rare cases even magnified—when viewed from the edge of the field. The light-reducing effect of the elliptical appearance of the aperture then disappears, and with such lenses the illumination follows a $\cos^3\omega$ law or is still better, instead of a $\cos^4\omega$ law.

The introduction of barrel distortion (§ 82) also increases the illumination towards the edge of the field. This indeed makes fish-eye lenses a practical proposition, since otherwise the illumination at 70° or more to the principal axis would be so low as to make the image virtually invisible even with a $\cos^3\omega$ law. The gain in edge illumination is directly derived from the geometry of the distortion involved: In the simplified representation of Fig. 8.40 the actual angle between the optical axis and the rays reaching the edge of the field is α where in a lens without distortion it would be β. In the $\cos^4\omega$ (or $\cos^3\omega$) law, ω therefore becomes α instead of β, with a consequent gain in edge brightness.

Amongst the devices used for compensating for this variation, even approximately, may be mentioned: (i) an opaque stop or a truncated cone placed at some distance in front of the lens to cut off some of the central rays; (ii) a star-shaped diaphragm, placed in front of the lens and rotated by blowing, during exposure; (iii) a graduated neutral filter placed in front of the photographic plate: this may consist of a negative of a uniformly illuminated surface taken

with the same lens, or a plano-convex lens of neutral glass cemented to a plano-concave lens of clear glass to form a plane-parallel plate.

The most usual compensating device employed nowadays is a graduated neutral density filter placed at a specific distance in front of the lens. Such a graduated filter—densest in the centre and decreasing towards the outside—must be matched in its gradient to the actual lens being used, to obtain a reasonable correction. Even then the compensation is still only approximate, since it is difficult to make a filter with anything other than a linear density graduation, while the reduction of illumination from the centre to the edge of the field is non-linear. Fig. 8.41 shows how a reasonable compromise may be achieved. The shaded area A there represents the decrease in image brightness from the centre C to the edge D of the field. The absorption characteristic of the filter B provides an approximate match—near enough to be acceptable in practice in most of the field.

87. Field Illuminated; Field Covered. We have just seen that the image plane receives no light at an angle greater than a certain value. Rotation of the secondary axis corresponding to this angle round the optical axis generates a cone of which the vertex angle (twice this limiting inclination to the axis) is the *angle of the field illuminated*. This cone cuts the image plane in a circle.

The image, which is sharp at the centre of the circle, becomes as a rule useless at the edge as much from want of sharpness as from insufficient illumination. If we agree to accept a certain minimum standard of definition, then at a certain aperture of the diaphragm the images of distant objects will be useful within a circle,

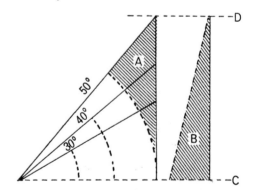

FIG. 8.41. GRADUATED FILTER TO COMPENSATE
LOSS OF EDGE ILLUMINATION WITH
WIDE-ANGLE LENSES

concentric with the circle of illumination, which is the *circle of good definition* under the given conditions. The vertex angle of the cone formed by the secondary rays passing through this circle is the *angle of field covered sharply*. If the plane of the focused image moves away from the lens (as when the object approaches it) the angle of field sharply covered remains the same, but the circle of good definition, being the intersection of the cone with a plane farther from the vertex, increases.

The employment of a small stop to improve the definition of the oblique images and to equalize the illumination over the field often has the effect of increasing the field of view as well, but this must not be taken as a general rule. Lens catalogues indicate (or should) the *angle of field* covered sharply for each lens at different apertures, or the diameters of the circles covered, for an object at infinity. Any rectangular shape that can be inscribed in that circle will then receive a sharp image. This amounts to saying that all plate sizes of which the diagonal is less than this diameter will be sharply covered in the specified circumstances.

Lens specifications generally quote the diagonal angle of view with the film or plate format for which the lens is used. This may be smaller than the angle of field covered. For interchangeable lenses used in technical cameras where camera movements are involved (see also § 136) the angle sharply covered is generally given. When used with a given camera and film format, the horizontal or vertical angles across the image are important when establishing the subject field of view at a given distance, since a camera is almost invariably used with either the length or the width of the negative horizontal. If the diagonal angle of view for a given format is known, the angle across the width or height of that format can be calculated from the equation:

$$\tan \tfrac{1}{2}s = \tan \tfrac{1}{2}d \times S/D$$

where s is the angle across the side S (height or width) of the format, d is the diagonal angle of view and D is the diagonal of the format. This latter value can be obtained from the tables in § 134.

88. Loss of Light in Passing through a Lens. A beam of light passing through transparent matter undergoes loss, partly by absorption and partly by reflection at the entrance and emergence surfaces.

Loss by absorption within the glass of a modern lens is generally very small, often negligible, for visible rays. The mean values of transmission (not reckoning loss by reflection, to be examined later) are indicated below for different total thickness of glass, expressed in centimetres—

Thickness in cm	1	2	3	4	5	6
Transmission %	97·6	95·3	93	90·7	88·5	86·4

This loss is much greater for ultra-violet radiation, which is, however, useless and indeed often harmful in general photographic practice. The loss of light by absorption may be considerable in old lenses, certain glasses of which have a pronounced yellow coloration.

Loss by reflection at the surfaces of the lens is generally more considerable than loss by absorption. In systems containing one or more cemented lenses the loss is negligible at the cemented surfaces (about 1 per cent); we need therefore to consider only losses at glass-air surfaces. The mean values of transmission (not reckoning loss by absorption, examined above) are given below for one, two, three, or four lenses of a glass of refractive index around 1·55 in air, supposing that the polish is perfect.

Number of glass-air surfaces	2	4	6	8
Transmission %	90	80	72	65

To obtain the total transmission approximately, reckoning both causes of loss, it would be sufficient to multiply one factor by the other, e.g. a lens containing six glass-air surfaces in which the total of the thicknesses of the components is 3 cm transmits approximately.

$$72 \cdot 1 \times 0 \cdot 93 = 67 \text{ per cent.}$$

89. Anti-reflection Coatings. The reflectivity of glass may be reduced considerably by coating the surface with a thin film of suitable material. This phenomenon was first observed by H. D. Taylor in 1892, and was put to practical advantage by J. Strong in 1935, by depositing a film of calcium or magnesium fluoride on the lens surface in vacuum. Virtually all modern lenses—and most better quality lens attachments (filters etc.)—have all their surfaces treated in this way.

This reduction in reflectivity, with a corresponding increase in transmission, is an interference phenomenon. The reflectivity can be reduced to zero, for a given wavelength of radiation, and a given angle of incidence. In the case of normal incidence, the first condition is that the thickness of the film should be an odd multiple of the half-wavelength of light, the best results being obtained when a half-wavelength thickness is used. The second condition is that the refractive index of the surface film should be equal to the square root of the refractive index of the glass on which it is deposited. This condition would appear unattainable, since no suitable substance has a refractive index lower than 1·4, whilst the required index must be 1·22 to 1·3 when the index of the glass is 1·5 to 1·7. Fortunately, in these thin films the refractive index is much lower than that of the same substance when measured in the bulk.

In practice, coating can reduce the reflectivity of an air-glass surface from around 5 per cent to about 1 per cent; so with a 3-element lens (six glass-air surfaces) the transmission would rise from 72 to about 96 per cent (ignoring absorption). The gain is even more spectacular with glasses of high refractive index, where the light loss by reflection is much greater (due to the greater difference in refractive index between the glass and air). There coating can reduce the light loss to a much lower level, because the refractive index of the coating material comes nearer to the square root value of the glass. Thus for a glass of refractive index 1·8 the light loss at each uncoated surface is around 8 per cent; coating reduces this to as little as 0·1 per cent.

Coating is important in modern lens systems for two reasons. One is the light loss already mentioned; while this is not very significant with one or two elements, it becomes vital when a complex lens with 10 or 12 glass-air surfaces is involved. Without coating, the light loss in such a lens is around 50 per cent, and five separate components thus represented just about the limit to which lens designers could go (and hence a limit on the correction of aberrations possible) before lens coating came into use. Equally, the use of modern highly refractive glasses with their much greater loss factor would have been impractical in uncoated systems. By contrast, present-day designers can—for special lens systems—work with 8 or 10 separate elements and thus achieve a correspondingly higher degree of correction. Yet with the use of glasses of high refractive index, the actual light loss through surface reflection at the twenty surfaces involved can be under 10 per cent.

Originally it was considered desirable to reduce by coating the reflectivity to a minimum for green light (550 mμ) as being the approximate middle of the visible spectrum. Such a coating appears purplish in colour by reflected light, since the reflection of green is surpressed most

and the reflected light consists predominately of the red and blue wave bands. The coating can also be arranged to reduce reflections most in the blue band—when it will appear yellowish, or in the yellow band when it will appear bluish.

In practice the variation of light loss over the spectral range is not very great—for instance with a coating which supresses reflections most in the yellow region, the minimum light loss is around $\frac{1}{2}$ per cent there, and still well under 1 per cent in the red region. The colouration of coatings is utilised in practice therefore more to match the colour transmission of a lens to a specific energy distribution. This is significant with interchangeable lenses used on one camera; these lenses may need to employ different types of glass with small residual selective absorptions. When used for colour photography, it could thus happen that one lens yields a cooler colour rendering on the same make of colour film than another lens for the same camera. By balancing the colour transmissions with the aid of different coatings it becomes possible to match the colour rendering of all lenses of a set produced by a manufacturer for a given camera. That would ensure that colour photographs taken by the camera always yield the same colour rendering even when we use alternative lenses during a series of exposures.

The second advantage of lens coating is that the elimination of reflections also reduces the amount of light which is scattered towards the image surface. This scattered light or *flare* at the best reduces the contrast—and hence also the general definition of the image and at the worst produces ghost images and flare spots (§ 90).

The different methods of producing anti-reflection coatings can be divided into two groups, according to whether the film is deposited on the glass (physical, or additive method) or is made by surface action on the glass (chemical, or subtractive method). Chemical methods are applicable to certain types of glass only, and are therefore not so universal. The physical methods consist either of evaporation *in vacuo* or of spinning by centrifuge. The latter has received some attention, but the majority of coated lenses are prepared by Strong's method. Heating the lenses during the process leads to exceedingly hard films.

90. **Effect of Internal Reflection.** The light reflected at each free surface is, unfortunately, not lost; a part of the beam which has suffered several internal reflections is sent back to the

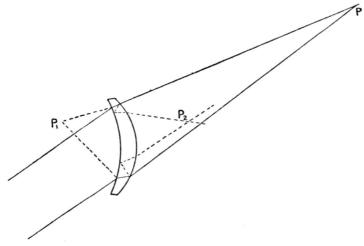

FIG. 8.42. IMAGES BY INTERNAL REFLECTION

object, but another part passes on to the film. In Fig. 8.42 it is seen that the beam which forms the image P also gives an image P_1 on the side of the object, after one internal reflection, and an image P_2 on the side of the image P after two internal reflections. If the incident beam is sufficiently intense, and if the exposure is sufficiently long, these images will register on the film or plate as circular or elliptical areas of relatively large dimensions. The number of parasite (ghost) images reflected to the plate will be greater the greater the number of glass-air surfaces. The intensity of the images diminishes according as the number of reflections the beam has undergone is greater.

Number of glass-air surfaces	.	.	2	4	6	8
Number of ghost images	.	.	1	6	15	28

These ghost images appear frequently in photographs taken at night, which have had a long exposure and where the view contains light-sources of great intensity towards the edge of the field. Owing to the symmetry of the lens round its axis, the secondary axis of the different beams arising from the same original beam are contained in a meridian plane. The centres of the areas corresponding with a single point source are thus all situated on the straight line which joins the image of the point and the point where the optical axis cuts the sensitive surface. Fig. 8.43 (from R. Schüttauf) shows the limits of the six ghost images given by a rectilinear lens (symmetrical lens of two groups each consisting of two cemented lenses, so that there are in all four glass-air surfaces) where the object is a

bright point on a black background. This phenomenon may easily be observed by placing a piece of opaque paper on the focusing screen of a camera, midway between the centre and a corner. If the camera is now directed towards the sun, so that the image of the sun falls on the opaque paper, a number of bright circles will be seen, which would have been invisible if the brighter image of the sun had remained within the field.

In some of the old lenses one of the internally reflected beams gave almost a sharp image of the stop in the image plane, somewhat enlarged, centred on the optic axis, and superposing a bright patch (called the *central flare spot*) on the image.

In regular photographic work these ghost images are not seen individually, but the light directed towards the plate after internal reflection forms a slight fog over the whole image,

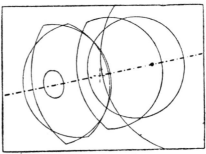

FIG. 8.43. FALSE IMAGES
(R. Schüttauf)

reducing contrast. Fig. 8.44 (from measurements made by E. Goldberg) shows the effect of these internal reflections for an $f/6\cdot8$ objective containing four independent lenses (eight glass-air surfaces) photographing a landscape of which HH is the horizon. Successive reflections of the light from the sky produce on that part of the plate on which the landscape is recorded an amount of light which decreases as the distance from the horizon line becomes greater. The circles in dotted lines correspond to different obliquities of the beam; the curves in full line join points of the image in which the parasite light has an intensity equal to 6 per cent, 5 per cent, . . . 2 per cent of that in the image of the sky. The intensity of this parasitical light is reduced appreciably when the lens is stopped down.

The same author has been able to establish the fact that from these reflections and from the unavoidable light scatter at the surfaces, even if perfectly polished and kept perfectly clean, the extreme contrast in the image yielded by a lens is always less than in the subject itself examined from the same viewpoint. A subject having a range of contrasts infinitely great is reduced to a contrast about 200 : 1 with a single lens and to about 60 : 1 with an anastigmat giving a sharp image over a relatively large field. It should be noted that the stray light which produces this reduction in contrast does not represent a fraction of the light coming from the subject, but a fraction of the *total* light falling on the lens, including that which is outside the field of view. To obtain maximum contrast, a lens hood should always be used.

Goldberg's measurements confirm the experience of the old photographers, who used for landscape work a single objective consisting of a number of lenses cemented together, considering that this type gave more *brilliant* images.

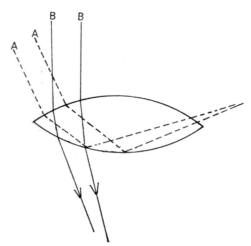

FIG. 8.45. ELIMINATION OF STRAY LIGHT BY TOTAL INTERNAL REFLECTION IN A LENS

With modern coated lenses the intensity of the scattered light and of ghost images is of course greatly reduced as the amount of reflection is cut down. The arguments for simple lenses against more complex ones therefore do not apply nowadays. But the geometry of flare image formation remains valid and even with a coated lens light sources actually within the picture area can produce strong enough images (especially in night photography where most of the picture area is detailless shadow) which become visible in the picture. Occasionally it has proved possible to reduce at least some of the flare under such circumstances by having in the lens a surface of such a curvature that light rays from outside the image area are totally reflected (§ 66) back again towards the object. Thus in Fig. 8.45 (showing the phenomenon in a very simplified form) the rays AA strike the lens at such an angle, that at the lower lens surface (which is convex towards the image) they follow the dotted path out of the lens again, while rays BB at a smaller angle to the axis can pass through. This total internal reflection is however generally an incidental benefit of a particular lens construction, rather than a deliberate measure.

91. Stereoscopic Effects. A lens of very large diameter, such as some at one time used as portrait lenses, gives an image of a near object in which appear certain parts of the subject which an eye (placed as close as possible to the lens) would see only if moved from right to left

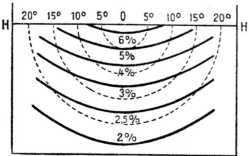

FIG. 8.44. VEIL FROM INTERNAL REFLECTION
(E. Goldberg)

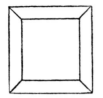

FIG. 8.46. SMALL CUBE AS SEEN BY A LARGE LENS

FIG. 8.47. DUPLEX DIAPHRAGM

(Brewster, 1860) and up and down. The image of a small cube isolated in space, e.g. a dice suspended by a thread in the optical axis of such a lens, would show five faces (Fig. 8.46), presenting thus the appearance of a truncated pyramid seen from the direction of the small end.

It has long been recognized that it is possible to obtain with such a lens, fixed with respect to the object photographed, two stereoscopic images by using an eccentric stop, rotated through 180° between the exposures, the aperture being $1\frac{1}{4}$ in. in a horizontal direction from the centre, so that two successive positions of the aperture are at a distance apart equal to the mean separation of the eyes. The diaphragm merely extracts from the complete image certain details by isolating certain light-rays.

It has also been proposed (Lehmann, 1878; Boissonas, 1900, etc.) to use with large lenses a diaphragm with two apertures (Fig. 8.47) to obtain a single image in which the doubling of certain outlines would suggest some idea of relief.

The above are however primarily optical curiosities. A lens large enough to show such phenomena to any extent would also have to be so close to the object—in relation to its focal length—that the depth of field (§ 110 ff) would be too small to show more than just the end face of the cube in Fig. 8.46 sharply.

In practice stereoscopic photography involves the production of two separate images by two separate optical systems a given distance apart. These images then have to be viewed in such a way, that each eye sees only the image corresponding to its own viewpoint. The lens with a twin diaphragm mentioned above (as in Fig. 8.47) is hardly a practical way of doing this.

92. Faults in Lenses. Apart from the lens aberrations already discussed, lenses may exhibit certain defects of materials and workmanship. The aberrations are optical factors, and the performance of a lens in this respect is limited by its design. A lens of higher performance tends to be accordingly more expensive. Certain more mechanical aspects of workmanship and materials can however also impair the lens performance. The factors involved here are:

(a) The accuracy of manufacture—how closely the curvatures of the lens elements follow the specifications laid down by the designer;

(b) Inhomogeneity of the glass (see also § 69)—a fault in glass making; and

(c) Lack of precision in centering and mounting.

Reputable lens manufacturers carefully check both their raw materials—to eliminate faults under (b) above—and their finished lenses for faults (a) and (c) before passing them for sale. With costly lenses such tests and inspections are naturally more stringent than for cheaper ones, and the tolerances closer (and hence the rejection rates higher), the higher the expected performance. Not all manufacturers are equally strict in this respect however, and this is responsible for sometimes appreciable variation in the performance of different specimens of what is nominally the same lens.

Want of homogeneity is not usually evident except in lenses of large diameter; it can be recognized by forming on a ground glass screen the image of a point source of light (e.g. the image of the sun in a well-polished metal ball or small silvered bulb) close to the axis of the lens. If now the screen is moved out of focus until a circle of light of about $\frac{1}{2}$ in. diameter is obtained, any defect will be visible as striæ or dark zones.

Optical inhomogeneity can also arise through uneven stresses within the glass of a lens. The most usual cause is uneven annealing, i.e. insufficiently controlled cooling of the glass during manufacture. If parts of a glass lens cool more rapidly than others, internal stresses are set up which lead to *double refraction* of the light rays (a doubling of the image in certain circumstances). Normally this can only be seen by examination in polarised light in an optical laboratory provided with the proper equipment. If the lens is placed between crossed polarising filters (§ 189), stresses show up as alternate light and dark rings or bands. Mechanical stresses can also arise through uneven pressure on the lens in its mount.

Isolated tiny bubbles are occasionally found in lens elements of certain glass types. These bubbles were at one time inevitable in optical glass manufacture, and in their small size and number have no measurable effect on the image. (They merely scatter a tiny fraction of a per cent of the light—about as much as one or two single grains of dust on the lens.)

To counter popular apprehensions about the presence of such occasional tiny bubbles, some optical manufacturers went as far as to claim that these bubbles were a sign of high quality optical glass. With modern optical glasses and glass making methods present lenses very rarely show bubbles.

One defect occasionally met with in inexpensive lens systems is faulty centering due to incorrect alignment of the mounts. In bad cases this can be detected by looking at the images of a point source of light reflected in the lens surfaces; these images should lie exactly on a straight line.

There are two main centering faults: The optical axes of the individual elements may be tilted with respect to each other (even a fraction of a degree is sufficient to affect lens performance), and they may be straight but not in line. Apart from inadequate care in manufacture and assembly, the first of these faults can be caused by distortion of the lens mounting through mechanical knocks (for example dropping the lens), and the second by unscrewing individual lens elements. This is likely to lead to decentering if the optical axis of the whole lens system, though in line, was not absolutely in the centre of the mount. Such overall decentering can be checked by rotating the whole lens on a test bench; during such rotation the image projected on a screen by a lens with a slightly decentered axis wanders on the screen.

CHAPTER IX

FOCAL LENGTH OF LENSES: IMAGE SCALE: CONJUGATE POINTS

93. Conjugate Points. When a point R' is the image of a point R (Fig. 9.1) formed by an optical system, the point R is also the image of R' (principle of *reversibility* of light rays); the points of such a pair are two *conjugate points* of the optical system considered. Various formulae and simple graphical constructions enable us, when the focal length of a lens and the positions of the nodal points or foci (§§ 73 and 74) are known, to determine the position of the image of a point the position of which is known.

The principle of reversibility means only that the path of an *individual* light ray through an optical system is the same, irrespective of which of the two ends of the path the ray originates from. It does not mean that when light rays from an object form an image, the image would send back light rays only along the same paths and no others. The light from such an image formed would in fact follow a number of paths, some of them coincident with the original light paths from the object and some of them completely different.

It is a misinterpretation of this fact which has at times led to assumptions that an unsharp image produced by a lens can be made sharp again by reprojecting it through the same lens system. If a number of points at different distances from the lens have been photographed on a flat film or plate, a reversal of the process does not make the images of the photograph points coincide again with the system of points photographed. Similarly, no optical reversal system can produce a sharp image from one degraded by lens aberrations; these deteriorate the image each time it is reflected through the lens, as the aberrations add up at each stage. The only exception is distortion; when an undistorted original on projection through a lens system forms a distorted image, then reprojection of this distorted image backwards produces again an undistorted picture.

In the theoretical discussion which follows we assume that the lens does not suffer from aberrations. Except when otherwise stated, all distances are measured from the appropriate nodal point.

The *power* of a lens (*convergent power* or *convergence*) is the reciprocal, $1/f$, of the focal length; when the focal length is measured in metres the power of the system is expressed in *diopters*. Thus, for example, a lens of 0·20 m (200 mm or 8 in.) focal length has a power of $1/0·20$, or 5 diopters.

The effect of an optical system is to add its convergence (or subtract, in the case of a divergent system, i.e. of negative *vergence*) to that of the light beams passing through it. A point at distance u from the front nodal point sends to the system a divergent beam of which the

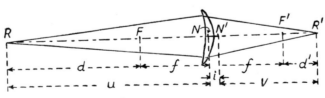

FIG. 9.1. IMAGE FORMATION

vergence is $-1/u$. If the convergence (positive vergence) $1/f$ of the system is greater than the negative vergence of the beam $(-1/u)$, the emergent beam will have vergence $1/v$ where

$$1/v = \frac{1}{f} - 1/u$$

or $1/v + 1/u = 1/f$

If, instead of considering distances from the nodal points, we measure our distances from the front and back focal points (i.e. by replacing u and v by $d + f$ and $d' + f$ respectively), we obtain the law of conjugate points in the convenient form given by Newton—

$$d \times d' = f^2$$

Expressed in words, this means that the distance from the object to the front focal point, multiplied by the distance from the image to the back focal point, is equal to the square of the focal length.

Among the different methods of graphically representing the law of conjugate points, the following (Lissajous, 1870) enables us to account for all the practical consequences of this relationship at first sight. Construct a square (Fig. 9.2) $NFMF'$, of which the sides are equal to the focal length of the lens considered, and produce the sides NF and NF' to X and Y respectively. From the origin N mark off NR on NX equal to the distance (u) of the object point (FR is thus the extra-focal distance d); join RM and produce it to meet NY in R'. The length NR' is equal to the distance v of the point-image and $F'R'$ is the focal distance d'. If now

RR' is rotated about M, its intersections (produced if necessary) with NX, NY correspond to two conjugate points. It is seen that as R moves away from the lens, R' moves nearer to it, and vice versa. When R moves to infinity, the straight line MR becomes parallel to NX, and R' coincides with F'. Inversely, if R approaches F, the straight line RM becomes parallel to NY and consequently R' recedes to infinity.

If the point R approaches closer to the lens than the focal length, e.g. to the position marked T, the straight line MT no longer meets NY, but its prolongation NY', in T', corresponding to a virtual image (§ 72).

A particularly interesting case is that in which the distance from the object S to the nodal point is twice the focal length. In this case $FS = MF$, and the straight line MS is inclined at 45°, and S' is such that $NS' = NS$. The two points S and S' at equal distances from their respective nodal points are called the *symmetrical points* of the lens; their separation is the shortest distance that can exist between a point object and its real image. Another particular case, but of no practical interest, is that where the points R and R' coincide with N; this leads to the fact already mentioned (§ 73) that the nodal points are conjugate.

94. Relations between the Size of Object and Image. If we consider a lens without appreciable distortion or curvature of the field (which would obviously not be the case with the meniscus represented in Fig. 9.3), we know that the images of all points on a plane perpendicular to the optical axis lie on another plane also perpendicular to the optical axis. Knowing also that

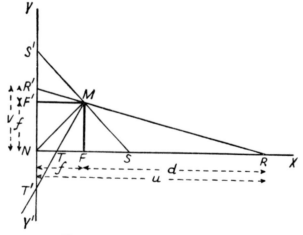

FIG. 9.2. LAW OF CONJUGATE FOCI

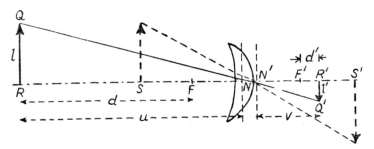

FIG. 9.3. SCALE OF IMAGE

the exterior parts of a secondary axis are parallel straight lines (lines joining object and image points to the corresponding nodal points), we can determine the *scale of the image* (relation between corresponding dimensions of object and image) of an object of which the position is known relatively to a lens of known focal length.

Let us suppose that the length of the image of an arrow RQ (Fig. 9.3) of length l perpendicular to the axis, at a distance v, is to be determined. Join by a straight line the point Q to the front nodal point N, and draw through the back nodal point N' a line parallel to QN to meet in Q' the straight line $R'Q'$ through R' (the image of R), parallel to RQ. The point Q' is the image of Q, and the element of line $R'Q'$ is the image of RQ. The length l' of this image can be ascertained from l, since the triangles RQN and $R'Q'N'$ are similar.

The scale of reproduction m is then equal to the ratio of the ultra-nodal distances of image and object

$$m = l'/l = v/u$$

By replacing u by v/m in the expression $1/u + 1/v = 1/f$, we find that

$$u = (1 + 1/m)\,f$$
$$\text{and } v = (1 + m)\,f$$

It is often useful to know the distance between object and image in terms of the magnification and focal length.

This is given as

$$u + v \pm i = \frac{(m+1)^2 f}{m}$$

where i is the inter-nodal distance, which can usually be neglected.

Another expression relating object and image is the distance x' which the lens (or focusing screen) must be moved from the infinity position when the object is moved from infinity to a finite distance u. This is

$$x' = f^2/(u-f)$$

There is a reduction whenever the object is farther from the lens than its image, and magnification whenever the object is closer to the lens than its image. The scale is zero when the object is at an infinitely great distance (e.g. the stars). The distance between the images of two distant objects cannot be determined from considerations of scale. It is determined from the angle seen to subtend the two object points, e.g. the solar disc is viewed from the earth under an angle of 32 minutes of arc (*apparent diameter*) i.e. about 1/100th of its distance. The image of the sun will thus be equal to 1/100th of the focal length of the lens used. The mean diameter of the lunar image is about the same size as that of the sun.

When the object photographed has a certain depth, it is no longer possible to speak of the scale of the image, since this will vary from point to point. It should be mentioned here that in the most general case, where such an image is photographed on a plane perpendicular to the axis, the relative dimensions of the different parts of the image are inversely proportional to the ultra-nodal distances of the corresponding point objects, and not to their ultra-focal distances, the image points being all on the same plane and no longer the *conjugates* of the object points.

95. Graphical Construction of the Image Formed by an Optical System. Knowing the position of a point object Q relatively to the foci F and F', and the nodal points N and N' of an optical system, the position of the image Q' can be determined as follows: Draw the optical axis FF' (Fig. 9.4), and at N and N' draw perpendiculars to it to indicate the nodal planes. From Q draw a straight line parallel to the axis,

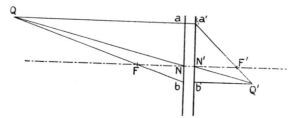

FIG. 9.4. GEOMETRY OF IMAGE FORMATION

meeting the nodal plane of emergence in the point a'; a' is the image of a, the intersection of the ray with the front nodal plane. The emergent ray will then pass through the focus F', since all incident rays parallel to the axis, after refraction, meet the optical axis at the back focus. Draw another line QF and produce it to meet the front nodal plane in b; the image of b is b' on a line through b parallel to the axis, which is also the emergent ray. Q', the intersection of $a'F'$ and bb', is the image required. The accuracy of the construction can be tested by seeing whether QN, $Q'N'$ of the secondary axis are parallel to one another.

96. Image of a Plane Inclined to the Axis. Consider a lens of which the foci and nodal points are F, F' and N, N' respectively (Fig. 9.5), and let R and R' be two conjugate points. If a plane perpendicular to the plane of the paper meets the optical axis obliquely at R, all the points in this plane (at least all those not far from the axis) form their images on another plane, also meeting the optical axis obliquely at R' and perpendicular to the plane of the paper. This image plane is defined by the condition that its intersection M' with the back nodal plane should be the image of the intersection M of the object plane with the front nodal plane.

It is easily seen that the image is deformed relatively to the object. In particular the points on the line X, the intersection of the object plane with the front focal plane, will be imaged at infinity, the secondary axes NX, $N'X'$ being parallel. In the same way infinitely distant points of the object plane in the direction NY will be imaged on the straight line Y', the intersection of the image plane with the back focal plane. On this straight line all the vanishing points of parallel straight lines in the object plane will be imaged, while all lines meeting in X will be parallels in the image plane.

This manner of distorting is made use of for correcting the perspective of photographs accidentally taken on an inclined plane (by making all the vanishing points of vertical lines in such a perspective meet in X, they will be *corrected* in the image), or for making lantern slides which are to be projected obliquely.

Distortion apart, the same principle can be applied when we want to form an image sharp overall of a number of object points at different distances from the lens, provided these object points lie in a single plane. In most cameras the orientation of the image plane is fixed at right angles to the optical axis, and imaging sharply objects at different distances is possible only by making use of the depth of field (§ 110). In Fig. 9.6 the object points A, B and C form their images at A', B' and C' in the planes J, H and G respectively. The photographic film or plate in any of these three planes can show one of the object points sharp, with the other two blurred.

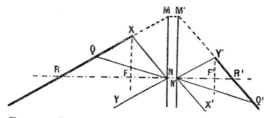

FIG. 9.5. IMAGE FORMATION ON INCLINED SURFACE

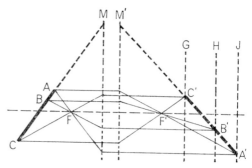

FIG. 9.6. TILTING THE IMAGE PLANE TO IMAGE SHARPLY OBJECT POINTS AT DIFFERENT DISTANCES FROM A LENS

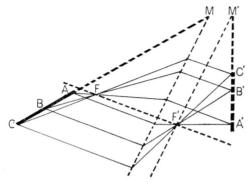

FIG. 9.7. TILTING THE LENS FOR OVERALL
IMAGE SHARPNESS

To obtain simultaneously a sharp image of
A, B and C, we have to tilt the image plane (the
film or plate) to the position shown by the heavy
broken line in Fig. 9.6. By a construction similar
to Fig. 9.5, the prolongation of the object plane
and the image plane meet the front and rear
nodal planes of the lens at M and M'. This
condition is also known as the Scheimpflug
condition after T. Scheimpflug. Such tilting of
the image plane is possible in technical and
view cameras.

In practice the exact location of the nodal
points does not really have to be known, since
with such a camera we are likely to adjust the
image sharpness on the focusing screen, altering
the inclination of the latter until the image
points corresponding to the nearest and the
farthest point required on the object plane are
sharp.

The same result, in terms of sharpness, is
achieved if we tilt the lens from its original
position (axis at right angles to the image plane)
until the nodal planes of the lens intersect with
the inclined object plane and the image plane
(shown simplified in Fig. 9.7). Tilting the lens
however displaces the optical axis away from
the centre of the image, and the angle of coverage
of lens must be adequate to allow for this.

**97. Experimental Determination of the Focal
Length of a Lens.** The method of measuring
the focal length usually described consists in
focusing a distant object (distant at least
1,000 times the focal length to be measured) in
the camera, then focusing an equal size image
of an easily measurable geometrical figure (e.g.
a circle or equilateral triangle). The amount
the camera has to be extended between the
two positions is exactly the focal length.

This, like the following methods, circumvents
the need for establishing the exact location of
the rear nodal point of the lens—usually a
difficult procedure without a fairly elaborate
optical bench.

If it is not possible to extend the camera front
sufficiently to obtain an equal-size image, it is
sufficient to obtain a second position at a reduction of m. The distance through which the
focusing screen is moved is thus $v - f$. Since
$v = (m + 1)f$, it follows that $f = \dfrac{v - f}{m}$. It
should be noted that m should be as large as
possible, to avoid errors in measurement.

Instead of focusing on a distant object, two
finite object distances can be used. The method
is to focus a scale at two different magnifications,
m_1 and m_2, and to measure the difference
$v_2 - v_1$ between the two image distances. Then,
since $v = (m + 1)f$, we have

$$v_1 = (m_1 + 1)f$$
$$v_2 = (m_2 + 1)f_1$$

whence $f = \dfrac{v_2 - v_1}{m_2 - m_1}$

In other words, the focal length is the difference in extension measured, divided by the difference between the two scales of reproduction.

If, for example, the test object is an equilateral
triangle of which the sides are 120 mm long,
reduced in the two positions to 90 and 40 mm
(scales of reduction 0·75 and 0·33 respectively)
and that the increase in camera extension is
70 mm, the focal length will be given by

$$70/0·42 = 167 \text{ mm}$$

The position of the back focus could be easily
found by measuring the ultra-focal distance
nf from one of the positions of the image
towards the lens. The position of the back
nodal would be given by measuring a further
distance f towards the lens.

In both of these methods care should be taken
to ensure parallelism between object plane and
focusing screen, and it is convenient to reverse
the focusing screen so that the images can be
measured directly on the ground glass side.

Where the only camera available is capable
of only a small range of focus (which is the case
with a large number of hand cameras) the above
method is not possible, and the following method
can be used based on the formula

$$u + v \pm i = \frac{(m + 1)^2 f}{m}$$

given in §94 (Debenham, 1879). Having focused the image of a geometrical figure and determined the scale m, the total distance l between object and image is measured. This distance is the sum of the two ultra-nodal distances u and v increased or diminished by the nodal interval i (separation of the nodal points) according as the nodal points are in the normal position or crossed (the *nodal points* are said to be *crossed* when the back nodal point is the nearer to the front focus, which is opposite to the case of the systems previously considered).

If m is very small (which will always be the case in small cameras) $1/m$ will be very large, and consequently the error arising from neglecting the internodal distance will be divided by a number generally greater than 10 and will therefore nearly always be negligible, except in telephoto and single lenses of convertible sets. If, for example, a lens of 150 mm focal length has an internodal distance of 4 mm, if the scale of reduction is 1/10, and the total separation between object and image is 1·82 m, the formula gives a focal length of 148 mm, which is sufficient approximation for all practical purposes.

A variation of this method will avoid the error arising from neglecting the internodal distance, whatever its value, and at the same time determine it. Having measured the total distances l and l' for two scales m and m', the focal length F and internodal distance i are given by

$$F = \frac{l - l'}{\left(m + \dfrac{1}{m}\right) - \left(m' + \dfrac{1}{m'}\right)}$$

$$i = l - \left(2 + m + \frac{1}{m}\right)F$$

respectively.

If, for example, it has been found that, for

$$m = 1/5 \qquad l = 110 \text{ cm}$$
$$m' = 1/3 \qquad l' = 82 \text{ cm}$$

it follows that

$$\frac{28}{1\cdot866} = 15 \text{ cm}$$

and

$$i = 110 - 15(2 + 5 + 1/5)$$
$$= 110 - 108 = 2 \text{ cm}$$

These methods of measurement of focal length presuppose that the lens is free from distortion. That is to say, if a ray is directed towards the front nodal point so as to make an angle β with the principal axis (Fig. 9.8) it will strike the focal plane at a distance y' from the principal axis such that $y' = f \tan \beta$. The equivalent focal length can be measured in the laboratory, using a single collimator whose direction can be changed, or a number of collimators placed at fixed angles to the principal axis. The values of y' can then be found, and the equivalent focal length is defined as the limiting value of $y'/\tan \beta$ as β approaches zero.

The British Standards Institution recommend that the equivalent focal length so measured should be within $\pm$ 4 per cent of the value marked on the lens. A similar tolerance is specified by other national standards and has been adopted by the majority of photographic and optical manufacturers. Some of these also indicate the actual equivalent focal length for each individual lens, possibly by means of a figure code.

By international standards also, focal length on photographic lenses are nowadays almost invariably marked in millimetres. This is naturally the nominal value subject to the tolerance described above. Lenses marked in centimetres are usually of older manufacture (generally before 1960). In Britain and the U.S.A.

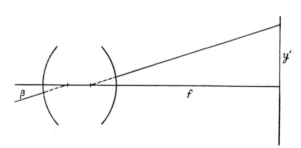

FIG. 9.8. COLLIMATOR METHOD OF DETERMINING FOCAL LENGTH

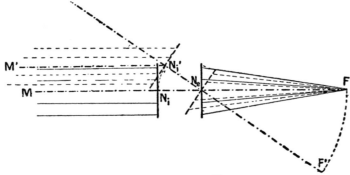

FIG. 9.9. THE MOËSSARD TOURNIQUET

focal lengths on lenses are still often marked in inches, but the millimetre notation is spreading here, too.

For accurate photogrammetric work it is necessary to know the *calibrated focal length*. If the lens suffers from distortion, however slightly, the distance of the image from the principal axis will be greater or less than the value given by the $y' = f \tan \beta$ formula. That is,

$$y' = f \tan \beta + \Delta y'$$

where $\Delta y'$ is a measure of the distortion. To measure the calibrated focal length it is necessary to carry out the laboratory method described above for the equivalent focal length, and then find a value of f which will give equal maximum and minimum values of $\Delta y'$. For this type of work the British Standards Institution recommend that the value of the calibrated focal length should be within $\pm$ 0·1 per cent of the value marked on the lens.

98. Direct Determination of the Position of the Nodal Points and the Focal Length. If the lens is rotated about an axis perpendicular to the optical axis, and containing the back nodal point, the images of very distant points remain fixed during the rotation, at least if it is not large and if the angle between the secondary axis to the object point and the optical axis is never very great (Moëssard, 1889).

To explain this, consider a lens (Fig. 9.9) which, for the sake of simplicity, we suppose to be reduced to the nodal planes $N_i N_e$. The image of an infinitely distant object in the direction $N_i M$ on the axis is formed at the focus F. After rotation about an axis perpendicular to the optical axis through the nodal point of emergence N_e, the nodal point of incidence will move to N_i'. The object point being infinitely

distant, the secondary axis $N_i' M'$ to this point is parallel to $N_i M$. By virtue of the definition of the nodal points (§ 73) the two exterior parts of the secondary axis are parallel to one another; the secondary axis thus emerges from the lens in the direction $N_e F$.

This property, which is made use of in the greater number of panoramic cameras, can also be utilized to determine the position of the nodal points and the focal length directly. The lens being mounted so that it can be moved to and fro on a platform which can rotate about a vertical pivot, the image is formed on a fixed screen and observed while the lens is moved on the platform until a position is found such that the images of distant points remain stationary while the lens is rotated. The nodal point is then on the axis of rotation and the distance of this axis from the screen is the focal length required (Moëssard Tourniquet, 1893). Turning the lens end for end, the other nodal point can be found similarly, and a second measurement made of the focal length, which gives a useful check on the first measurement.

The displacements of the image noticed when the angle of rotation is large enable us to determine the form of the focal surface point by point, and to study the various aberrations of the image.

99. Automatic Adjustment of Object and Image. The relations between the ultra-focal distances of two conjugate points, or of planes perpendicular to the axis passing through them, can be translated geometrically so that automatic linkages between these planes can be made, so dispensing with all focusing in enlarging or reproduction. The only adjustment to be made is that for the scale of reduction, obtained by the displacement of one of the conjugate planes, the image remaining sharp

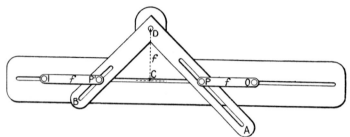

FIG. 9.10. SELF-FOCUSING LINKAGE
(Carpentier)

throughout. Numerous solutions of this problem have been given; we shall indicate only
some of them, selected from the most characteristic.

We shall suppose, in what follows, that the
nodal points coincide with the optical centre.
If this is not accurately true, it will be necessary
to assign to one of the nodal points the position
indicated by the centre, and move the conjugate
point corresponding to the other nodal point
in an appropriate direction by an amount equal
to the nodal interval.

1. Consider (Fig. 9.10) two points O and I,
free to move in a slot parallel to the optical axis.
At C, the intersection of the slot with the plane
drawn through the optical centre at right angles
to the optic axis, erect a perpendicular CD,
of length equal to the focal length f. By making a
bent lever, pivoted at D and having slots of which
the axes meet at right angles in D (J. Carpentier,
1898), rotate, it is possible to constrain two studs
P and P' in the axial slot to move so that their
distances d and d' from the point C will always
satisfy the relationship between the ultra-focal
distances of two points, viz.

$$dd' = f^2$$

This is possible since in the right-angled
triangle $P'OP$, in which a perpendicular is
dropped from the right-angle D to the hypotenuse PP', $P'C \times CP = (DC)^2 = f^2$.

It will then only be necessary to join P and
P' to O and I respectively by two connecting
rods, of length equal to f, to make certain that
O and I are conjugate points, and consequently

also the two planes perpendicular to the axis
through them.

2. Another linkage (G. Koenigs, 1900) is
formed of an articulated lozenge $P'AP''B$ (Fig.
9.11) and two equal rods AC, CB, pivoted at their
joint. If we represent by m the common length
of the four sides of the lozenge and by n that of
the connecting rods, the lengths $d = CP'$ and
$d' = CP''$ (which, by reason of symmetry, are
obviously in a straight line) will always be
such that

$$dd' = m^2 - n^2$$

This expression is derived from the fact that a
circle with A as centre and radius m will pass
through the points P' and P''. Now the product
of the distances of any point C from the two
intersections of the circle by a chord through C,
i.e. the product $CP' \times CP''$, is equal to the
difference between the squares of the radius m
and the distance n of the point C from the centre
of the circle.

We then only need to give to the constant
value of this product (dd') the square of the
focal length to get the required linkage. But
in these circumstances the jointed lozenge would
generally be of very great dimensions; by magnifying the movements transmitted from P'' to
P by means of a pantograph $CaP''a'Pb'P''bC$,
the size is considerably reduced. If the two
coupled lozenges of the pantograph have sides
of length l and L respectively, it will only be
necessary to satisfy the relationship

$$m^2 - n^2 = f^2 \frac{l}{L + l}$$

FIG. 9.11. SELF-FOCUSING LINKAGE
(Koenigs)

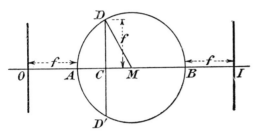

FIG. 9.12. PRINCIPLE OF FOCUSING LINKAGE.

3. Let (Fig. 9.12) the points O, I on the optical axis of the lens C be the intersections with the axis of the object plane and the image plane. From these points mark off towards the lens two distances equal to the focal length f. The points A and B thus obtained must be at distances from C such that $CA . CB = f^2$. Using AB as a diameter draw a circle with a centre M and through C draw the chord DD' perpendicular to AB. Elementary geometry teaches that $CA . CB = CD . CD'$, hence $CD = f$. The rays MA, MB, MD are evidently equal and, conversely, by this last equation the respective distances of the conjugate points OC, IC can be definitely determined (P. R. Burchall, 1933). Among the methods of linking based on this principle may be mentioned (A. Bonnetain, 1934) a system of three racks engaging in M on one and the same toothed wheel.

4. Finally, there are numerous arrangements based more or less directly on the hyperbolic cam (G. Pizzighelli, 1889). This follows from the fact that relation $dd' = f^2$ is the equation of a rectangular hyperbola with the asymptotes as axes. The vertex is at a distance f from the two asymptotes.

For instance, a table T on which the optical centre C is fixed can slide on two rails RR (Fig. 9.13) perpendicular to the object plane P.

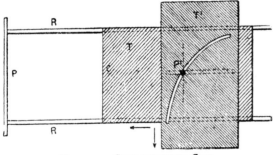

FIG. 9.13. SELF-FOCUSING CAM
(Pizzighelli)

Movement of the table T is communicated by means of racks and pinions to a table T', but in a direction at right angles. A slot in T' in the form of a rectangular hyperbola acts on a stud P' which is constrained to move in an axial slot in T. Any plane perpendicular to the optic axis and containing P' will be conjugate to P.

The hyperbolic cam is—in numerous variations—the most popularly used device for coupled focusing in enlargers, commonly described as "automatic". A practical difficulty is that the cam generally has to be shaped separately for every individual lens, since its parameters depend on the exact focal length, and this varies for production series lenses within the tolerances indicated under § 97. (This applies to all the above mechanical focusing linkages). The hyperbolic cam has the practical advantage of being probably among the easier types to machine; it is even possible to have a number of cams on for instance an automatically focusing enlarger for use with interchangeable lenses. The equipment must however always be used with the specific set of lenses for which the cams are dimensioned.

Some linkage arrangements have appeared in which an adjustment can compensate reasonably closely for slight variation in the focal length. In practice the precision of mechanical focal linkages is in any case governed by mechanical factors such as wear on the cam or the cam roller (or follower). This may after considerable use call for readjustment and possibly even for reshaping or replacement of the cam or certain linkage elements.

For this reason there have been numerous attempts to produce automatic focusing systems where the adjustment of the lens-to-image plane distance is governed by optical measurement of the image sharpness. While sharpness cannot be measured as such, it is possible to assess the image definition by the fact that loss of sharpness also results in loss of image contrast. And contrast can be measured, for instance by photo-electric devices, which can in turn control servo systems to bring the image plane (or the lens) into a position of optimum sharpness.

100. Optical Automatic Focusing. Another aspect of automatic image plane adjustment is concerned with keeping the object or image plane automatically in a constant position relative to the lens. This arises when the object plane is liable to move unpredictably within small distances and has a special application in slide projectors where the object plane is a film transparency liable to buckle or "pop" through heating in the projector.

In the arrangement of Fig. 9.14 a light ray *OM* (derived from the projector lamp) is reflected by the mirror *M* on to the image plane of the transparency *T* and from there to the gap *X* between two photo cells *P* and *P'* (or evenly on to the two cells). At this stage the system is balanced, and set up so that the lens *L*, rigidly linked with the mirror *M*, throws a sharp image on the screen. If the plane of the transparency moves to a position *T'*, the light ray from the surface of the transparency is reflected along the dotted path to the photo cell *P'*, which activates a servo motor *S* to move the lens *L* in the direction of the arrow. This brings the mirror to the position *M'*, so that the light beam reflected from *T'* again falls in the gap *X* between the two photo cells. If the transparency plane moves in the opposite direction, the reflected ray would fall on the photo cell *P*, making the servo motor drive *L* in the opposite direction. This system therefore ensures a constant distance between *T* and *L*.

Such an optical linkage could also be extended to control the lens movement by the movement of the projection surface, for instance the paper plane in an enlarger. Thus in Fig. 9.15, *N* is the negative plane in an enlarger, *O* the paper plane with a light source projected via the mirrors *M* and *M'* at the negative plane and from there towards the photo cells *P* and *P'*.

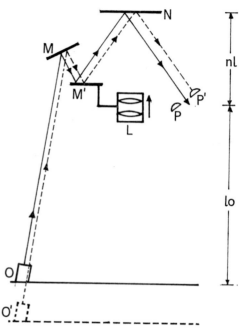

FIG. 9.15. OPTICAL FOCUSING COUPLING IN AN ENLARGER

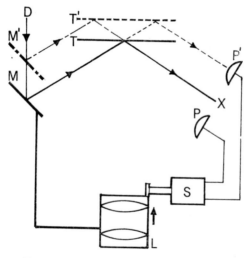

FIG. 9.14. OPTICAL FOCUSING COUPLING FOR SLIDE PROJECTORS

When the paper plane moves to the position *O'*, the projected ray is displaced along the dotted path and reaches the photo cell *P'*. To restore the reflected ray to a path where it falls between the two photo cells again, the lens *L* with the mirror *M'* has to move upwards. By suitable positioning and inclination of the fixed mirror *M* and the moving mirror *M'* it will be possible to ensure that the distances *nl* and *lo* always remain conjugate. That way the image in the plane of *O* would remain sharp when the scale of reproduction is altered by changing the distance *lo*.

101. Combination of Lenses or Optical Systems. It sometimes happens that another system, convergent or divergent, has to be added to a lens, and it is desirable to be able to determine the focal length of the combination, the optical axes of the different components being assumed to coincide (centred system).

For thin lenses in contact the law that *the power* (§ 93) *of the system is the sum of the powers of the components* may be considered exact, it being understood that negative powers (corresponding with divergent lenses) are to be subtracted.

Calling *f* and *f'* the focal lengths of the

components and F that of the resultant system, then

$$1/F = 1/f + 1/f'$$

In general, however, this rule is not applicable, and account must be taken of the *spacing of the combination*, i.e. the separation between the back nodal point of the first system and the front nodal point of the second. Calling e the separation as defined above, the resultant focal length is given by

$$1/F = 1/f + 1/f' - e/ff'$$

The resultant focus is at a distance D from the back focus of the second system, equal to

$$D = \frac{f'^2}{e - (f - f')}$$

The focal length of the combination can be found by considering the separation δ between the back focus of the first system and the front focus of the second. The interval δ is connected with the interval e by the relation

$$\delta = e - (f - f')$$

from which it may be shown that the resultant focal length is

$$F = ff'/\delta$$

These rudiments will have an application to the case of lenses in which focusing is effected by varying the separation of their components (§ 159), to supplementary lenses (convergent or divergent, § 181) and to telephoto lenses (§§ 152 to 154).

To determine the focal length of a divergent lens the procedure is the same as for a convergent lens but a *virtual object* must be used, which can be the image of an object formed by a convergent system of relatively great focal length, the divergent lens being placed between the convergent system and the real image.

For an approximate value of the focal length, the lens may be directed towards the sun, and the distance from the lens to a screen measured when the diameter of the circle of light on it is double that of a circular aperture placed against the lens; or a thin divergent lens may be neutralized by placing it in contact with a thin convergent lens of the same focal length (the method used by oculists).

CHAPTER X

DIAPHRAGMS AND RELATIVE APERTURE : EFFECT ON PERSPECTIVE AND INTENSITY

102. Relative aperture of diaphragm—effective aperture—maximum relative aperture. 103. Aperture scale—stopping down—normal and fractional stop intervals—aperture scales. 104. Numerical aperture. 105. Different types of diaphragms—iris diaphragm—rotating diaphragm—Waterhouse stops—slotted blade diaphragms. 106. Centre stops—for optical correction.—for light control. 107. Pupils of an optical system—entrance pupil and exit pupil—pupil magnification. 108. Photographic perspective—perspective drawing by a lens. 109. Perspective and viewpoint. 110. Depth of field—standards of sharpness. 111. Relative depth of field—calculation in terms of convergencies. 112. Absolute depth of field—depth and image size. 113. Depth of field indicators—depth of field scales—semi-automatic aperture coupled indicators. 114. Factors affecting depth of field—focal length—aperture—subject distance—definition. 115. Depth with interchangeable lenses—the need for absolute sharpness standards. 116. Choice of lens for depth—depth and image scale. 117. Close-up depth of field. 118. Hyperfocal distance—simplified depth calculations. 119. Absolute hyperfocal distance calculation. 120. Direct hyperfocal distance calculation. 121. Depth of field limits from the hyperfocal distance. 122. Influence of the corrections of the lens on the depth of field and hyperfocal distance—effects of spherical aberration—aberrations and circle of confusion—depth of field and focus shift. 123. Accuracy of depth of field tables—when to round off—rate of sharpness fall off—sharpness near the limits of the depth of field. 124. Fixed focus cameras—hyperfocal zoom coupling. 125. Focusing scales—hyperfocal distance scale. 126. Depth of focus—latitude in the image plane—factors affecting depth of focus. 127. Effect of relative aperture on the brightness of the image—aperture and focal length—transmission stops. 128. Effect of the scale of an image on its brightness—exposure corrections in close-up photography. 129. Measurement of the effective aperture. 130. Measurement of the pupillary magnification.

102. Relative Aperture of a Diaphragm. The diameter of the beam of rays incident parallel to the axis which, after refraction through the lens components in front of the diaphragm, completely fills the latter is called the *effective diameter* of the diaphragm. Thus, *D*, *D'* and *D''* (Fig. 10.1), although of different diameters, all have the same effective diameter *d*

If, without altering the position of the stop, the real diameter is altered, its effective aperture varies proportionally. The constant ratio between the effective and the real aperture is sometimes called the *coefficient of the effective aperture*, and is equal to 1 only if the beam of light reaches the stop before meeting the lens

(the case with some single lenses). In the general case, in which the stop has in front of it one or more lenses forming a convergent system, the coefficient is greater than 1. As the value depends on the construction of a given lens, obviously no rule can be given, but it may be stated that with symmetrical anastigmats it generally lies between 1·1 and 1·15, whilst with anastigmats consisting of three separated lenses it often amounts to 1·3.

If the front element or group of elements of a lens system has a net diverging power (as in inverted telephoto designs—§ 156), the coefficient of the effective aperture may be less than 1. Values may here lie between 0·6 and 0·9. With normal telephoto lenses (§ 152) where the rear element is strongly diverging, the coefficient values may go much higher—up to or even exceeding 2·0. The same applies even more to tele-converters—diverging lens systems placed behind a normal lens to double, treble or further increase its effective focal length (§ 183).

If the diameter of the effective aperture is 1/*n*th the focal length *f*, the aperture is said to

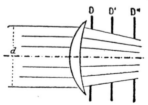

FIG. 10.1 EFFECTIVE APERTURE

be f/n, where n is also called the *relative aperture* of the diaphragm considered. If, for example, the real diameter is 0·8 in. and the effective aperture is 0·92 in. of a lens of 4·6 in. focal length, the relative aperture is $f/5$. This is often designated as the *f-number*, sometimes written also as $f5$, $f:5$, or $1:5$.

The relative aperture of the largest stop a lens can use is called the **maximum relative aperture**, or, more simply, the maximum aperture of the lens. We shall see later (§ 127) that the maximum relative aperture of a lens is the principal factor governing its speed. It was seen in § 86 that the illumination in the focal plane is reduced as the angular separation from the axis is increased, so this statement is true for the centre of the field only.

103. Aperture Scales. The light transmitted by a lens is a function of the area of the relative aperture—in turn a function of the square of the diameter. Doubling the f-number (e.g. reducing the relative aperture—also known as *stopping down*) from $f/4$ to $f/8$ halves the diameter and therefore reduces the light transmission to $\frac{1}{4}$. As this is rather a large interval between successive steps of exposure adjustment, lens aperture scales are invariably marked in steps which double or halve the light transmission. In terms of f-numbers this means that the latter must increase by a factor of the square root of 2 from step to step, for instance $f/1$, $f/\sqrt{2}$, $f/2$, $f/2\sqrt{2}$, $f/4$ etc.

The internationally accepted scale of aperture markings on lenses is in fact based on this series and runs $f/1$, $f/1\cdot4$, $f/2$, $f/2\cdot8$, $f/4$, $f/5\cdot6$, $f/8$, $f/11$, $f/16$, $f/22$, $f/32$, $f/45$, $f/64$ and so on. Some of these values are rounded-off approximations of the $\sqrt{2}$ series; for example $f/11$ should really be $f/11\cdot3$, but in practice this difference can be neglected.

The series can also be extended to larger apertures (lower f-numbers) than $f/1 : f/0\cdot7$ and $f/0\cdot5$. The latter is the theoretical limit for lenses with an air space between the lens and the image plane; it has been approached but not reached.

The above series of aperture numbers based on the $\sqrt{2}$ factor is commonly referred to as having normal *stop intervals*. It is also possible to have reduced stop intervals, for instance half stops, $\frac{1}{3}$ stops or $\frac{1}{4}$ stops. These are not normally marked numerically, but frequently indicated on the aperture scale of a lens by dots or by mechanical click stops. Smaller intervals are rarely indicated; $\frac{1}{3}$ and $\frac{1}{4}$ stops can often

COMPARISON OF APERTURE SCALES

f-number			Relative Light Passing Power	Decrease in Light Passing Power (Nearest 1/3 Stops)
1			10,000	0
	1·1		7,937	1
		1·2 (1·3)	6,300	2
1·4 (1·5)			5,000	3
	1·6		3,969	4
		1·8	3,150	5
2 (1·9)			2,500	6
	2·2		1,984	7
		2·5	1,575	8
2·8 (2·9)			1,250	9
	3·2		992	10
		3·5	788	11
4 (3·8)			625	12
	4·5		496	13
		5	417	14
5·6			312	15
	6·3		248	16
		7	209	17
8 (7·7)			156	18
	9		124	19
		10	104	20
11			79	21
	12·5		62	22
		14	52	23
16			40	24
	18		31	25
		20	26	26
22			20	27
	25		16	28
		28	13	29
32			9·9	30
	36		7·8	31
		40	6·5	32
45			5·0	33
	48 (50)		3·9	34

be set by estimation. Any finer subdivision than that is not only impractical but unnecessary since sensitized materials do not as a rule respond visibly to smaller exposure increments.

The maximum aperture of a lens may not necessarily fall into the above $\sqrt{2}$ series, for instance a fairly popular maximum aperture of $f/3\cdot5$ falls between $f/2\cdot8$ and $f/4$. The reason for this is partly the fact that the degree of lens correction achievable with a given design expenditure falls off very rapidly, as the lens aperture is increased beyond a certain limiting value which is in no way connected with the above arbitrary scale of aperture markings. It then has a certain propaganda and sales value for the optical manufacturer to utilise

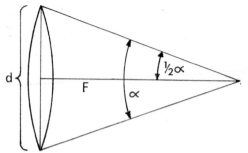

FIG. 10.2. RELATIVE APERTURE AND
NUMERICAL APERTURE

and publicise even a fractional gain of light transmission over the next smaller standard stop figure—however insignificant this may be in terms of practical exposure. The British Standards Institution (and other standards organizations) recommend that the marking of the maximum aperture should be within ±5 per cent of the true relative aperture.

One or two other aperture scales based on the $\sqrt{2}$ factor but with a different starting point have been used in the past, but are now obsolete. The series $f/1\cdot1$, $f/1\cdot6$, $f/2\cdot2$ etc. used to be popular in central Europe before the Second World War. Attempts have also been made at times to mark aperture scales in arithmetic numbers indicating the relative exposure required. Such scales are still found on enlarger lenses, where it is more important to know relative exposures for different positions of the lens diaphragm than the $f/$ number as such.

104. Numerical Aperture. An alternative way of specifying the relative aperture, derived from microscopy, is the numerical aperture. The relative aperture, as the ratio of focal length to effective aperture diameter (F/d), can be expressed as

$$f\text{-number} = \frac{1}{2 \tan \tfrac{1}{2}\alpha}$$

where α is the angle subtended by the effective aperture at the focal point on the lens axis (Fig. 10.2). The numerical aperture A is then given by:

$$A = n \times \sin \tfrac{1}{2}\alpha$$

where n is the refractive index of the medium in which the lens is being used. For air, $n = 1$, and A becomes $\sin \tfrac{1}{2}\alpha$. The table below lists numerical aperture equivalents of the standard series of f-numbers for a lens in air:

NUMERICAL APERTURES AND f-NUMBERS

$f/$	0·7	1	1·4	2	2·8	4	5·6
A	0·57	0·45	0·34	0·24	0·18	0·12	0·09

Where $\tfrac{1}{2}\alpha$ is smaller than 10°, i.e. with apertures of $f/4$ or smaller (higher f-numbers), the sine and the tangent of the angle are nearly the same, and the approximate relationship between numerical aperture and f-number becomes:

$$f\text{-number} = \frac{1}{2A}$$

105. Different Types of Diaphragms. In order to be able to get all possible apertures with a lens, modern objectives are usually fitted with an *iris diaphragm* (Fig. 10.3) having an aperture which can be varied by means of a rotating ring or external lever on the mount. In Fig. 10.3 the guiding slots of the movable ring are shown radial, which for a long time used to be the accepted form. By sloping them it is possible to make the usual markings of apertures almost equidistant (Lan Davis, 1911). That means that equal angular displacements of the aperture setting ring (which controls the iris diaphragm) results in equal proportional increases or decreases of the light passing power of the

FIG. 10.3. IRIS
DIAPHRAGM

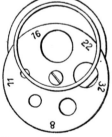

FIG. 10.4. ROTATING
DIAPHRAGMS

FIG. 10.5. WATERHOUSE
DIAPHRAGMS

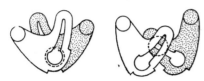

FIG. 10.6. TWO-BLADE DIAGRAM

lens. This is the usual form with modern lenses where the iris disphragm is often mechanically coupled with the exposure time setting on a linear scale (for instance for an exposure value system) or with an exposure meter. The thin blades of the iris are of ordinary steel or ebonite. Though ebonite has the advantage of not rusting, like steel, in damp climates, care must be taken not to subject it to great heat. Hence an ebonite iris should not be used in an enlarger or projector using a condenser, or there will be danger of the blades melting or burning.

In inexpensive amateur cameras—and sometimes also with lenses of which the component glasses are too closely spaced to accommodate an iris—a *rotating diaphragm* is employed (Fig. 10.4). Here an eccentric disc has a number of different apertures, which, by rotation of the disc, are brought into position concentric with the axis of the lens. The size of the aperture in position is indicated by a number engraved on the part of the projecting disc opposite the aperture.

In many old lenses and in modern lenses for process work, *Waterhouse stops* (Fig. 10.5) are inserted through a slot in the side of the lens tube. The making of negatives through screens, as used in preparing half-tone blocks or in lithography, requires stops with non-circular openings (generally square), and capable of being variously orientated in the lens tube.

Another type of diaphragm uses one or two slotted blades which change their position relative to each other (or relative to a fixed opening) as shown in Fig. 10.6. By appropriately designing the shape of the slot it is possible to arrange for the mechanical movement to take place in linear intervals corresponding to equal stop intervals. Such systems are widely used in comparatively simple cameras with automatic exposure control (especially cine cameras). Since the blades are light enough to be moved by electrical energy derived from a photo cell, the light falling on the cell directly adjusts the lens opening.

With slotted blade systems the shape of the opening is no longer circular, but may vary from a near circle to a square or a rhomboid. In theory this may influence the evenness of illumination in the image plane, though in practice the effect is not very significant. A non-circular aperture may also cause non-circular discs (rather than circles) of confusion (§ 79) because the image of the discs reproduces the shape of the lens aperture.

106. Centre Stops. Under certain circumstances special stops are used to hold back or obstruct the centre of the light beam rather than —or in addition to—its outside diameter. Such centre stops may be permanently incorporated in a lens (for instance neutral density spots of specific diameter evaporated or otherwise applied to the centre of one of the lens components), or they may be separate units such as a piece of plane glass with a central opaque stop for fitting in front of the lens.

Such centre stops can serve various purposes:

(*a*) In soft focus lenses. Here the lens system is left deliberately undercorrected for spherical and/or chromatic aberration. Stopping down the lens with the iris diaphragm for exposure control would however modify the balance between corrected central and uncorrected zonal rays. So where small lens stops are required for exposure purposes, the centre stop is fitted in front of the lens and the iris diaphragm can remain at or near its full opening. The minimum aperture to which the diaphragm can be stopped down has the same effective diameter as the diameter of the centre stop used (in soft focus lenses often between $f/4$ and $f/5 \cdot 6$).

(*b*) In rare cases where the best balance for optical correction is achieved predominantly for zonal rays, the centre stop simply eliminates the central image forming rays which in this case contribute to unsharpness rather than to sharpness.

(*c*) With lenses of short focus used with small negative formats the degree of unsharpness introduced by diffraction becomes significant at small apertures. While the size of the Airy disc (§ 85) depends on the relative aperture of the lens, the diameter of the disc is important in relation to the image size. Thus an Airy disc of about $0 \cdot 25$ mm diameter (obtained with a lens stopped down to $f/22$) has a much greater effect on a 24×36 mm negative than on a 4×5 inch one. The latter is liable to be enlarged much less in print making than the former. For this reason some manufacturers limit the smallest aperture setting of the lenses to somewhere between $f/11$ and $f/22$ when the lens is intended for small negative sizes. If however a centre stop is used in the system, a light control equivalent to very small apertures becomes possible without reducing the actual diameter of the iris to a degree where diffraction effects become disturbing. In any case, very small openings of an iris are difficult to calibrate accurately, and the purely mechanical setting error becomes greater.

107. Pupils of an Optical System. The beams of light passing through an optical system are limited by the aperture of the diaphragm. Now the components of the system in front of the stop (lens L_1, Fig. 10.7) form a virtual image (called the *entrance pupil*, P_i) of the stop D. The entrance pupil is such that the prolongation of rays through L_1, which afterwards are just bounded by the diaphragm D, reach the outline of the entrance pupil. The diameter of the entrance pupil is thus equal to the effective aperture of the diaphragm (§ 102).

In like manner the components behind the diaphragm (L_2 in Fig. 10.7) form a virtual image of its aperture, called the *exit pupil* P_e, the outline of which is reached by the prolongations of those rays which (before passing through L_2) just reached the outline of the diaphragm D (E. Abbé, 1890). The two pupils are thus conjugate with respect to the complete lens.

The pupils must not be confused with the windows (German, *Luke*), consideration of which is less frequent in treating of photographic lenses. The windows are the images formed by the two systems L_1 and L_2 of the aperture limiting the field of view (the mount of the lens or the aperture of some attachment to the lens), and thus correspond to the field stops in observational instruments.

The ratio of the exit pupil diameter to the entrance pupil diameter is also known as the pupil magnification. For most normal lenses this is in the neighbourhood of 1; for telephoto lenses (§ 152) it may be appreciably less than 1 and for certain types of wide angle lenses—the inverted telephoto type (§ 156)—it is generally greater than 1. Where the pupil magnification deviates appreciably from unity, this affects the calculation of exposure factors for close-ups (§ 128) as well as certain depth of field formulae (§ 117).

From the definition given above, the pupil magnification depends also on the orientation of the lens with respect to the image plane. If a lens is inverted (mounted on the camera back to front), the pupil magnification similarly becomes the reciprocal of its previous value. So a lens with a pupil magnification of say 1·5 when used the right way round, has a magnification of 0·67 when reversed back-to-front.

If we suppose the diaphragm (Fig. 10.7) gradually reduced to a small opening O on the axis, admitting but a single ray of light, this single ray would be the one originally directed to the point I, the centre of the entrance pupil, and would appear to emerge, after passing through the lens, from the point E, the centre of the exit pupil. The ray RR' forms what is sometimes called a *principal ray*.

In the particular case where the stop is placed with its centre at the optical centre of the instrument (which frequently happens with symmetrical lenses), the centres of the pupils coincide with the nodal points, but this coincidence does not occur with single lenses, convertible sets, nor telephotos, and in other types of lenses is not always aimed at.

Just as by consideration of nodal and focal points it is possible to determine the dimensions of the image without considering the construction of the optical system forming it, so by consideration of the pupils it is possible to determine the perspective and the centre of projection of images without having to be concerned with the optical system. The pupils in fact determine which of the rays are used in the formation of the image, without upsetting in any way the conclusions that have been drawn, as to the position and dimensions of this image, from the positions of the nodal points and the foci.

108. Photographic Perspective. The photographic image is an exact perspective rendering of the objects represented, the viewpoint of which, relatively to the objects, is the centre of

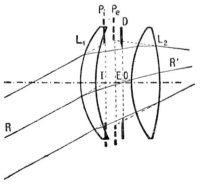

FIG. 10.7. PUPILS OF A LENS

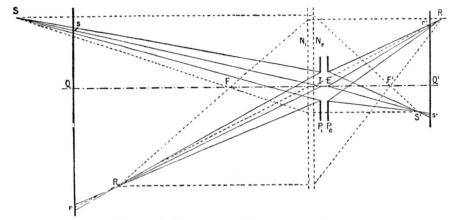

FIG. 10.8. PERSPECTIVE DRAWING BY A LENS

the entrance pupil; relatively to the image, the viewpoint is usually identical with the nodal point of emergence.

Consider (Fig. 10.8) the two conjugate planes QQ' of an optical system represented by its nodal points, foci, and pupils, and let us find how the points R and S outside the plane Q will be reproduced on the plane Q', R' and S' being the respective images of R and S (the graphical construction is indicated by dotted lines) and being themselves outside Q'.

The bundle of rays used in the formation of the image of the point R is limited by the cone with apex R and base P_i (the entrance pupil). After passing through the lens it forms another cone, having the exit pupil P_e as base and R' as apex. These two cones form circular patches (*circles of confusion*) on the *focused plane* Q and on its conjugate Q', where the focusing screen or photographic film is placed. The circles of confusion are conjugate, with their centres r and r' at the intersections of the principal ray with the respective planes, and the ratio of their sizes is equal to the ratio of the distances of Q and Q' (say m). If the patch at r' is sufficiently small and the photograph is viewed at a sufficiently large distance, the patch is indistinguishable from the geometrical point image of r (the secondary axis corresponding to r has been drawn in Fig. 10.8).

The photographic image thus coincides with a photograph, made on a scale of reproduction m, of the perspective of the objects projected on the plane Q from a point coinciding with the centre of the entrance pupil. It is thus itself a perspective view if the lens is free from distor-

tion and the diameter of the entrance pupil is a small fraction of the distance of the objects represented, so that stereoscopic effects are avoided (§ 91).

Now it is known that different perspectives obtained by proportional enlargement or reduction have their principal distances proportional to their respective scales (§ 31). The principal distance of the perspective at Q' (the photographic image) is thus the product of the distance of Q from the entrance pupil, multiplied by m.

When the object distance is large compared with the distance between the entrance pupil and the front nodal point, the principal distance of the photograph can be taken as the image distance, and the viewpoint as the back nodal point (L. P. Clerc, 1923).

109. Perspective and Viewpoint. The fact that the construction of the lens (except in the case of very pronounced distortion) and its focal length have no influence on the perspective of the image can be proved by photographing an architectural subject *from the same viewpoint* successively with a pinhole (§ 62) and with lenses of different focal lengths. The different images thus obtained will be identical except for size.

From a close viewpoint such an image will show an exaggerated and often unpleasant perspective; this is however due entirely to the close viewpoint (§ 35) and not—as sometimes assumed—to the use of a short-focus lens. The latter, especially if it is the only lens available with a camera, does however tempt the photographer to go comparatively close to the scene to be photographed, to obtain an image of reasonably large scale. Unless the photographer is specially trained, he does not notice, when examining the view, the exaggerated perspective arising from too close a viewpoint, the brain making the objects appear at their correct relative size, whilst binocular vision places them in their correct relative positions. On the plane image these compensations do not exist, and the so-called distortion becomes actually offensive, especially if the image is viewed from a position other than the correct viewpoint (§§ 32 to 35). These anomalies disappear in stereoscopic vision if the images are viewed at the principal distance although the angle of view may then be too large for the eye to view the whole picture without rotating.

When it is stated that a lens of short focus gives "faulty perspective," which should be translated as "geometrically correct but unpleasant perspective," it is understood, then, that the photographer has tried to compensate for the smallness of the scale of his image by approaching too close to his subject.

The position of the camera should be chosen without any consideration of scale. If, when the viewpoint is chosen, it is found that the lens is not of sufficient focal length to give directly as large an image as desired, the small image should be subsequently enlarged.

The descriptions "short focus", "normal focus" etc. are of course relative to the film size being used (§ 134). A wide-angle lens is often used as a short-focus lens, but the two are not the same. See § 134.

110. Depth of Field. The image of the point outside the plane focused on (for example points S and R which lie beyond and short of the object plane Q respectively in Fig. 10.8) is a circular patch in the image plane (r' and s'). If these circular image patches are small enough, they are practically indistinguishable from points and the image still appears adequately sharp. There is thus a range of object planes, behind Q towards S and in front of Q towards R, which gives rise to image patches of sufficiently small diameter in the plane Q' (sufficiently small circles of confusion) to form a sharp image. This range of object distances from Q to S and from Q to R in Fig. 10.8 is the depth of field, and the limits of this depth can be determined.

The calculations for doing this are however very arbitrary in many respects: they assume a subjective tolerance of unsharpness, and they are based on geometrical optics, and which take

no account of the distribution of light within the patch. Moreover, it is assumed that the lens is perfect, giving aplanatic, anastigmatic, and plane images, conditions which are unfortunately unattainable. The results of these calculations must be regarded only as indicating in what direction the depth of field changes when the focal length, relative aperture, and object distance are changed. Practical results may differ considerably with lenses of different types, even though the focal length and relative aperture are the same. Some of these aspects are dealt with in more detail in § 122.

It is necessary, first of all, to decide upon the tolerance on sharpness which can be permitted, and this tolerance may either be fixed as an *absolute* value or a *relative* value. In the first case it is usual to fix a maximum value to the diameter of the circle of confusion, of, for example, 0·1 mm, a size which, when viewed at a distance of 25–30 cm is indistinguishable from a point.

This convention is purely arbitrary, and is too severe for pictures which are to be viewed at a greater distance, as when placed on a wall, and is not sufficiently severe for a small image which has to be subsequently enlarged by projection or examination under a magnifier (the case of stereoscopic pictures). In the second case the maximum diameter of the circle of confusion is defined as a fraction (say, 1/2,000) of the normal distance of viewing, and therefore of the image distance. This convention is more logical for pictorial photography than the absolute method.

Whichever convention is used, the diameter of the circle of confusion assumed—absolute or relative—remains completely arbitrary. This fact is the primary reason for the discrepancy often found in depth of field values obtained from different sources (tables or calculators) for lenses of the same parameters used under the same conditions.

Alternative frequently used values for the circle of confusion are 0·4 mm as an absolute value and 1/1000 of the image distance—in practice of the focal length.

111. Relative Depth of Field. Let q and q' (Fig. 10.8) be the ultra-nodal distances of the object plane Q and its conjugate Q' on which the photographic image is recorded, respectively; f/n the relative aperture of the lens, r and s the ultra-nodal distances of point-objects respectively in front of and behind the plane Q, r' and s' the ultra-nodal distances of their focused images.

The dimensions of the circles of confusion in the plane of the image (r) and (s) are expressed by

$$\frac{(r)}{f/n} = \frac{r' - q'}{r'}, \quad \frac{(s)}{f/n} = \frac{q' - s'}{s'}$$

In order that the blurs (r) and (s) should have the maximum permissible diameter aq' (the coefficient a being, for example, $1/2{,}000$), the distances r' and s' must be such that

$$\frac{naq'}{f} = \frac{r' - q'}{r'} = \frac{q' - s'}{s'}$$

which may be written

$$1/q' - 1/r' = 1/s' - 1/q' = na/f$$

and as (§ 93)

$$1/q' = 1/f - 1/q, \quad 1/r' = 1/f - 1/r$$
$$1/s' = 1/f - 1/s$$

it follows that

$$1/r - 1/q = 1/q - 1/s = na/f$$

The difference between the extreme convergences (§ 93) of R and S and the convergence of the plane Q focused on is then represented by $n/2{,}000$ths of the power of the lens, all measurements being expressed in diopters; and the total depth of field (distance between R and S measured parallel to the optical axis) corresponds to a difference in convergence equal to $n/1{,}000$ths of the power.

The calculation of depths of field in terms of convergences may be a little unfamiliar at first, but is convenient in practice. The convergences are simply the reciprocals of the distances involved (focal length and appropriate object distances). The advantage of these reciprocals is that they can easily be added and subtracted and are thus simpler to handle. A useful aid is however a table of reciprocals of numbers from 1 to 1000 for making calculations rapidly and of sufficient accuracy in problems relating to depth of field. Alternatively, a slide rule with a reciprocal scale is fully adequate.

For a lens of 110 mm focal length, i.e. 0·11 m, or a power of $1/0·11 = 9·09$ diopters, with an aperture of $f/6$, the total tolerance of convergence will be $(9·09 \times 6)/1{,}000$, or 0·05454 diopters, which has to be divided between the near and far points. If the object focused on was at 5 m, corresponding to a convergence of $1/5 = 0·2$ diopters, the convergences of the two limits of

depth of field will be 0·20 ± 0·02727, corresponding to object distances of $1/0·22727$ and $1/0·17273$, or 4·40 and 5·80 m respectively.

It should be noted that the sharp field extends less in front of the plane focused on than behind it (0·6 and 0·8 m in the example above).

It may be said that the depth of field is that part of the object space in which the entrance pupil appears to have an approximately constant angular size, the variations being less than the permitted angle of confusion (A. Jonon, 1925).

Calculations of a similar degree of simplicity enable us to work out the aperture at which the lens must be used in order to give a sharp image of objects at different distances from the lens, and on what plane the lens ought to be focused. The convergences of the extreme points at distances of 2 and 8 m respectively, are $\frac{1}{2} = 0·5$ and $\frac{1}{8} = 0·125$ diopters. The difference is thus 0·375 diopters. In order that the tolerance in convergence may be equal to this, which represents $375/9·09$ thousandths of the power of the lens (say $41/1{,}000$) the lens must be stopped down to $f/41$. In practice, the nearest marked aperture of the iris, $f/45$, is used, and this will give ample guarantee of the sharpness and depth required.

The distance to focus on will be given by the mean of the extreme convergences $(0·500 + 0·125)/2 = 0·312$ corresponding to a distance of $1/0·312$ m $= 3·2$ m. That is, $q = 2rs/(r + s)$. This distance is independent of the sharpness tolerance, either relative or absolute whether based on geometrical or physical considerations.

112. **Absolute Depth of Field.** To conform to tradition we shall deduce the formulae for depth of field in terms of an absolute diameter of the circle of confusion e (e.g. $e = 0·1$ mm), and not, as above, a constant fraction of the ultranodal distance of the plane of the photographic plate.

Assigning a limit e to the diameter of the circle of confusion, and calling (R) and (S) the image patches projected on the plane Q by beams having their apices at R and S, and bounded by the diaphragm, we find, in the same notation as above, that

$$\frac{R}{f/n} = \frac{q - r}{r}, \quad \frac{S}{f/n} = \frac{s - q}{s}$$

If the image Q' of the plane Q is reduced on a scale $1/m$, which implies that $q = (m + 1)f$, the diameters (r) and (s) of the images are equal to $(R)/m$ and $(S)/m$ respectively. If these are to be equal to the maximum diameter e, then (R) and (S) are equal to me, and r and s (the distances of the near and far planes which will be rendered sharply) will be calculated from

$$\frac{em}{f/n} = \frac{q - r}{r} = \frac{s - q}{s}$$

$$q/r = 1 + nme/f, \qquad q/s = 1 - nme/f$$

whence, after simplification

$$r = \frac{(m + 1)f^2}{f + nme} \qquad s = \frac{(m + 1)f^2}{f - nme}$$

In the above equations m is the reduction factor, equal to object size/image size. This makes the formulae simpler than using the scale of reproduction M ($=$ image size/object size), though the use of M is more useful for small reduction scales, in other words real magnifications from 0·1 upwards (§ 117).

Using the same numerical values as in the previous example, we have a value of $m =$ approx. $5/0·11 = 44·5$. With an object at a distance of 5 metres, a lens aperture of $f/6$ and taking 0·1 mm as the maximum diameter of the circle of confusion, we get $s = 6·6$ metres and $r = 4·02$ metres. Hence the depth of field obtained is much greater than previously calculated.

This is because the tolerance of definition is greater in this case. The variations in the values obtained *do not however affect the actual image sharpness* in any way, only the standard of what we choose to call "adequately sharp" or "no longer sharp enough".

In this case a limit of the circle of confusion of 0·1 mm is adequate for a large negative—say about 5 × 7 inches or 13 × 18 cm or larger—but decidedly inadequate for a 24 × 36 mm miniature camera negative which is likely to be

appreciably enlarged. With an average magnification scale of 5 times, the original 0·1 mm patch would become 0· 5 mm, which is very noticeably blurred when it appears on a print viewed around 25 to 30 cm away. This therefore confirms the logic of selecting a relative value value for the sharpness tolerance as indicated in § 110. This is however subject to one reservation discussed in § 115.

113. **Depth of Field Indicators.** If the camera carries a scale by which the change in camera extension can be measured, it is possible to avoid the above calculations.

The procedure is here to focus the lens in succession on the near and the far limits of sharpness required, and note each time the position of the movable part of the distance scale. The camera is then set to the midway position (in actual extension, not in engraved distance values), which sets the lens to optimum sharpness. To cover this range with a degree of sharpness equivalent to a circle of confusion of 0·1 mm, the f-number is 5× the change in the camera extension in millimetres (G. Cromer, 1911).

If for instance the movement is 4 mm, the required aperture is $f/20$. For a sharpness standard of 0·2 mm or 0·05 mm, half or double the factor (2·5 or 10 times respectively) must be taken, yielding $f/10$ or $f/40$ respectively in the above case.

This principle is a basis of depth of field indicators incorporated in the focusing movement of a camera (Fig. 10.9). Most such movements are helical ones where the lens is moved forward and back by rotating a screw ring; this has the advantage that a comparatively small axial shift is translated into a larger radial displacement, so that the scale can be spread out more. Since it is the relative displacements which matter, this does not affect the working of the

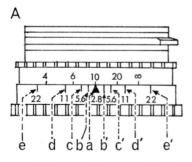

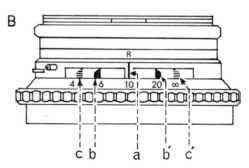

FIG. 10.9. DEPTH OF FIELD INDICATOR SCALE (A) AND COUPLED INDICATOR (B)

depth of field indicator. It works in the same way even with a lens which has front cell focusing—i.e. where the distance setting is adjusted by slightly altering the focal length of the lens.

The depth of field indicator consists usually of a series of index marks or lines arranged in pairs symmetrically about the central focusing index a in Fig. 10.9A, so set up that the depth of field scale moves relative to the distance scale (or vice versa) during focusing. The line pairs are marked with different f-numbers. When the lens is set to any given distance so that the latter on the distance scale is opposite the index a, any pair of lines marked with the same f-number indicates the near and far limits of the depth of field zone at that aperture. Thus in Fig. 10.9A the lens is focused at 10 metres, and the index lines for $f/5\cdot6$ are opposite positions corresponding on the distance scale to approximately 7 and 16 metres respectively. The nearest distance within the depth of field range for adequate sharpness is thus 7 metres, the farthest distance 16 metres. The different f-numbers against various index lines show how the depth of field varies with the aperture setting (§ 114). The calibration of this scale automatically takes care of all other parameters in the depth of field computation—focal length of the lens and standard of sharpness—while the movement of the distance scale automatically gives the depth at different object distances.

The standard of sharpness is—especially on cheaper cameras—often appreciably lower (greater tolerance or larger circle of confusion) than we have assumed so far because with such cameras it is assumed that the average size of enlargements will be smaller. To get the depth of field for a higher standard of sharpness, simply stop down the lens—after having read the depth of field off the scale—by 1 or even 2 stops.

Semi-automatic depth of field indicators simplify the procedure still further. Here the scale with its series of index lines is replaced by a pair of movable pointers as in Fig. 10.9B, which are coupled with the aperture setting of the lens. The pointers thus directly indicate the depth of field on the distance scale. On opening the lens aperture the pointers move together, for instance to position b and b'; on stopping down the pointers move apart to, say, positions c and c'. Other types of indicator use sliding masks, coloured dots etc. which come into, or go out of, view as the aperture is adjusted.

114. Factors Affecting Depth of Field. The depth of field (distance between near and far planes in focus) can be expressed by one or other of the following formulae, according as the permissible circle of confusion is a constant fraction a of the distance of the image, or a fixed amount e. The formulae give the difference $(s - r)$ of the distances previously calculated—

$$(1)\ \frac{2naq^2f}{f^2 - n^2a^2\ ^2} \qquad (2)\ \frac{2neq(q-f)f^2}{f^4 - n^2e^2(q-f)^2}$$

in each of which the second term of the denominator is generally negligible unless q is very great, so that we can replace these by the simpler formulae below, which lead to a slightly smaller value—

$$(1A)\ \frac{2naq^2}{f} \qquad (2A)\ \frac{2neq(q-f)}{f^2}$$

In this form it is seen at once that, all conditions remaining the same, with the exception of the one factor considered—

1. Depth of field is less with a lens of greater focal length; it is inversely proportional to f if the tolerance is defined as an angular constant, and inversely to the f^2 when the tolerance is fixed by an absolute value.

2. Depth of field is proportional to n and is thus greater the smaller the stop.

3. Depth of field is greater for greater object distances, being proportional to q^2.

4. Depth of field, based on the value of a or e, is greater the less exacting the requirements of definition are.

It should be noted that the laws of physical optics lead to the result that the relative depth of field is independent of the focal length f, and is inversely proportional to the square of the diameter of the effective aperture (T. Smith, 1928).

115. Depth with Interchangeable Lenses. We have seen (§ 110) that a relative standard of sharpness—as a fixed fraction of the image distance—is more logical than an absolute standard. This applies however only for a lens of normal focal length relative to the film format with which it is used, in other words approximately the diagonal of the format (§ 134). Where a series of interchangeable lenses of different focal lengths is used with one film format, the same value for the circle of confusion has to be used for all the alternative focal lengths. The depth of field can then be established from the formulae (2) or (2A) in § 114, taking, e as equal to $f_N/2,000$, where f_N is the focal length of the normal or standard lens. (This is a good enough approximation for reasonably great subject distances where the image distance is not very much greater than the focal length.) If the hyperfocal distance (§ 121) is used for calculating the actual limits of the depth of field, the procedure becomes simpler still as we only have to establish the hyperfocal distance for the standard focal length and multiply it by the ratio $(f/f_N)^2$ to get the hyperfocal distances for the alternative focal lengths f (§ 118 ff).

116. Choice of Lenses for Depth. When photographing an object of a certain depth from a given viewpoint, it is sometimes of interest to know whether it is preferable to use (a) a long-focus to obtain a specified large image scale, or (b) a very short-focus lens giving a small image which is subsequently enlarged.

Taking the same numerical data as in § 111, but supposing this time that the focal length is 330 mm (0·33 m), or a power of 3·03 diopters, we will find the depth of field for the same circle of confusion after equalization of the sizes of the two images. The distance of the plane focused on being the same in the two cases, the sizes of the two images are proportional to the respective ultra-nodal distances, and it will be sufficient to give a the same value, 1/2,000. The total tolerance of convergence is thus found to be $(3·03 \times 6)/1,000 = 0·0182$ diopters, and consequently the convergences of the limits of the field—with an object distance of 5 m—are $(0·2 \pm 0·0091)$ diopters, corresponding with ultra-nodal distances of $1/0·2091 = 4·78$ m and $1/0·1909 = 5·24$ m with a total depth of field of 0·46 m only, instead of 1·4 m in the case of the lens of 110 mm focal length.

It remains to examine whether, to obtain a reproduction at the same size by direct photography, supposing that aesthetic considerations allow an alteration of viewpoint, there is any advantage as regards depth of field, in using a lens of shorter focus, or if, on the contrary, it is preferable to get farther back from the view and use a long-focus lens.

From the formula (1) of § 114, remembering that $q = (m + 1)f$, it is possible to deduce the expression for the total depth of field $(s - r)$

$$s - r = \frac{2\,a\,f\,(m + 1)^2 n}{1 - (m + 1)^2 a^2 n^2}$$

The scale of reduction m being constant, the camera extensions are proportional to the focal lengths, and in order to have the same limits for the diameter of the circle of confusion in the photographs taken with lenses of different focal lengths, the product af must be constant $= k$ (say), whence $a = k/f$, and the above expression reduces to

$$s - r = \frac{2\,k(m + 1)^2 n}{1 - (m + 1)^2 n^2 (k/f)^2}$$

The $f/$No. n being supposed constant, it is seen that, if f increases the denominator increases and $(s - r)$ decreases.

We can derive a similar result from formula (2) of § 114, using an absolute diameter of the circle of confusion e, in which case we get:

$$s - r = \frac{2nef^2 m(m + 1)}{f^2 - n^2 e^2 m^2}$$

$$= \frac{2nem(m + 1)}{1 - n^2 e^2 m^2/f^2}$$

where $(s - r)$ again decreases as f increases.

117. Close-up Depth of Field. The above expressions are valid for reasonably great subject distances, where m is of the order of 10 or larger. When m becomes less than around 10, or the scale of magnification M greater than about 0·1, the term $n^2 e^2 m^2/f^2$ tends to become negligible in comparison with 1, unless n is very great (apertures very small). Under these conditions the total depth of field then becomes virtually independent of f and is for all intents and purposes a function of m or of M. Using the reduction factor m

$$s - r = 2nem(m + 1)$$

On the other hand, taking the magnification factor $M (= 1/m)$ we get:

$$s - r = 2ne(M + 1)/M^2$$

At higher magnifications in macro-photography with M greater than around 10, the difference between $M + 1$ and M becomes negligible and the total depth of field is directly proportional to $1/M$.

A further factor intruding into close-up depth of field arises with lenses of telephoto or inverted telephoto construction where the pupillary magnification (§ 107) is appreciably greater or smaller than 1. This affects the effective aperture n_2, the modification being given by

$$n_2 = n(1/mP + 1) = n(M/P + 1)$$

where n is the nominal aperture (f-number). If m is large (i.e. M small) the term $1/mP$ or M/P is negligible and the pupillary magnification (the ratio of the exit pupil diameter to the entrance pupil diameter) has little effect on the depth of field.

At larger scales of reproduction—where $1/m$ or M is greater than around 0·1, the value of n in the equations for close-up depth of field should be replaced by n_2, established by the formulae just given.

118. Hyperfocal Distance. The depth of field formulae derived so far are fairly complex, but all contain a number of recurring parameters—n, f, e (or a). For calculating near and far limits of the depth of field it becomes somewhat laborious to employ these parameters repeatedly. A simplification is possible by incorporating several of them in a value called the *hyper-focal distance*.

From the point of view of geometric optics, the hyperfocal distance is the nearest limit of the depth of field when the lens is focused on infinity. The hyperfocal distance is a function of the lens aperture, focal length and the degree of tolerance of unsharpness.

When the lens is focused on the hyperfocal distance, the far limit of sharpness just reaches to infinity.

If we agree to adopt as the tolerance a constant fraction a of the ultra-nodal distance of the image (still supposing that the pupils coincide with the nodal points), the hyperfocal distance H of a lens of focal length f and aperture number n, is easily calculated if we consider that the convergence of the far plane is zero, this being at infinity. Calling l the distance to the near plane, the preceding formulae for the depth of field become

$$1/l - 1/H = 1/H = na/f$$

whence $H = f/na$ and $l = f/2na = H/2$

With the lens focused on the hyperfocal distance, the near limit of sharpness thus extends to half the hyperfocal distance. The distance H is therefore the setting for maximum possible depth of field from infinity downwards with the focal length, aperture and standard of sharpness considered.

Thus with a lens of a focal length of 50 mm and assuming $a = 1/1,000$, the hyperfocal distance H at an aperture of $f/8$ is

$$H = 50 \times 2,000/8 = 12,500 \text{ mm} = 12·5 \text{ m}$$

The camera, when focused on this distance, would give a sharp image of everything from 6·25 metres to infinity.

It may be remarked that when the limit of sharpness is defined by an angular value the hyperfocal distance is proportional to the focal length and inversely proportional to the $f/$No. It is also greater the more severe the standard of good definition is.

This is easily explained by noticing that the *hyperfocal distance* thus defined is the *distance from which the effective aperture subtends the angle of tolerance*. If, for example, the angle is $1/2,000$ (circle of confusion $= 1/2,000$ of the principal distance), the hyperfocal distance is 2,000 times the useful aperture of the stop. Similarly, if the angle were $1/1,500$ or $1/1,000$, the hyperfocal distance would be 1,500 or 1,000 times the useful aperture.

119. Absolute Hyperfocal Distance. If we agree to adopt, as limit of definition, a diameter e for the circle of confusion, we calculate H by the condition that s is infinitely great, which requires the denominator of the fraction for s (§ 112) to be zero, so

$$f = nme, \text{ whence } m = \frac{f}{ne}$$

As the plane focused on, reduced in the ratio $1/m$, is at an ultra-nodal distance $(m + 1)f$, we get $H = f(f/ne + 1)$, and for the corresponding length l, by replacing m by the value above in the expression for r,

$$l = H/2$$

If instead of measuring H from the front nodal point, we measure it from the front focal point, we get

$$H' = f^2/ne$$

It may be remarked that, when the limit of sharpness is thus defined as an absolute value, the hyperfocal distance is, for equal relative apertures, proportional to the square of the focal length, i.e. for lenses of focal length half, double or triple that of the lens in the example, the hyperfocal distances would be respectively one-quarter, four times, and nine times, the value calculated above. This applies naturally also to comparative focal distances with interchangeable lenses used with the same camera and image format (§ 115).

If the diameter of the aperture is reduced to half or one-quarter its value, the hyperfocal distance will be reduced to half or quarter the value calculated above.

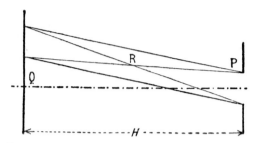

FIG. 10.10. GEOMETRY OF HYPERFOCAL DISTANCE

If, instead of fixing the limit at 1/250 in., it was taken as 1/125 or 1/500 in., the hyperfocal distance would be half or twice respectively the former value.

In every case the distance of the near plane is half the hyperfocal distance.

120. Direct Hyperfocal Distance Calculation. The formulae for hyperfocal distance can be obtained directly without using the formulae for depth of field.

Let P be the entrance pupil of the lens (Fig. 10.10). Every parallel pencil of light (i.e. coming from an infinitely distant point) will cut planes perpendicular to the axis (and plane Q in particular) in a circle of the same diameter as that of the pupil.

The beam, limited by the pupil and having as apex any point R half way between Q and the pupil, cuts Q in a circle of the same size (which will coincide with the former if R is on the principal ray of the beam). If we focus the lens on Q, the condition that all point-objects from R to infinity shall be sharp is that the images of the circles on Q, reduced $1/m$th, must not exceed the limit e assigned to the diameter of the circle of confusion. Now, the diameter of the pupil is f/n; the condition is therefore $f/n \times m = e$, and gives $m = f/n \times e$, whence, the distance H of the plane reduced $1/m$th being $(m + 1)f$,

$$H = (f/ne + 1)f$$

H derived in this way differs from the value of H obtained in § 119 only by the value of f, which is negligible in comparison with f^2/ne.

121. Depth of Field Limits from the Hyperfocal Distance. From the equations in § 112 we can derive values for r and s as follows—taking $m = (q - f)/f$:

$$r = \frac{qf}{f + ne(q - f)/f}$$

Multiplying by f/ne and taking $H = f^2/ne$, we get

$$r = \frac{qf^2/ne}{f^2/ne + (q - f)} = \frac{qH}{H + (q - f)}$$

Similarly we have for the far limit s:

$$s = \frac{qH}{H - (q - f)}$$

As long as q is more than about $10f$, we can ignore f in the denominator and the equations further simplify down to:

$$r = \frac{qH}{H + q} \qquad s = \frac{qH}{H - q}$$

Thus once the hyperfocal distance for a given aperture and focal length is known, this can be used fairly rapidly to establish the near and far limits of sharpness at any object distance.

When q is greater than H, the value of s becomes infinitely large, in other words the far limit of sharpness is infinity.

122. Influence of the Corrections of the Lens on the Depth of Field and Hyperfocal Distance. It cannot be too strongly emphasized that the depth of field and hyperfocal distance calculated from the formulae given in the foregoing paragraphs, or taken from charts and diagrams based on them, have only relative accuracy. It may be noted in passing that few of these tables indicate the degree of sharpness on which they are based.

Firstly, it was assumed in deducing the formulae that the nodal points coincided with the centres of the corresponding pupils, which is not always true, particularly for telephoto and inverted telephoto lenses. The necessary correction affects especially close-ups (§ 117).

Secondly, it was assumed that the lens was ideal, having a flat field free from all aberrations.

Thirdly, it was assumed that the circles of confusion were uniformly illuminated. Actually a patch of light of large area can give a reasonably sharp image if there is a concentration of light at its centre.

These formulae lead to the conclusion that depth of field is the same for different lenses of the same focal length and aperture, a conclusion which is not always borne out in practice. In fact a perfectly corrected lens has less depth of field than one having residual aberrations (D. Brewster, 1867).

Compare, for example, two lenses of the same

focal length and aperture, one, *A*, free from spherical aberration, the other, *B*, having positive spherical aberration at apertures greater than $f/16$. The aberration of *B* being positive, the caustics of each beam will be formed between the sharpest image and the lens, approaching the latter as the aperture increases, and thus affecting only the lower limit to the depth of field. At $f/16$ the lenses give equal depth; at an aperture slightly larger the caustics due to spherical aberration make their appearance with *B*. A beam limited by a caustic would be restricted more rapidly than one limited by a cone, so that the depth of field would diminish less quickly with the uncorrected lens. If objects situated in front of or behind the focused plane are considered, this difference between the two lenses increases as the aperture is increased. At a certain aperture the caustic, meeting the sensitive surface, gives practically a constant circle of confusion, and thus sets an almost invariable lower limit to the depth of field, whilst with the perfect lens every increase of aperture increases the diameter of the circles of confusion, and thus limits the depth of field. A negative aberration would affect the back limit in the same way (C. Welborne Piper, 1903).

It has been suggested that to increase the depth of field, one of the lens elements should have an aspherical surface to provide over-correction of spherical aberration in the central zone and under-correction in the marginal zone (A. Warmisham, 1932).

In most cases however, the lens aberrations simply impose a larger circle of confusion as the standard of sharpness, and the depth of field gained as a result is rarely greater than what would be gained by relaxing the sharpness tolerance of a perfect lens. These considerations suggest that it does not always make sense to assume too high a standard of sharpness for depth of field calculations.

A related depth of field anomaly arises with lenses subject to a focus shift on stopping down (§ 77). If the use of a smaller aperture moves the plane of average optimum definition towards or away from the lens, depth of field calculations would apply essentially to the new position of the optimum image plane. If this shift is not taken into account, the depth may appear to increase more towards the nearest subject plane (or towards the more distant one—depending on the direction of the focus shift) than would be expected from the depth of field

formulae. In extreme cases the depth could even decrease with respect to *either* the near *or* the distant limit on stopping down the lens.

123. Accuracy of Depth of Field Tables. Tables of depth of field values published by different camera and lens manufacturers for lenses of similar focal length and application may disagree, as already indicated (§ 110) owing to the assumption of different standards of sharpness; they may sometimes also attempt to allow in a rudimentary way for the influence of lens aberrations (§ 122).

In applying such tables it is worth noting that the figures obtained from whatever calculations are used imply a greater accuracy than can ever be attained in practice. It is therefore logical to round off such tables extensively, especially where great sharpness zones are involved. Thus it makes little sense to try to allow for a depth zone of for instance 24 feet 11 inches to 89 feet 9 inches (or in metric terms, 7·58 to 27·45 metres)—yet published tables often pretend an even greater accuracy, usually stemming from conversions between feet and metric values. It is fully adequate to assume the zone to extend from 25 to 90 feet or from $7\frac{1}{2}$ to 27 metres respectively.

In practice it is unnecessary to work out a depth of field zone more accurately than within about 15 to 20 per cent of its *total* extent. For instance if the total zone ($s - r$ in § 112 and later) amounts to 6 metres, a difference of $\pm 0·5$ metre (1 metre total) would not show any very noticable difference in sharpness. This $\pm 0·5$ metre would of course be split *pro rata* between the zone in front of and behind the sharply focused plane, according to the relative extent of these zones.

Since the fall-off in sharpness in front of and behind the sharply focused object plane is gradual, changes in the depth of field affect the sharpness of subject items near the limits of the sharp zone only. Apart from the effect of the lens aperture on aberration-limited definition, larger or smaller apertures would not noticeably affect the image sharpness in regions already within the depth of field zone at the larger aperture, since it is the marginal regions which count here.

Attention is once more drawn to the fact that with a given lens, distance setting and aperture the actual image sharpness is in no way affected by the assumption of different depth of field limits based on different sharpness tolerances (§ 112). In other words, if we obtain a total acceptably sharp zone of say 2·6 metres by one set of calculations and 1·4 metres by another, the difference is only due to our own assumption of what we will accept as sharp, and not to any change in the image on the ground glass screen or the film.

124. Fixed-focus Cameras. In many very cheap cameras for beginners, no adjustment for focus is provided. The lenses used on these cameras being nearly always simple or achromatic, poorly corrected, with maximum aperture rarely exceeding $f/11$, the hyperfocal distance is very short, and consequently the minimum distance of sharp objects (half the hyperfocal distance) is small enough to allow almost all subjects (except portraiture, properly so-called) to be attempted.

In addition to this category of cheap cameras with fixed focus there is a second category of very short-focus lenses of high aperture which are also used at a fixed focus. Examples of this may be found in narrow gauge cinematography.

Reducing the aperture in fixed-focus cameras does not make use of all the increased depth of field, since the lens ought then to be refocused for the new hyperfocal distance. Narrow gauge cine cameras use such fixed-focus (more correctly, fixed-distance) settings even with variable-focus or zoom lenses (§ 160). Here, too, the lens should be refocused to its appropriate hyperfocal distance when the focal length setting is changed. At least one make of cine camera zoom lens couples its focal length adjustment with a focusing movement, so that the lens automatically focuses on the hyperfocal distance appropriate to its focal length—although the lens does not carry any manual distance settings. As the aperture of such lenses is often controlled by automatic exposure metering systems, the hyperfocal distance setting applies to the largest aperture. Hence in practice the depth obtained—especially when shooting in good light conditions—is even greater.

The expression *fixed-focus lens* is in any case unfortunate. It is liable to be taken not only as a lens of fixed focal length (as distinct from variable focal length) but may also imply a special lens design. This is of course not the case; the extreme depth of field given by lenses of short focus and small aperture is due exclusively to the general application of the laws governing depth of field.

125. Focusing Scales. Focusing the image on a ground glass or other focusing screen is possible only with technical or view cameras on the one hand (where the screen is changed for the film or plate holder before the exposure) and with reflex cameras on the other—where a mirror system permits alternate viewing of the image on the screen and projection on to the film. Other camera types—even when fitted with focusing aids such as rangefinders—are nearly always provided with a scale graduated in object distances, so that the lens can be set to any distance within the limits of the scale. (Under special conditions—such as in poor light—even reflex cameras may have to be focused by scale.)

The mark on this scale corresponding to objects at a great distance (generally marked by ∞, or the letters "INF") usually indicates the focal plane for objects on the horizon, and, sometimes, the focus for objects at the hyperfocal distance of the lens at the maximum aperture. Some makers indicate the focus both for infinity and the hyperfocal distance, the latter being indicated by a mark of different colour or the letter H. It must be remembered that when the focus is set for infinity the nearest plane that is sharp is at the hyperfocal distance, while when focus is set for the hyperfocal distance the nearest plane that is sharp is at half this distance.

The distances on the scale are often chosen quite arbitrarily. It would be better to divide the hyperfocal distance by the consecutive numbers 0, 1, 2, 3, . . . , i.e. infinity, the hyperfocal distance, half, one-third, one-quarter etc. of the hyperfocal distance. Such a scale possesses an interesting property when used with the appropriate diaphragm and when the tolerance of sharpness used in its construction is accepted. When the focus is adjusted for one of the distances on the scale, the depth of field extends to the contiguous distances.

This can be derived from the depth of field equations based on hyperfocal distance in § 121. Take x as the whole-integer denominator of the hyperfocal distance for the above series of subject distances, so that $q = H/x$. The equations in § 121 then becomes:

$$r = \frac{H}{x+1} \qquad s = \frac{H}{x-1}$$

In other words, at for instance a focusing distance of half the hyperfocal distance, the depth extends from the hyperfocal distance itself to $1/3\,H$; when focused on $1/3\,H$ it extends from $\frac{1}{2}H$ to $\frac{1}{4}H$ and so on.

As a practical example of such a hyperfocal distance scale we could take a lens of 80 mm focal length and assume a circle of confusion of 0·05 mm—which would be appropriate for a $2\frac{1}{4} \times 2\frac{1}{4}$ inch (6 × 6 cm) roll film reflex. At $f/4$ this has a hyperfocal distance of 32 metres; rounding this off to 30 metres, we could have a distance scale marked: ∞, 30, 15, 10, 7·5, 6, 5, 4·3, 3·75, 3·3, 3, 2·7, 2·5, 2·3, 2·15, 2, 1·9, 1·75, 1·65, 1·58 and 1·5 metres. With each of these distance settings the depth of field at $f/4$ extends automatically to the next lower and the next higher marked distance.

The scale still remains useful at other apertures; thus at $f/8$ the depth would extend in each direction to the next but one marked distance, at $f/11$ to the next but two, at $f/16$ to the next but three and so on.

The same argument would be valid for a focusing scale marked in feet; for the lens just mentioned the hyperfocal distance at $f/4$ would then be about 100 feet and the sub-division would follow the same fractional rule. We can also note that in such a hyperfocal scale all distance markings are spaced at equal intervals on the focusing mount or ring.

Cameras and lenses made in Great Britain, the Commonwealth and the U.S.A. (or produced for the market in those countries) are generally fitted with a focusing scale in feet, while cameras of or for most other countries have a metric scale. Many modern lenses however carry a dual scale marked in both feet and metres, usually in different colours.

126. Depth of Focus. If the plane on which the image is formed is slightly separated from the position of the sharp image of a point, the image will be a disc which can be considered as a geometrical point if its diameter does not exceed a certain fraction a of the ultra-nodal distance of the sharp image, or does not exceed a constant limit e (§ 110 and 111).

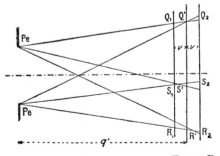

FIG. 10.11. DEPTH LATITUDE IN THE FOCAL PLANE

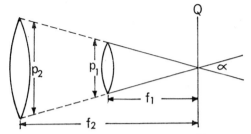

FIG. 10.12. CONSTANT DEPTH OF FOCUS
INDEPENDENTLY OF FOCAL LENGTH

Knowing (Fig. 10.11) the diameter of the aperture f/n and the ultra-nodal distance q' of the focused image (supposing again that the pupils coincide with the nodal planes) it is easy to calculate the distance v, the error in the position of the image plane which can be tolerated. Assigning the diameter of the disc of confusion at Q_2 the value (Q'), consideration of the similar triangles having their apices at Q' gives

$$\frac{(Q')}{f/n} = \frac{v}{q'}$$

Now, according to the convention adopted in fixing the tolerance in sharpness, we have

$$(Q') = aq' \quad \text{or} \quad (Q') = e$$

which gives[1]

$$v = \frac{q'^2 \times a}{f/n} \quad \text{or} \quad v = \frac{eq'}{f/n}$$

The tolerance is the same in front and behind the focus.

The sum of these equal tolerances is the *depth of focus*, a term which is often erroneously used when depth of *field* is meant.

This tolerance is greater the smaller the useful aperture of the stop (other things being equal).

The depth of focus tolerance is influenced by some of the factors affecting depth of field, but not necessarily in the same way. As in the case of depth of field, the use of a smaller aperture (larger f-number or n) increases the depth of focus in direct proportion to the value of n. The focal length for a given relative aperture however has no affect on the focusing tolerance (Fig. 10.12), since in the equations above the ratio f/n remains constant if the effective absolute diameter of the aperture is

[1] Considerations of physical optics ascribe to depth of focus a value proportional to the wavelength of the radiation and expressed as $k\lambda \left(\frac{q'}{F/n}\right)^2$

increased in the same ratio as the focal length—
in other words for a given value of n. Thus in
Fig. 10.12 the angle α, which governs the degree
of tolerance in the position of the image plane,
depends only on the ratio p_1/f_1 which is the
same as p_2/f_2 for a given value of n for the two
lenses of focal length f_1 and f_2.

The depth of focus is less at great subject
distances and increases with nearer objects
because the value of q' (Fig. 10.11) then has to
increase to permit focusing at a nearer object.

It is necessary to add that this latitude can
only be made use of in photographing plane
objects perpendicular to the axis, or in the
photography of objects of negligible depth. *It
is impossible to make use of depth of focus and
depth of field at the same time.*

If images at R' and S' of points in front of
and behind Q are also to be photographed at
the same time as Q' it is seen that they will form
image patches in one of the limiting planes, of
diameter greater than the tolerance.

In particular it should be remembered that
depth of focus has already been taken into
account when a lens having curvature of field
is used.

**127. Effect of Relative Aperture on the Bright-
ness of the Image.** In the photography of a landscape in which all the objects are at a very
great distance from the lens, the brightness of
the image at the centre of the field (on the optical
axis) is, apart from loss by absorption and reflection (§ 88), inversely proportional to the square
of the relative aperture n (§ 102). It is easily
seen that for equal losses in passing through
the lens, two lenses, of the same focal length but
of different effective apertures, give images the
brightnesses of which are proportional to the area
of the effective aperture, which, in fact, limits
the beam of light from a distant object, just
as a tap restricts the amount of liquid passing
through. If the diameter of the effective
aperture is doubled its area will be four times
as great. The images being of the same size,
since the focal length is assumed to be the same
in each case, the brightness will vary in the
same ratio.

Let us now consider two lenses of the same
effective aperture but of different focal lengths.
If the focal length of one is double that of the
other, all dimensions in the plane of the image
of distant objects will be doubled, and consequently the areas will be four times as great.
Both will receive the same quantity of light,
but that formed by the longer-focus lens will be

one-quarter as bright, so that the brightness
of the image is directly proportional to the
square of the diameter of the lens and inversely proportional to the square of the focal
length.

If B is the brightness of an element of the
object situated on the axis and perpendicular
to it, the intensity of illumination of its image
is $E = t\pi B/4n^2$ where t is the *transmittance.*

In complex systems the losses by reflection
and absorption reduce the apparent advantage of
a large aperture compared with a simpler lens
of smaller aperture. This used to be particularly
serious before lenses had anti-reflection coatings
(§ 89) when in fact gains of lens speed by increasing the number of elements (to ensure
acceptable correction) were very much subject
to the law of diminishing returns. With
modern coated lenses this loss is of course greatly
reduced—as is the parasitic illumination which
finds its way to the image plane as fog. Lenses
of different complexity do however still differ
in their transmittance even at the same relative
aperture. Attempts have been made to get
round this problem by adopting a method of
aperture calibration known as the *T-stop system*
(1949). The T-number of a lens is the f/number
divided by the square root of the transmittance,
i.e.

$$T\text{-No.} = n/\sqrt{t}$$

The image illumination formula given above thus
becomes

$$E = B/4(T\text{-No.})^2$$

Lenses calibrated in T-stops have found favour
in the motion picture industry, where it is most
desirable that interchangeable lenses can be
used without upsetting exposure. On the other
hand, since the T-stop is not directly correlated
with the geometry of the lens system, the T-stops
cannot be used for the determination of the
depth of field (§ 109), and for this reason it is
unlikely that the T-stop system will find
universal adoption.

We can say then that the speed of the lens is
chiefly determined by its relative aperture. If
two lenses have for instance apertures of $f/4$
and $f/11$, the first gives an image which at its
centre (neglecting loss of light) is brighter than
the second in the ratio of $11^2/4^2 = 121/16 = 7\cdot5$
approx.

With lens stops marked in the international
aperture series, the geometrical progression
from one stop to the next is the ratio of $\sqrt{2} = 1\cdot4$,

and hence the illumination at the centre of the image is doubled when going from any stop to the next larger one (§ 105).

128. Effect of the Scale of an Image on its Brightness. If an object, illuminated equally in all cases, is photographed several times with the same lens at the same aperture but on different scales, by moving the lens closer and closer to the object, it will be found that the image falls off in intensity as the size increases.

The image illumination formula then becomes

$$E = \frac{t\pi B}{4n^2(1 + M)^2}$$

This amounts to saying that when the image is formed, not in the focal plane, but at a distance $(M + 1)f$ from the rear nodal point, the relative aperture of the stop f/n is reduced to $f/n(M + 1)$. This assumes that the entrance pupil contains the front nodal point; if it does not, the scale of reproduction M (image size/object size) is replaced by the expression M/P, where P the pupillary magnification (the diameter ratio of the exit to the entrance pupils of the lens—§ 107). With a telephoto lens, where P is smaller than 1, the image illumination is therefore reduced even further; with a wide angle lens of inverted telephoto construction P is greater than 1 and the image illumination decreases at a lesser rate.

The above image illumination formula is also the basis for the exposure correction applied in macro-photography at scales of reproduction greater than about 0·1. The simplest way is to determine the exposure in the normal way and increase the exposure time by a factor of $(M + 1)^2$ or by $(M/P + 1)^2$ if the pupillary magnification deviates appreciably from 1. The value of $(M + 1)^2$ becomes significantly greater than 1 when the magnification M is 0·1 or larger; at $M = 0·1$ the exposure factor is 1·21 which is about the smallest exposure increase to which a photographic emulsion responds visibly. As the magnification increases, the factor grows very rapidly: when $M = 1$ (same-size reproduction), the exposure factor—assuming P for the moment to be 1—becomes $4\times$; when $M = 2$ the factor becomes $9\times$ and so on.

Alternatively, we can assume a modified effective aperture $n(M + 1)$ or $n(M/P + 1)$, as explained above. This modified aperture is then used in place of the nominal f number n for exposure determination.

These close-up exposure corrections do not apply when the exposure is measured through the lens by a exposure meter cell in the image plane or an equivalent image plane—as is the case with a number of present-day cameras.

129. Measurement of the Effective Aperture. The effective aperture of a lens can be measured by placing a small source of light (such as an illuminated pinhole) in the centre of the focal plane. If a rule is then placed perpendicular to the axis of the lens, the free diameter can be measured (Fig. 10.13). A permanent record can be made by placing a photographic plate in front of the lens, when after development a black disc corresponding to the free aperture will be obtained. It should be noted that it is necessary to measure the focal length fairly accurately (§ 97) in order that the relative aperture may be calculated.

130. Measurement of the Pupillary Magnification. The pupillary magnification of a lens can be measured in a similar way by measuring the effective aperture from the front of the lens as described above, and again from the rear with the lens turned round. The first measurement

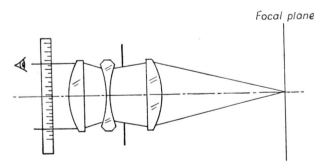

FIG. 10.13. MEASUREMENT OF EFFECTIVE APERTURE

gives the diameter of the entrance pupil, the second that of the exit pupil. The magnification is then the ratio of the exit pupil to the entrance pupil (§ 107), the value being reversed if the lens is used back-to-front. This last point is significant because in close-up and macro-photography is sometimes expedient to mount a lens in reverse; on some cameras this provides a greater lens-to-film distance (and hence greater achievable magnification) and often offers better image quality when a lens is corrected pre-dominantly for distant objects (§ 76).

A very rough and ready way of measuring the pupil diameters is to hold the lens at arm's length pointing at the sky or a suitable brightly lit surface, and to measure the diameter of the clear circle of light of the iris with a ruler held across the front of the lens. To obtain the pupillary magnification this measurement is again repeated from the back.

CHAPTER XI

CHOICE OF A LENS: LENS TYPES

131. Preliminary Remarks. The qualities required of an objective depend on whether the lens is intended for artistic photography, commercial photography, process work, enlargement or photogrammetry (measuring by photography) —or any one of numerous special purposes in industrial, scientific etc. photography.

The qualities to be considered for these purposes primarily concern image definition and the degree of lens correction. Significant are also the angle of view, lens speed and required scale of reproduction; these three factors are however linked with the lens correction since the latter is invariably a compromise. The lens designer therefore has to optimize the performance of a lens to the purpose of application correcting preferentially, those aspects which matter most, at the expense of less important ones. This becomes particularly important with lenses for specialised uses where the designer tends to minimise those aberrations which would be most harmful; such a lens might not perform satisfactorily when used for a different purpose.

132. Definition Requirements. In pictorial photography the demand on definition used to be least stringent. What was required was "firm" drawing without hardness, breadth proportional to the scale of the image, and suppression of unnecessary detail, translating only the general form.

For this purpose some photographers used to

employ lenses of incomplete spherical correction and even without chromatic correction. As the older schools of pictorial photography rarely used very wide angles of view or large lens apertures, oblique aberrations (astigmatism, coma or curvature of field) did not appear too disturbingly. In portraiture such partially corrected lenses sometimes help the pictorial effect of getting the centre of the face sharp and the outlying areas less sharp.

Modern pictorial trends however often achieve their styles by other means (special lighting effects, tone abstractions, viewpoints etc.) so that the lenses are expected to give good definition in the first place, any softening being introduced by lens attachments during taking or printing (§ 190).

Definition requirements, including the demand for distortion-free reproduction, are highest in photographic applications where dimensional reproduction is important, such as the graphic arts field, aerial photography and photogrammetry and certain aspects of copying. Electric micro-circuitry in which integrated circuits prepared as full-size diagrams are reduced down to a scale where line details are under 1 micron thick requires lenses giving extreme detail resolution.

In copying and graphic arts application a lens is often optimally corrected for a given scale of reproduction. Thus lenses for micro-miniaturisation may yield their optimum performance at reductions of 1:30, while process lenses for normal photo-mechanical reproduction might be corrected for best performance between scales of 1:4 and 4:1. There is no need, in this case, for a large aperture, but the chromatic corrections need to be very good if three-colour work is to be done; the different component pictures obtained through selective filters should be capable of being exactly superposed and be of equal sharpness.

The requirements of a lens for enlarging are much the same as those for process work, except that the correction should be made for an enlargement of 2 to 15 times linear.

For photogrammetry the optimum performance is usually required with the lens focused at infinity. Such lenses must also cover a very wide angle of view (§ 149) and must be absolutely free from distortion and curvature of field. They also need good colour correction if colour materials are being used—especially infra-red sensitive ones; where the lens is intended for photography on black-and-white

materials through a yellow or orange filter, chromatic correction may be a simpler matter.

133. Requirements of Lens Speed. In commercial photography and a great deal of press and amateur work lenses of high speed are often called for. Only the very simplest amateur cameras have lenses slower than about $f/8$ which permit instantaneous exposures only in good light. Even the cheapest cameras however are provided with flash contacts for synchronised firing of a flash bulb with the shutter, which extends the use of these cameras to poor light conditions.

Most better modern amateur cameras have anastigmat lenses of apertures around $f/2\cdot8$; while professional camera lenses for larger image formats may have apertures of around $f/4\cdot5$. Here the compromise adopted is one between image performance and speed. More expensive cameras, especially of the miniature type for 24×36 mm negatives, often have lenses of $f/2$ or even faster for greatest versatility in poor light and with fast shutter speeds to arrest rapid movement.

Lenses have been made for general photography with apertures down to $f/1$ and for special applications down to $f/0\cdot7$ and even faster. However as the large apertures also mean greatly reduced depth of field, the applications of ultra-speed lenses are somewhat limited. Moreover the compromise between speed and definition here often favours the former on the assumption that a picture—even if optically not perfect—is better than no picture, a point of view which is valid for instance in press photography. Except with miniature cameras, the interest in pushing lens speeds to the limit for general photography has declined with the appearance of increasingly more sensitive films; in the past twenty years the speed of ultra-fast films for general photography has increased by a factor of 5–10 times.

The value of ultra-speed lenses in miniature cameras is linked on the one hand with the fact that the necessary correction of aberrations at large aperture is easier with shorter focal lengths and on the other with the more favourable depth of field obtained at such focal lengths.

134. Focal Length and Image Size. The focal length of a camera lens depends primarily on the film or plate format it has to cover, assuming of course that the lens design covers the corresponding angle of field (§ 87). Where the camera lens is permanently built in, this point is automatically taken care of by the camera manufacturer; the lens is usually one of "normal focus" which in this context means that it has a focal length corresponding approximately to the diagonal of the image format. This corresponds to an angle of field between 50° and 55°, though in practice the field angles of cameras with fixed lenses may range between 45° and 60°. With camera systems using interchangeable lenses designed for the camera in question (usually the case with more advanced 35 mm miniature cameras and some roll film reflexes) the standard lens of normal focal length is also set by the camera manufacturer who however in addition offers shorter-focus wide-angle lenses and longer focus tele-lenses.

The two terminologies involved here must be distinguished. The terms "short-focus" and "long-focus" refer to the focal length relative to the standard or "normal focus" lens, i.e. approximately to the diagonal of the film or plate format used, and are thus a function of the latter rather than of the lens. On the other hand "wide-angle" and "narrow-angle" refers to the angle of the sharply covered field (§ 87) and depends only on the lens design. In this terminology normal angle lenses have an angle between about 45° and 60°; lenses with an angle of 60° to about 80° are regarded as wide-angle lenses and over 80° as ultra-wide-angle lenses.

At the other end of the scale, narrow-angle lenses cover anything with an angle below about 40°—in all cases irrespective of the image format. The term tele-lens is often applied indiscriminately to all lenses of longer than normal focal length among interchangeable camera lenses, covering both ordinary long-focus lenses and true telephoto lenses; the latter description strictly refers however to a specific type of lens construction (§ 152).

With system cameras (minature and roll film types), alternative focal lengths are provided to enable the photographer to control the image scale without changing his viewpoint (or the perspective without changing the scale of the main subject). Here a short-focus lens invariably has to be a wide-angle lens as well, since the shorter focal length in conjunction with the fixed film format implies an increased angle of field.

Conversely, long-focus lenses for such cameras are deliberately designed only for the angle they have to cover. It is easier to achieve a higher level of image performance if the correction compromises can be made over a narrower field angle and hence reduce obliquity of the image forming rays (§ 81). This is the reason why a normal focus lens of for instance a 35 mm miniature camera cannot be used as a wide-angle lens on a 6 × 6 cm or 2¼ inch square roll film reflex: the lens would not cover the larger angle required. A long-focus lens for the larger camera could be used with the smaller image format to yield a still greater image magnification (relative to the standard lens for the picture format), but as explained before the lens performance is likely to be better when the lens is designed for the smaller picture size from the outset. (This does not necessarily apply to extreme tele-lenses with angles below about 10° where the considerations of lens correction do not change very much with decreasing angle of converage.)

In characterising lenses by the angle of field sharply covered, the angle in question is that between the secondary axes to the extremities of the diameter of the circle of the sharp image, or to the two extremities of the diagonals of the rectangle which can be inscribed in this circle. The first of the two tables below indicates the factor by which the focal length should be

DIAMETER OF THE SHARP IMAGE (THE FOCAL LENGTH BEING TAKEN AS UNITY)

Angle of field	Diameter of image	Angle of field	Diameter of image	Angle of field	Diameter of image
10°	0·17	55°	1·04	100°	2·38
15°	0·26	60°	1·15	105°	2·61
20°	0·35	65°	1·27	110°	2·86
25°	0·44	70°	1·40	115°	3·14
30°	0·54	75°	1·54	120°	3·46
35°	0·63	80°	1·68	125°	3·84
40°	0·73	85°	1·84	130°	4·28
45°	0·83	90°	2·00	135°	4·84
50°	0·93	95°	2·18	140°	5·50

Image Sizes, their Diagonals and Corresponding Normal Focal Lengths

Image format cm	(nominal) inches	Dia-gonal mm	Usual normal focal length mm
0·8 × 1·1	(0·31 × 0·43)[1]	13·6	15
1·0 × 1·4	(0·39 × 0·55)[1]	17·2	20–25
1·2 × 1·7	(0·47 × 0·67)[1]	20·8	25
1·8 × 2·4	(0·71 × 0·95)[2]	30	30
2·4 × 2·4	(0·95 × 0·95)[2]	34	35–40
2·8 × 2·8	(1·1 × 1·1)[3]	39·6	35–40
2·4 × 3·6	(0·95 × 1·42)[2]	43·3	45–55
3 × 4	(1·18 × 1·58)	50	50–60
*4 × 4 (4·2 × 4·2)	$1\frac{5}{8} \times 1\frac{5}{8}$[4]	59·3	60
*4 × 6·5 (4·2 × 6·4)	$1\frac{5}{8} \times 2\frac{1}{2}$[4]	76·5	75
*4·5 × 6 (4·5 × 5·7)	$1\frac{3}{4} \times 2\frac{1}{4}$[5]	72·6	75
*6 × 6 (5·7 × 5·7)	$2\frac{1}{4} \times 2\frac{1}{4}$[5]	80·5	75–80
5·7 × 7·2	$2\frac{1}{4} \times 2\frac{7}{8}$[6]	92	100
*6 × 9 (5·7 × 8·2)	$2\frac{1}{4} \times 3\frac{1}{4}$[5]	99·7	100–110
*6·5 × 9 (6·4 × 8·9)	$2\frac{1}{2} \times 3\frac{1}{2}$	110	110
8·2 × 10·8	$3\frac{1}{4} \times 4\frac{1}{4}$[7]	137	135–150
9 × 12	$(3\frac{1}{2} \times 4\frac{3}{4})$	150	150
(10·1 × 12·7)	4 × 5	162	150–180
9 × 14	$3\frac{1}{2} \times 5\frac{1}{2}$	166	150–180
10 × 15	(4 × 6)	180	180–210
12 × 16·5	$4\frac{3}{4} \times 6\frac{1}{2}$[8]	204	200–210
(12·7 × 17·8)	5 × 7	219	210–240
13 × 18	$(5\frac{1}{8} \times 7\frac{1}{8})$	222	210–240
16·5 × 21·6	$6\frac{1}{2} \times 8\frac{1}{2}$[9]	272	270–300
18 × 24	$(7\frac{1}{8} \times 9\frac{1}{2})$	300	300
20·3 × 25·4	8 × 10	325	300–360
24 × 30	$(9\frac{1}{2} \times 11\frac{3}{4})$	384	360–400
25·4 × 30·5	10 × 12	396	400
28 × 35·5	11 × 14	450	450–500
30·5 × 38·1	12 × 15	488	500
30 × 40	$11\frac{3}{4} \times 15\frac{3}{4}$	500	500

* Nominal format; actual image size indicated in brackets (not usually quoted).

1 Ultra-miniature formats (on 16 mm and 9·5 mm film)
2 Formats available with normal 35 mm film
3 Instant-pack (No. 126) image size
4 Formats available with No. 127 roll film
5 Formats available with No. 120, 620 and 220 roll film
6 "Ideal" format on No. 120, 620 and 220 roll film
7 "Quarter-plate"
8 "Half-plate"
9 "Whole-plate"

multiplied to obtain the diameter of the sharp image when the angle of field is known (in other words twice the tangent of the semi-angle of field). The second table gives the lengths of the diagonals corresponding to different film and plate formats, together with the usual normal focal lengths used in corresponding cameras. The focal lengths are thus seen to range to either side of the mean length of the image diagonal; with small image formats below 6 × 6 cm or $2\frac{1}{4} \times 2\frac{1}{4}$ inches square the focal length of the normal (or fixed) lens is most of the time slightly longer than the image diagonal. Some of the image formats, especially in the metric sizes, are nominal and the true sizes—which are not usually quoted—are shown in brackets. (For instance 6 × 6 cm is really 5·7 × 5·7 cm, i.e. the true metric equivalent of $2\frac{1}{4} \times 2\frac{1}{4}$ inches.) The inch formats (other than those quoted in brackets) have been used mainly in Great Britain and the U.S.A.; film manufacturers however quote the metric equivalent as well.

135. Choice of Focal Length and Angle. With technical and view cameras it is more usual to select the camera and lenses separately, but similar considerations apply for general photography. In normal work the focal length of the lens chosen should correspond approximately to the image diagonal (as indicated in table under § 134), i.e. equivalent to an angle of about 50° which is about the angle taken in by the eye. There is a tendency to choose a lens of the shortest focal length in the maker's catalogue that will cover the image format, often in an effort to include in a photograph as much as possible even if part has afterwards to be sacrificed in the print to unify the composition. There is no real need for this in commercial photography, since lenses for technical cameras are available in a wide range of focal lengths to cope with different subject conditions and field angles. There is on the other hand no serious disadvantage in employing a lens covering a larger angle of view on the film or plate format if only part of this angle is used in the photograph. But in this case care must be taken to avoid light reflected from the sides of the camera fogging the image. A detachable lens hood is then called for. (But see § 136 for occasions where a normal focal length of a wide angle of coverage is needed.)

Particular considerations limit the choice of focal length of studio portrait lenses. On the one hand it is very desirable, in order to avoid foreshortening and exaggeration of near parts, to place the camera at least 3–4 metres or 12 ft away from the sitter for a head and shoulders or half-length portrait, and at least 6 metres or 20 ft for full-lengths or groups. On the other hand, it is obviously necessary to take into account the dimensions of the studio and the distance available between sitter and camera, since the sitter cannot be placed against the wall and the operator must have room behind the camera for focusing and manipulating the dark slides, both of which requirements take away at least 2 metres or 6 ft from the actual length of the studio. Finally, in industrial towns, where dust is plentiful in the air, the light diffused by the dust (when the space between the camera and sitter is illuminated) will produce a slight haze over the image if the distance between sitter and camera exceeds about 12 metres or 40 ft.

Allowing a mean height of 1·70 metres or 67 in. for an adult, and that the head is about one-seventh the height, i.e. 24 cm or 9½ in., it is easy to find, by using the rules formulated in § 94, the distance the sitter must be away from the lens in order to obtain an image of any desired size, or, inversely, to determine what is the greatest focal length which, in the space available, will allow of a given degree of reduction. For a small print (head about 2 cm or 0·8 in., or full length about 7 cm or 2¾ in. on 6·5 × 9 cm or 2½ × 3½ in. paper), a lens of 280 mm focal length will require a distance of 7 metres or 23 ft, so that the studio must be 9 metres or 30 ft long. For larger portraits (a head measuring about 4 cm or 1·6 in. or a full-length figure 4 in. on paper 4 × 5 in.), or for postcards 9 × 14 cm or (3½ × 5½ in.), the same length of studio would allow the use of a lens of 550 mm focal length for head and shoulders, or a lens of 370 mm focal length for a full-length portrait, these focal lengths being the shortest which permit the camera to be placed sufficiently far from the subject to produce an agreeable perspective.

The table below indicates the distances between the sensitive material and the subject necessary to obtain the image of a head or of a full-length figure, of given dimensions, taking the focal length (f) as unit of distance—

HEAD (LENGTH 24 CM OR 9½ IN.) REDUCED TO				
2 cm	4 cm	6 cm	8 cm	12 cm
0·8 in.	1·6 in.	2·4 in.	3·2 in.	4·8 in.
14·1f	8·2f	6·25f	5·33f	4·5f

FIGURE (LENGTH 1·7 METRES OR 67 IN.) REDUCED TO				
7 cm	10 cm	15 cm	20 cm	25 cm
2·8 in.	4 in.	6 in.	8 in.	10 in.
25·6f	18·6f	13·1f	10·4f	8·75f

The only calculation to be done is to multiply the number given in the bottom rows above by the focal length of the lens to be used.

It is no good trying to use a large aperture with lenses of very great focal length, since the depth of field would be insufficient even for a profile portrait; it would constantly be necessary to use the lens at a much smaller aperture. $f/3\cdot5$ can be taken as a practical limit for a lens of 300 mm focal length, $f/5\cdot6$ for 500 mm, and $f/8$ for 750 mm. (See § 113 on "Factors Affecting the Depth of Field.")

136. Angles of Coverage with Camera Movements. In technical and view cameras the lens is usually displaceable normal to its own axis and also rotatable about one or two axes normal to the optical axis. The first movement is parallel displacement, the second the lens tilt or swing. The latter is used both for perspective control (§ 38) and especially for depth of field control (§ 96). Parallel displacement is used to raise or lower the horizon, especially when photographing high buildings, while keeping the optical axis of the lens horizontal. When choosing a lens for a camera with parallel lens displacement, the diameter of the field covered sharply must considerably exceed the diagonal of the rectangle defining the image.

If we consider, for example, a plate 9 × 12 cm (Fig. 11.1), of which the diagonal is 150 mm, a field of 150 mm diameter would cover it if the

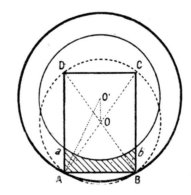

FIG. 11.1. IMAGE SIZE IN RELATION TO LENS FIELD

lens were always centred on the plate, i.e. if its optical axis always met the plate in the point O, the intersection of the diagonals of the rectangle $ABCD$. But if the lens is to be decentred 30 mm parallel to the long sides, so that it comes opposite O', the lens considered above would no longer cover the shaded area $AabB$, and in order then to cover the plate, the field covered sharply should be equal to the circle with O' as centre and radius $O'A$, i.e. a diameter of 200 mm, which would cover a plate about $12 \times 16 \cdot 5$ cm in the absence of decentring. A margin of a few millimetres corresponding to the rebate on the dark slide to hold the plate, should, to be exact, be deducted from the normal plate size.

Accordingly, instead of sharply covering an angle of about $53°$, the lens would have to cover nearly $68°$. This is thus a case of a wide-angle lens (as defined in § 135) of normal focal length (relative to the film or plate format). In practice wide-angle lens designs are often used as "normal" focal lengths on technical cameras, especially when the amount of parallel displacement is rather great (which may be the case when this displacement is obtained by tilting both the lens plane and the image plane). Equally, wide-angle lenses used with parallel displacements must be ultra-wide-angle designs.

Although the geometry of image formation is slightly different when the lens axis is tilted, the considerations governing the required angle of coverage are similar since in effect the lens axis meets the image plane at a point displaced from the centre of the film format.

The angle of coverage of a lens does not change substantially when the lens is used for subjects at different distances from the camera. The angle subtended by the film format however does decrease as the distance from the lens to the image plane increases. This means that when a lens is used for instance for macro-photography, it can cover a larger image format. In Fig. 11.2 the lens at O (shown here as a single lens for the sake of simplicity) covers an image diagonal AB when focused at infinity, where the distance OO' is equal to f, the focal length. The sharply covered angle is then AOB. When used for same-size reproduction the image plane has to move back to $A'B'$ so that OO'' equals $2f$. The angle of field $A'OB'$ is halved in this case, as is the corresponding angle of the subject field covered. The angle the lens can sharply cover however remains substantially unchanged, i.e. COD (which is equal to AOB)

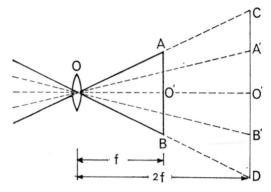

Fig. 11.2. Lens Angle in Relation to Image Scale

and the lens could cover a larger image diagonal of CD.

For the image format equivalent to the diagonal CD the lens is thus a short-focus lens, though its angle of coverage is normal (in other words not wide-angle). In practice this means first, that at close subject distances the allowable parallel displacement (and also tilt) of the lens axis is greater than implied in Fig. 11.1. Secondly, the use of a normal-angle short-focus lens is often desirable for close-up and especially macrophotography since the shorter focal length permits greater image magnification with a given camera extension. At the same time it is of course easier to correct a short-focus lens of normal angle for optimum image performance than a short-focus lens of wide angle. Special macro lenses offered by a number of manufacturers are of this type.

137. **Optical Glass Types in Lens Design.** Since the image produced by a simple converging lens is imperfect in many respects, the various aberrations (§ 75 to § 83) are corrected—within the scope of the compromises possible—by combinations of single and cemented lens elements which are assembled to form a complete lens system. The tools available to the lens designer for the correction of aberrations are the choice of the curvatures of individual lens surfaces, the number of elements employed and the use of glass types of different optical properties. The properties mainly involved here are the refractive index (§ 66) and the dispersion or Abbé number (§ 68). We have already seen (§ 75) that a measure of chromatic correction becomes possible by combining a lens of a glass with a high refractive index and low dispersion with one of similar or not much

higher refractive index but comparatively high dispersion. By tradition going back to craft methods of glass manufacture the highly dispersive glasses are generally known as flint glasses and those of lower dispersion (higher Abbé number) as crown glasses. The boundary is generally taken to lie at an Abbé number of 55 for glasses of refractive index below 1·6 and at $\nu = 50$ for glasses of higher refractive index.

Chemically, these glasses contain mainly alkali silicates as well as oxides of certain other elements; flint glasses in particular generally contain lead oxide.

Originally the number of glasses with different combinations of refractive index and dispersive power was limited. In 1886 the Schott glass works in Germany brought out a wide range of new glasses with further combinations of high and low refractive indices and dispersive powers respectively; this was largely responsible for the rise of the German optical industry before the first World War. These glasses contained phosphates, borates, barium and other metallic oxides. After the second World War a further rapid development of new glass types took place, utilising various rare earths and heavy metals (lanthanum, thorium, etc.).

For the lens designer the refractive index and dispersion remain the important parameters of a glass. To help him in his choice, glass manufacturers usually show on charts the location of the glass types they offer in terms of refractive index and Abbé number. Fig. 11.3 shows the form of such a chart, indicating also the historical development of glass types and their main groups. The area within the solid bold line indicates glass types available up till the 1880s; here HC and SC are the classic crown glasses (hard crown and soft crown), while SF (short flint), ELF (extra light flint), LF (light flint), F (flint) and DF (dense flint) represent the classical flint glass varieties. The area within the heavy broken line covers locations in terms of Abbé number and refractive index of glass types developed since the 1880s up to the end of World War II. Here the crown glasses extend from borosilicate and fluoride crowns (BSC and FC) through phosphate crowns (PC) to the barium crowns (light barium crown $LBaC$, medium barium crown $MBaC$, dense barium crown $DBaC$). Flint glasses in turn cover light to dense barium flints ($BaLF$, BaF, $BaDF$) and extra dense flints (EDF). Developments after 1945 mainly produced glasses containing lanthanum and other rare earth elements—both among lanthanum crowns and special crowns (LaC, SpC)

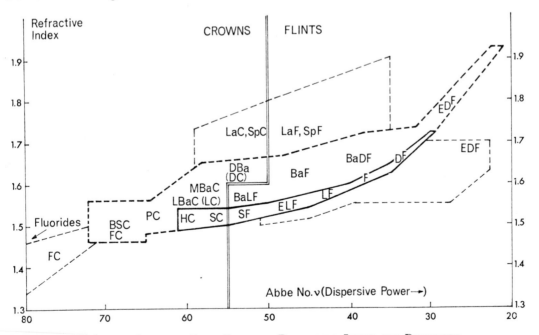

FIG. 11.3. CHART OF GLASS TYPES BY REFRACTIVE INDEX AND DISPERSION

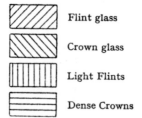

Flint glass

Crown glass

Light Flints

Dense Crowns

FIG. 11.4. SHADING REPRESENTING THE DIFFERENT
TYPES OF GLASS

and the corresponding flints (*LaF, SpF*). New glasses also include a range of extra dense flints of very high dispersive power and crown glasses of extremely low dispersion. Crystalline fluoride materials also lie in this direction; these are used in ultra-violet transmitting optics (§ 164). Naturally the greater the number of glass types a designer has at his disposal, especially with extreme refractive index and/or Abbé number, the greater his scope in producing lens systems of advanced optical specifications and quality.

138. Survey of Principal Lens Types. In the following sections main lens types are briefly described, chosen partly for their historical significance and partly as representative examples of modern developments. The list cannot of course be complete on account of the extremely wide variety of combinations in use and the constant progress which is taking place in this field. To facilitate comparisons, the sectional drawings of historical lens types, reduced to their essential elements, have been made on a uniform scale corresponding to lenses

FIG. 11.5. WOLLASTON'S SINGLE MENISCUS, *f*/11

of 100 mm focal length. In these historical designs the principal optical glass types are indicated by conventional shading, following the key given in Fig. 11.4. The stop, where drawn, corresponds approximately to the maximum aperture.

139. Single Lenses. The simple non-achromatized lens was used in the camera obscura before the invention of photography. To obtain a relatively large field, W. H. Wollaston (1812) recommended the use of a convergent meniscus lens (Fig. 11.5), with stop in front, having an aperture of *f*/11, and covering a field equal to the focal length (angle 60°). This image, it must be understood, has every possible aberration, and in particular requires the adjustment after focusing to compensate for the difference between visual and chemical focus. In some fixed-focus cameras (§ 124) this is made once for all by the maker who also makes allowance for astigmatism, field curvature and coma by setting the film at a suitable distance from the lens.

The first photographs made by Daguerre were taken with a doublet lens made by C. L. Chevalier (1830), partially corrected for achromatism (Fig. 11.6), which, with stop *f*/14 (afterwards increased to *f*/12), covered sufficiently well a circle of diameter equal to half the focal length. At a smaller stop, *f*/70, the field was half as large again.

This form of lens was improved and brought to its present form of simple achromatic lens only in 1857 by Thomas Grubb. In his lens (Fig. 11.7) it is seen that the arrangement of Chevalier was reversed, the convergent lens this time facing the object. With an aperture, usually *f*/16, the field reached 60° with complete correction of achromatism and partial correction of spherical aberration for the central rays. By increasing the number of cemented lenses to three (Fig. 11.8), J. H. Dallmeyer (1865) was able to extend the aperture to *f*/11 and field to 70°

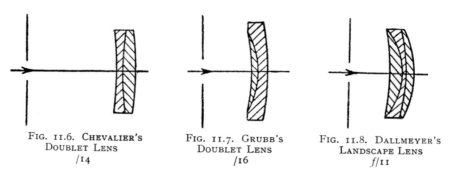

FIG. 11.6. CHEVALIER'S
DOUBLET LENS
/14

FIG. 11.7. GRUBB'S
DOUBLET LENS
/16

FIG. 11.8. DALLMEYER'S
LANDSCAPE LENS
f/11

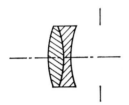

FIG. 11.9. GOERZ FRONTAR $f/9$

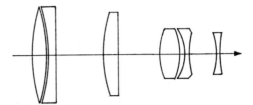

FIG. 11.11. PETZVAL-DERIVED $f/1\cdot2$
CINE PROJECTION LENS

(90° at $f/32$) in his " rapid wide-angle landscape lens."

Modern doublet lenses, still used in cheap box cameras, usually have the stop behind the lens, protected inside the camera. An example is the Frontar by C. P. Goerz (Fig. 11.9) which offers reasonably good correction of most aberrations (but not necessarily distortion), though of course the biggest limitation remains the comparatively small aperture of $f/9$.

140. Petzval Portrait Lens. This lens (Fig. 11.10),the first to be calculated by a mathematician, was only moderately successful when first brought out (1840). J. Petzval set out, by a proper choice of curvatures and thicknesses, to correct aberrations, and particularly curvature of the field, without the necessity of using a small stop, so as to shorten the very long exposures required in the Daguerreotype process. But this aim could only be accomplished at the expense of angle of field, the diameter of useful field being only about one-third the focal length (angle 20° to 25°), with an effective aperture of $f/3\cdot4$ to $f/3\cdot6$, subsequently enlarged to $f/2\cdot4$ by H. Zincke in 1870. It will thus be seen that the useful field of the lens was almost equal to its diameter.

In his first type Petzval had intentionally left in a little chromatic aberration, which subsequent optical designers adopting this type corrected in the endeavour to make the image a little more homogeneous.

The Petzval portrait lens, more or less modified, is still in use in a number of portrait studios, where the slight softness of definition away from the centre of the field was considered an advantage. Nowadays the Petzval lens is practically superseded by modern high-speed anastigmat systems, but it is still widely used—sometimes in modified forms—in projectors. There the maximum aperture may reach $f/1\cdot2$, though here additional elements may be added —for instance a field flattening rear element and an intermediate coverging lens as in Fig. 11.11.

At the time of the reaction against the exaggerated correction of lenses for portraiture, lenses of the Petzval type were successfully used (de Pulligny, 1904) with the back combination removed and replaced by a simple convergent meniscus of the same diameter but almost double the focal length. The whole lens can be used at about $f/5$. The chromatic fringe is then about one-third to one-quarter that of an anachromatic lens of the same focal length and relative aperture.

141. Rectilinear Lenses. At a time when the only successful lenses available to the photographer were the simple objective and the portrait lens, the need was felt for lenses covering a field comparable with that of the single lenses but perfectly corrected for distortion, which consequently could be used for copying and architectural photography. This correction was sought for in a symmetrical arrangement of the components, following that already used by Wollaston for microscope objectives. In 1866 H. A. Steinheil brought out his symmetrical

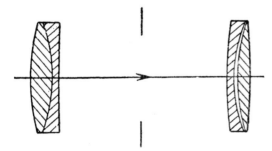

FIG. 11.10. PETZVAL PORTRAIT LENS, $f/3\cdot5$

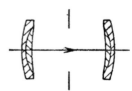

FIG. 11.12. STEINHEIL'S SYMMETRICAL APLANAT, $f/8$

aplanat (Fig. 11.12), and soon afterwards the rectilinear of Dallmeyer appeared, almost identical except as to detail. However, while this lens was indeed rectilinear, it was only very slightly aplanatic, so that it is the name given it by Dallmeyer that has become general for this class of lenses, which all lens designers tried, more or less successfully, to improve. In its original form it covered a field of 45° at $f/8$, and 60° at $f/30$. Steinheil succeeded in increasing the aperture to $f/7$ and even $f/6$ without much sacrifice of field (40°). These lenses attained considerable popularity, but were also displaced after about the turn of the century by anastigmat lenses with their greatly superior definition and speed. The rectilinear lens, being one of the simplest forms of symmetrical lens, offered automatic correction for lateral chromatic aberration, coma and distortion when the object and image were at the same distance from the lens, as in copying. For these each half of the lens system contributed these aberrations of equal but opposite sign so that they cancelled out. It was not, however, possible to correct both astigmatism and curvature of field.

Where optimum image quality was a less important consideration, symmetrical lens types like the rectilinear were sometimes made to permit the use of the back combination on its own, forming a single achromatic lens of double the focal length of the complete lens. The largest aperture, $f/8$ is then actually $f/16$ or a little less. Such an arrangement was the cheapest and simplest *convertible lens*, offering two focal lengths—provided of course that the camera had adequate bellows extension for the use of the back component on its own. The slight distortion and softer definition resulting from the removal of the front component did not seriously interfere with the use of this system in landscape photography.

142. Wide-angle Rectilinears. The somewhat large separation between the components of the rectilinear lens restricts the angle of field illuminated, and it is impossible, even by stopping down, to increase the angle to the extent required in many classes of work. In the 1860's were introduced the Globe lens of

FIG. 11.13. STEINHEIL'S WIDE-ANGLE, $f/18$

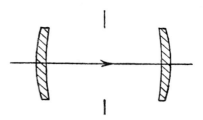

FIG. 11.14. PUYO AND PULLIGNY'S SYMMETRICAL ANACHROMATIC LENS, $f/6.5$

Harrison and Schnitzer (1863) and the Pantoscope of Busch (1866), symmetrical combinations of two achromatic lenses of the form shown in Fig. 11.7, covering 90° and 95° at maximum apertures of $f/17$ and $f/30$, with considerably less curvature of the field in the latter case. Steinheil subsequently succeeded, by modifying his aplanat but keeping the same principle, in making his wide-angle Aplanat (Fig. 11.13), covering 105° at $f/18$, showing marked superiority over its predecessors, particularly from the point of view of spherical aberration. These were the forerunners of wide-angle lenses proper (§ 149).

143. Anachromatic Symmetrical Lens. This lens, the use of which was recommended by Puyo and de Pulligny (1903), is based on Steinheil's Periskop but, there being no need for a large angle of field, the aperture was increased from $f/40$ to $f/6.5$. The symmetrical anachromatic consists of two identical convergent menisci placed one on either side of the stop, with their convex surfaces outwards and separated by at least one-sixth of their common focal length (Fig. 11.14). When the necessary correction is made for focus, very agreeable portraits can be made, covering a field of about 30°. This is thus a way of achieving a soft focus lens of deliberately imperfect definition (§ 132). As already mentioned, softness of focus can nowadays be controlled more efficiently with soft focus attachments (§ 190).

144. Antiplanats. A symmetrical construction reduces the resources of the lens designer in the matter of corrections, as both combinations must be separately corrected for several aberrations. With the glasses available at this period progress was only possible by giving up both symmetry and the separate correction of the individual components, each component, on the contrary, being left with considerable aberration, which compensated that in the other. This fruitful conception was first applied with real success by A. Steinheil (1881) in his Group Antiplanat (Fig. 11.15), covering at *f*/6·2, the central region being remarkably well corrected for astigmatism. The considerable weight of this lens was a serious drawback to its use on the light cameras which became fashionable with the introduction of the dry plate. Hence this lens and several variants of it made by R. Steinheil merely aroused curiosity, the more so as the approaching appearance of the anastigmat was to furnish a complete and more elegant solution of the problem of the photographic objective.

145. The First Anastigmats. The principles of the correction of astigmatism had been laid down in 1843 by Petzval, but none of the glasses available to opticians at that time allowed these conditions to be satisfied. The appearance of new glasses, dense crowns, and light flints, enabled P. Rudolph, at the instigation of E. Abbé, to design, after less successful attempts, a type of unsymmetrical, unconvertible doublet, Its appearance (1890) marks an event in the history of photographic optics, at least as important as the invention of the portrait lens or the aplanat. Each of the components of the different series of lenses made on the same principle (afterwards known as Protars) was formed of two cemented glasses, the dimensions, curvatures, and thicknesses varying as the requirements were for a lens of high aperture (field of 80° at *f*/7·2) or one of very large field (110° at *f*/18). Fig. 11.16 shows this type of wide-angle lens. A much better correction of astigmatism was obtained in 1893 by adding a glass to the rear component (Fig. 11.17), this

lens covering perfectly, without curvature of field, an angle of 57° at *f*/8 and still satisfactorily 75° when stopped down to *f*/22. In 1901 H. L. Aldis showed that an excellent image could be obtained with a considerably simpler construction (Fig. 11.18), covering a field of 51° at *f*/6 and 90° at *f*/32.

146. Convertible Anastigmats. The excellent results obtained by Rudolph encouraged many lens designers to use the new combinations of glasses, but they sought for a solution of the problem in another direction—returning to the convertible symmetrical lens. The German factories being almost the only ones at this period to possess research departments, the first of the new category to appear was the double-anastigmat calculated by E. von Hoegh (1893), (Fig. 11.19), covering a field of 72° at *f*/8 (afterwards increased to *f*/7·7 and then to *f*/6·8), and almost 90° at *f*/22, forming an excellent universal lens. Similar lens systems were also produced at about the same time by Voigtlander and Steinheil, with different arrangements of the individual elements in each component. Some of these lenses, like the Voigtlander Collinear Apochromat (Fig. 11.20) with apertures between *f*/9 and *f*/12·5 provided a high degree of chromatic correction. This type of lens is still used in process work at a scale of reproduction of or around 1:1.

A number of variants followed, from process lenses covering about 100° at *f*/11 to the French "Eurygraphe" lens, in which the aperture was enlarged to *f*/5 with the same field of 90°. The number of glasses cemented together in the components was subsequently increased to four, and even five.

The back component of such a lens, when used alone, forms an excellent single anastigmat, perfectly corrected for chromatic and spherical aberrations, but not for coma, and showing, at least at the edges of the field, a little distortion and curvature, but very suitable for landscape work. The focal length is usually about 1·8 times that of the complete lens, and the camera extension is rather more than doubled. The

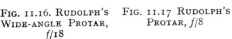

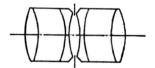

FIG. 11.20. VOIGTLANDER COLLINEAR APOCHROMAT (up to $f/9$)

FIG. 11.22. TAYLOR'S COOKE TRIPLET LENS, $f/6.5$

maximum effective aperture is then equal to the actual diameter of the largest stop, and the relative aperture about 40 per cent (mean value) less than that of the complete lens.

Meanwhile (1895) Rudolph, after having tried and rejected this arrangement, worked out a single anastigmat of four cemented glasses, which could be used either separately (field about 50° at a maximum aperture of $f/12.5$) or in pairs, forming either a symmetrical lens at $f/6.3$ or an unsymmetrical lens (Fig. 11.21), at an aperture from $f/7$ to $f/7.7$ (according to the degree of dissymmetry) covering about 45° at full aperture and 80° at $f/25$. This arrangement was later adopted by the greater number of designers some of whom have pushed the aperture to $f/5$ and that of the single components to $f/9$. These convertible unsymmetrical anastigmats form the simplest "sets of lenses" giving the photographer a range of three focal lengths in steps, generally in the ratio of 1 : 1.6 : 2 (or 1 : 1.5 : 2.2), the focal length of the complete lens being taken as 1. The single lens, when used by itself, is always placed behind the diaphragm; in the complete lens the shorter-focus component is behind and the longer component in front.

Nowadays the use of convertible symmetrical lenses to obtain a range of focal lengths is practically obsolete, since the optical performance of the longer focal length by using only part of the lens was appreciably below that of the complete lens. Alternative focal lengths are therefore almost invariably obtained by separate lens systems interchangeable as a whole on the camera. A special form of convertible lens, based on quite different principles, is however found on certain miniature cameras (§ 158).

147. Triplet Type Anastigmats. A completely different conception of the anastigmat led H. D. Taylor (1893) to design numerous types of specialized lenses, all consisting of a system of three separated lenses, among which the model shown in Fig. 11.22 is particularly designed for hand cameras, covering 70° at a maximum aperture of $f/6.5$. Among other forms by the same designer may be noted a portrait lens at $f/3.5$, covering about 40°, a wide-angle covering 97° at $f/6.5$, and a process lens at $f/8$ ($f/11$ and $f/16$ for the longer focal lengths) covering 55° at full aperture and about 80° at $f/32$.

The advantages of this relatively economical construction, which allows the designer the greatest number of variable factors with the minimum number of lenses, led to the appearance of a number of variants, in most of which, however, one of the single lenses was replaced by a system of two cemented lenses. Such is the case, for example, with the Tessar lens designed by Rudolph and E. Wandersleb (1902), of which there are several series. That shown in Fig. 11.23, intended especially for portraiture, covers a field of about 35° at $f/3.5$. Others at $f/4.5$ and $f/6.3$ cover respectively 55° and 65° at full aperture, and 70° with a small stop (about $f/36$).

The triplet design soon became—and still is—one of the most widely used anastigmat lens types and serves in medium to high-class amateur and professional cameras as well as

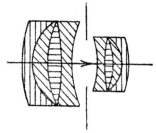

FIG. 11.21. RUDOLPH'S DOUBLE PROTAR, /7.7

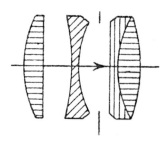

FIG. 11.23. RUDOLPH AND WANDERSLEB'S TESSAR, $f/3.5$

for numerous projection lens systems. As might be expected, it was followed by a considerable number of derivatives which mostly followed two lines of evolution.

The first was the splitting of one or more of the elements into separate air-spaced components. There exist versions with the front, the middle or the rear element replaced by an appropriate lens pair; in some designs even two of the three elements are thus split up.

The second approach was the replacement of one or more of the single elements of the Taylor triplet by cemented components. While the Tessar (Fig. 11.23) was the best known lens of this type, innumerable variants and derivatives again exist, differing in the arrangement of the elements within the cemented component, in the number of cemented components and using sometimes combinations of air-spaced and cemented multiple units to replace each of the three basic triplet elements. (Even modern Tessar lenses, produced in a wide range for 35 mm miniature, medium and large size technical cameras as well as copying and other special purposes, have many variants with different arrangement of the rear cemented component, different curvatures, glass types and dimensions of the other two components etc.).

Triplet types with cemented front and rear component are derived from the Heliar by H. Harting (1902) originally marketed as a lens of slight deliberate softness (Fig. 11.24). Lenses of this type were however also produced with very high apochromatic colour correction for process work. Further advances in correction became possible with modern highly refracting glasses, used for instance in the Elmarit $f/2\cdot8$ of 90 mm for minature cameras (Fig. 11.25). In several such systems central elements of considerable thickness are used, an almost classic type being the 135 mm Sonar $f/4$ (Fig. 11.26). Despite the complexity which triplet derivatives achieve, especially when applied to modern high aperture lenses, there has in fact been a trend back to the simple triplet broadly following the system of Fig. 11.22 for medium speed amateur camera lenses. The appearance of

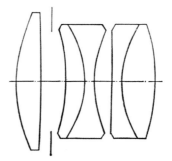

FIG. 11.25. 90 mm ELMARIT $f/2\cdot8$ FOR 24 × 36 mm

modern highly refracting lanthanum glasses since the 1940s provided appreciably greater scope for correction in the triplet lens type than had been possible before, so that the newest three element triplets are as good as—if not better than—the earlier four-element Tessar type. Such triplets are nowadays fitted on less expensive miniature cameras and have maximum apertures of around $f/2\cdot8$. Needless to say, the use of these new glasses permitted further improvement also in triplets with one or more cemented components, such as the Elmarit (Fig. 11.25) mentioned before.

With the triplet design slight variations in the spacing between the first and second elements alters the focal length without seriously affecting the general performance. Such lenses are therefore particularly suitable for front cell focusing (§ 158).

148. Symmetrical Anastigmats of Separated Lenses. With a view to simplifying the construction of symmetrical convertible anastigmats, many designers have sought to take advantage of the freedom given by combinations of separated lenses. One of the first of this type appears to be that calculated by von Hoegh (1898). Originally the maximum aperture was only about $f/10$ for the complete system, but it was extended by Zschokke successively to $f/7\cdot6$ (1903), and then to $f/5\cdot5$ and $f/4\cdot5$, according

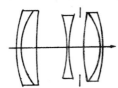

FIG. 11.24. HARTIG'S HELIAR $f/4\cdot5$

FIG. 11.26. 134 mm SONNAR $f/4$ FOR 24 × 36 mm

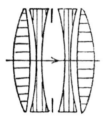

FIG. 11.27. ZSCHOKKE'S CELOR, $f/4\cdot5$

to the focal length (Fig. 11.27), the field being about 60° at the maximum aperture and 65° at a very small aperture.

The majority of modern symmetrical anastigmats is however derived from the so-called Gauss configuration (Fig. 11.28) in which the biconcave and biconvex elements of the Celor are replaced by diverging and converging meniscus lenses respectively, all surfaces being concave towards the centre stop, while the air space between the front two and the rear two elements also has a diverging meniscus shape. (Being an air space between glass elements it has in fact a converging effect.)

In modern Gauss type lenses the diverging meniscus elements are almost invariably replaced by cemented components and one or more of the converging meniscus lenses may become plano-convex or even biconvex. One of the

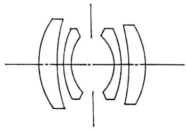

FIG. 11.28. THE BASIC GAUSS SYSTEM

earliest photographic Gauss type lenses was the Planar designed by P. Rudolph in 1896. This existed both with fixed elements (Fig. 11.29), as a modification with five elements (Fig. 11.30) and also in a modern form with seven elements (Fig. 11.31). The maximum aperture is usually $f/2\cdot8$, but special versions of this design have also been used for high aperture lenses up to $f/1\cdot4$ (§ 151).

The unmodified Gauss design is also still used occasionally in lenses of fairly long focal length covering an image angle up to 60°, but with the maximum aperture limited to around $/6\cdot3$.

The symmetrical Gauss configuration has also given rise to a large number of other derivatives, mostly with the front or rear components split into two or more separate elements or else with the inside components separated or replaced by multi-cemented units. The main purpose of most of these variants is to increase the maximum aperture for high aperture lenses (§ 151). Many of these systems became possible only with the introduction of lens coating (§ 89) which cut down the loss of light occasioned by the growing number of glass-air surfaces to acceptable levels. Before coating the usual limit of Gauss type leneses was set with four single or cemented components and hence eight air-glass surfaces.

149. Wide-angle Lenses. Although such a lens has only a very restricted use, we ought to mention, if only as a curiosity, the wide-angle lens (Fig. 11.32), calculated by von Hoegh in 1900 to cover a flat anastigmatic field of 140°, almost four-tenths of the complete horizon, at an aperture of $f/22$ (actually the full aperture is used only for focusing, and a smaller aperture used when the photograph is taken). The correction for astigmatism is only obtained by the use of extremely thin lenses; spherical and chromatic aberrations are not corrected, but the relative

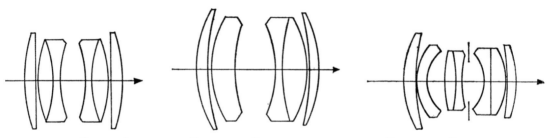

FIG. 11.29. RUDOLPH'S ORIGINAL PLANAR

FIG. 11.30. FIVE-ELEMENT PLANAR $f/2\cdot8$

FIG. 11.31. SEVEN-ELEMENT PLANAR $f/2\cdot8$

FIG. 11.32. Von Hoegh's Hypergon, $f/22$

aperture is so small, and thus the depth of focus is so large, that these aberrations do not affect the image in practice, and no correction for focus is necessary. When the field used exceeds 110° the difference of illumination between the centre and the edge is so great that it is necessary to use a star-shaped diaphragm (§ 86) to reduce the illumination at the centre for a considerable proportion of the exposure.

The large angle between the extreme secondary axes, and the fact that the focal length is scarcely one-fifth the diagonal of the plate covered, means that the lens can only be used on a specially-made camera; also it is generally impossible to use a shutter with it.

A prototype of more modern wide-angle lenses is the Dallmeyer $f/16$ (Fig. 11.33) which in fact follows the simple Gauss layout. This lens is focused at $f/6.5$, but must be stopped down to $f/16$ for exposure. The angular field at $f/16$ is 90° and increases to 95° at $f/32$.

Most wide-angle lenses—other than the retrofocus types (§ 156) are symmetrical and many of them are derived from the Gauss design. To increase the usable aperture, the elements can be made much more curved as in the Topogon (Fig. 11.34) which covers an angle

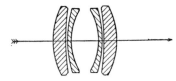

FIG. 11.33. Dallmeyer Wide-angle Lens, $f/16$

of about 83° at $f/4$. Another approach is to split the diverging meniscus elements into a cemented component and then cement this to the outer converging elements, producing a design like Fig. 11.35, one of the best known examples of which is the Angulon.

For a still greater angle of view at large apertures, symmetrical configurations or derivatives are used which however have nothing to do with the Gauss design as here the outer elements are diverging meniscus units with two converging inner components of two, three or more cemented elements. Examples are the Super-Angulon (Fig. 11.36) which can cover up to 90° on 24 × 36 mm miniature negatives with a maximum aperture of $f/3.4$. More complex derivatives may split one of the outer elements into two; an example is the Rodenstock Grandagon $f/5.6$ (Fig. 11.37) which covers 100° at full aperture. There are numerous variations on these basic forms, produced by nearly all major optical manufacturers.

Noteworthy among unorthodox wide-angle systems is the 15 mm Hologon $f/8$ (Fig. 11.38) which covers an angle of 110° and is used in a specially designed 35 mm camera. This lens has—apart from its shape—two unusual features: it only uses three elements and the fixed lens stop is set in glass and not in air, being a constriction in the central element.

150. **Fish-eye Lenses.** For most applications where wide-angle lenses are used, especially in technical and aerial photography, freedom from distortion (§ 82) is essential. This is one of the reasons why symmetrical designs with the stop in the middle are favoured for wide-angle purposes. In view of the falling off of illumination towards the edges of the wide-angle image field the maximum coverage of such lenses finds its limit at around 100°–110°.

This limitation disappears if we drop the

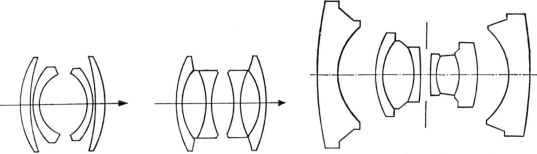

FIG. 11.34. Topogon $f/4$ FIG. 11.35. Angulon $f/6.8$ FIG. 11.36. Super-Angulon $f/3.4$

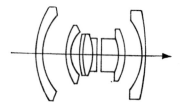

FIG. 11.37. GRANDAGON $f/5\cdot6$

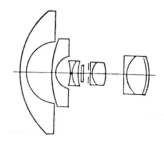

FIG. 11.39. 180° FISH-EYE NIKKOR

requirement of distortion-free reproduction. It then becomes possible to cover an angle of 180° and more, this being achieved by the introduction of very high degrees of barrel distortion. This at the same time counteracts the loss of image brightness towards the margins of the field and so gives acceptable results. Indeed, if the degree of distortion is precisely known, it is possible to rectify such an image during projection in a manner similar to that dealing with panoramic perspective (§ 39).

One of the earliest systems of this kind was R. Hill's cloud lens used for recording cloud formations over the whole sky. The distortion was here corrected by using the same lens again for projection of the image. Modern optical systems of this kind, mainly for miniature and cine cameras, are known as fish-eye lenses—largely because of the bulging out front element necessary to take in a 180° angle of view. A fairly elaborate example is that of the Fish-eye Nikkor $f/8$ (Fig. 11.39), which with a focal length of 8 mm covers a 24 × 36 mm image format. The 6·2 mm $f/5\cdot6$ Fish-eye Nikkor covers even a 220° angle. In many cases the image field of the fish-eye lenses is circular within the negative area; in other words the latter is fitted around the lens's field and not inside it.

151. Ultra-Speed Lenses. For every type of lens there is a maximum aperture beyond which it is practically impossible to obtain good definition; this limit may sometimes be exceeded by the use of glasses of unorthodox

types, but even then the increase in aperture is not striking. The zonal aberrations can be reduced to permissible limits only by using shallow surfaces, so that the refraction of extreme rays is slight for all surfaces. Most high-aperture lenses are related to a portrait lens designed by A. Clark (1889) in the U.S.A., which consisted of two combinations, each of two separated elements, of the type formerly designed by Gauss for telescopes, the lens being nearly symmetrical.

At a time when the maximum aperture of lenses used for general photographic work was around $f/3\cdot5$ to $f/4\cdot5$, lenses of $f/2\cdot8$ were considered as fast and $f/2$ as ultra fast. Nowadays $f/2\cdot8$ is the normal maximum aperture for most miniature camera lenses other than the very cheapest ones, as well as for lenses of roll film reflexes; most better miniature cameras have lenses of $f/2$ or $f/1\cdot4$. Ultra-speed lenses of apertures larger than $f/1\cdot4$ are also found for a number of cameras; advances in this direction are mainly limited by the practical problems of depth of field (§ 133). As these problems are less pressing with very short focal lengths, ultra large-aperture lenses are much more widespread among narrow-gauge cine cameras.

Most current large-aperture lenses are derived from the symmetrical Planar type design. Significantly early types were the Speed Panchro and H. W. Lee's $f/2$ Opic (1921), (Fig. 11.40), P. Rudolph's $f/2$ Kinoplasmat (Fig. 11.41), in

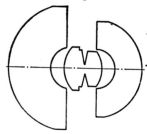

FIG. 11.38. 15 mm HOLOGON $/8$

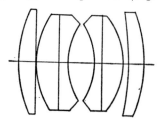

FIG. 11.40. LEE'S OPIC ANASTIGMAT, $f/2$

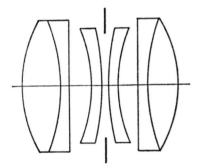

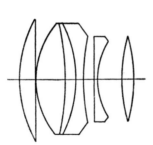

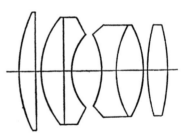

FIG. 11.41. RUDOLPH'S
KINOPLASMAT, $f/2$

FIG. 11.42. BERTELE'S
ERNOSTAR, $f/1\cdot8$

FIG. 11.43. MERTÉ'S BIOTAR, $f/1\cdot4$

which a small amount of spherical aberration is intentionally allowed, in order to produce "soft" images, A. Klugnardt's $f/2$ Ernostar, subsequently extended to $f/1\cdot8$ by L. Bertele (Fig. 11.42 (1924)), and finally W. Merté's Biotar of aperture $f/1\cdot4$ (Fig. 11.43).

Modern high-speed symmetrical lenses achieved both larger maximum apertures and improved correction of aberrations by the use of post-war highly refractive glass types. In some cases the lens systems obtained did not deviate very greatly from the Planar or Speed Panchro configuration, but usually high-speed systems split one or more of the outer (and sometimes also inner) elements into separate glasses. This became feasible once anti-reflection coatings had removed the crippling light loss penalty with more than eight air-glass surfaces. Examples of such modern types are the 50 mm Canon $f/1\cdot2$ and $f/0\cdot95$ (Fig. 11.44) for 35 mm cameras and the Nikkor $f/1\cdot1$ (Fig. 11.45), while the 50 mm Summicron $f/2$ splits up both the front components into separate air-spaced elements (Fig. 11.46). The latter two lenses thus each have a total of 12 air-glass surfaces. As another approach the Noctilux

$f/1\cdot2$ goes back to a four-component system (Fig. 11.47) but employs two outside aspheric surfaces for additional correction (§ 166).

Lenses of apertures larger than $f/1$ have been used for many years in fluorography, i.e. the photography of fluorescent images from radiographic and cathode ray tube screens. They are mostly Gauss derivatives, often with field flattening elements and with a limited colour correction to cover only the spectral emission range of fluorescent screens. Two extreme speed lenses of more general application are the 75 mm Voigtlander Super Farron $f/0\cdot87$ (Fig. 11.48) and the 50 mm Zeiss Planar $f/0\cdot7$ (1966) which covers a 30° angle (Fig. 11.49).

Extreme aperture lenses of this kind cannot be considered as interchangeable lens units for conventional cameras. As the lens diameter of a 50 mm $f/0\cdot7$ lens is around 80–90 mm, it has to be used in a specially designed camera which will also meet the demands of film flatness and mechanical tolerances required by the greatly reduced depth of focus.

Triplet derivatives are also found among high-speed lenses, though here the maximum

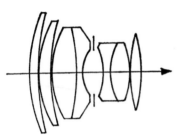

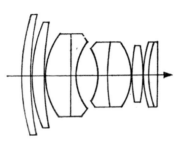

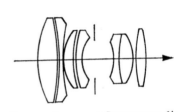

FIG. 11.44. CANON $f/1\cdot2$ AND $f/0\cdot95$

FIG. 11.45. NIKKOR $f/1\cdot1$

FIG. 11.46. 50 mm SUMMICRON $f/2$

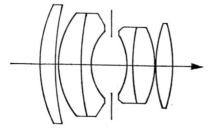

FIG. 11.47. 50 mm NOCTILUX $f/1\cdot2$

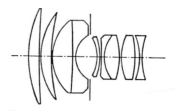

FIG. 11.48. SUPER-FARRON $f/0\cdot87$

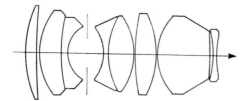

FIG. 11.49. 50 mm PLANAR $f/0\cdot7$

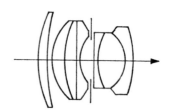

FIG. 11.50. SONNAR $f/1\cdot5$ TO $f/2$

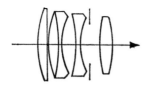

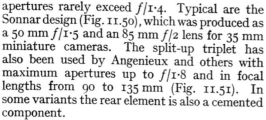

FIG. 11.51. ANGENIEUX $f/1\cdot8$ TO $f/2\cdot5$

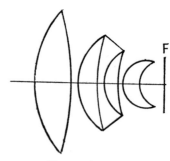

FIG. 11.52. YOSHIDO'S ASPHERIC $f/0\cdot519$

apertures rarely exceed $f/1\cdot4$. Typical are the Sonnar design (Fig. 11.50), which was produced as a 50 mm $f/1\cdot5$ and an 85 mm $f/2$ lens for 35 mm miniature cameras. The split-up triplet has also been used by Angenieux and others with maximum apertures up to $f/1\cdot8$ and in focal lengths from 90 to 135 mm (Fig. 11.51). In some variants the rear element is also a cemented component.

The high correction necessary for extreme apertures is less easy with triplet lens types than with symmetrical systems; however aspheric lens surfaces can again be used. With such a system Yoshido (1959) designed a three-component anastigmat with a cemented centre component of three elements and an aspheric front element, reaching a maximum aperture

of $f/0\cdot519$ (Fig. 11.52). The focal length here is 50 mm and the rear component is practically in contact with the film plane F. The lens diameter of around 100 mm makes this quite a cumbersome unit, despite its optical simplicity. This is also the main reason why extreme speed lenses are not designed in focal lengths above about 75 mm.

152. Variable-power Telephotos. A divergent lens had several times been used for enlarging the image given by an astronomical objective (L. Porro, 1851; Warren de la Rue, 1860), or by a microscope (Foucault and Donné, 1845; Borie and de Tournemine, 1869) when, in 1873, J. Traill Taylor pointed out the importance to photographers of obtaining large pictures of distant objects directly in the camera, by using an objective constructed on the principle of the Galilean telescope (opera glasses) but increasing the separation between the lenses and correcting them specially for this purpose. Such a system, in fact, constitutes an objective the focal length of which can be varied at will between very wide limits by altering the separation between the elements. Also, since the nodal points are thrown forward a great distance in front of the lens, so that the distance between the lens and the image is only a small fraction of the focal length, the use of the cumbrous cameras required for normal lenses of great focal length is thus rendered unnecessary. It was only in 1891 that this suggestion was exploited by T. R. Dallmeyer, followed closely by A. Miethe and Steinheil, and then by many other designers.

Consider (Fig. 11.53) a system formed of a convergent lens L_1 of focal length f_1 and a divergent lens L_2 of focal length f_2, so placed that the back focus f'_1 of the convergent lens falls between L_2 and its (virtual) front focus f_2. The image of a distant point in the direction R will be formed, in the absence of the divergent lens, at a point r in the focal plane of the front component. This point acts as virtual object to the divergent lens and closer to it than its focus, its image R' is real, and magnified in the ratio $F'R'/f_1'r'$.

The application of the formulae already quoted in § 101, bearing in mind that the focal length of the divergent lens must have the " minus " sign, gives for the resultant focal length

$$F = \frac{f_1 f_2}{f_1 + f_2 - e} = \frac{f_1 f_2}{\delta}$$

where e is the separation of the components, δ the optical interval, the distance between the foci f_1' f_2. The formula shows that when δ tends to zero the focal length becomes infinitely great (adjustment of the Galilean telescope for normal sight). Conversely, if the lens L_2 approaches the focal plane of L_1 there can be no

possibility of photographing the image. The optical interval δ can thus take all values between o and $(f_1 - f_2)$, the difference between the two focal lengths.

If the image given by the complete system is magnified m times relative to that which the convergent system alone would have given, the distance E of the divergent lens from the magnified image is

$$E = f_2(m - 1)$$

If, in the case of a telephoto, where $f_1/f_2 = s$, the distances O and I of the object and image respectively from the telephoto and the distances o and i for an ordinary lens of the same focal length giving an image of the same size, are calculated, it is found that—

$$O = o + [F(s - 1) + f_1]$$
$$I = i - [F(1 - 1/s) + f_2]$$

The ratio s being always greater than (or at least equal to) unity, it is seen that, for a photograph on the same scale, the distance of the object from the telephoto is always greater than it would be with an ordinary lens of the same focal length, and the more so the smaller the focal length of the amplifying negative lens compared with that of the convergent system. Conversely, the distance from the image to the telephoto is always less than it would be with a lens of the usual construction.

The first telephoto lenses used any ordinary photographic lens as the convergent system, and as amplifier a more or less complex divergent system. The two components were mounted so that the separation could be altered by a rack and pinion, the optical interval δ of the above formulae being marked on a scale on the outer tube, also, usually, the resulting magnification and the corresponding distance of the image.

The first simplification took place in 1896 by the construction of a complete system shown in Fig. 11.54, the divergent system being shown

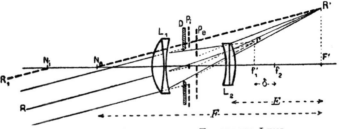

FIG. 11.53. OPTICS OF THE TELEPHOTO LENS

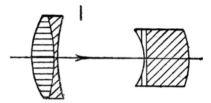

FIG. 11.54 VARIABLE POWER TELEPHOTO

in full lines in the position for a focal length of 100 mm, whilst in the position shown by the dotted lines the focal length is about 300 mm.

In one or other of these forms the telephoto requires careful handling on account of the very faint image, making focusing difficult when large magnifications are attempted. The use of an optical system with variable separation requires in fact that each of the components should be separately corrected, which is only possible with small apertures. This type of lens could thus be regarded as suitable only for special purposes. It was however the forerunner of the modern variable focus lens (§ 160).

153. Fixed-focus Telephotos. Very great improvement, at least in the construction of telephoto lenses for general use, was made when K. Martin (1905) abandoned the variable magnification and made a lens which, in view of its employment on hand cameras, would be more correctly described as a long-focus lens for short-extension cameras. The possibility of compensating the aberrations of each of the components by aberrations of opposite sign in the other, and the removal of the difficulty of centring which arises when two sliding tubes are employed (which must necessarily have a little play) enabled him to obtain an aperture of $f/9$ covering about 35° and giving an image of a quality comparable with that of a good rectilinear. The lens had the advantage that for a focal length of 240 mm (covering almost the whole of a 9 × 12 cm plate), the distance from the vertex of the back lens to the plate (practically the same as the distance from the camera front to the plate) was only 133 mm. That is, the equivalent focal length was 1·8 times greater than the back focal distance (i.e. the separation between the nearest part of the back surface of the lens and the focal plane). The aperture of these lenses was extended later to $f/7$ or $f/7·7$ (by the same designer), with a slightly smaller field, the focal length for the 9 × 12 cm plate being increased to 265 mm, without increase of camera extension.

The ratio of the equivalent focal length to the back focal length is sometimes called the *power of telephoto*, but the use of the term *power* in this connexion is rather unfortunate, as it is often used

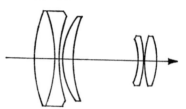

FIG. 11.55. FIXED-FOCUS TELEPHOTO, $f/4·8$ (LEE)

to designate simply the ratio of the equivalent focal length of the telephoto lens to the focal length of the standard lens for the same film format. A better term is *telephoto ratio*, and most telephoto lenses have a ratio of about 2. This incidentally also provides a definition of a real telephoto lens, in other words one in which the ratio of the equivalent focal length to the back focal length is greater than 1.

At the same time this relationship affects the pupillary magnification (§ 107). This is approximately the reciprocal of the telephoto ratio (the approximation being due to the fact that the exit pupil is not located exactly in the rear surface of the lens) and indeed provides a useful way of establishing roughly the telephoto ratio of a lens by measuring the pupil magnification (§ 130).

154. Modern Telephoto Lenses. The basic form of the fixed focus telephoto was that shown in Fig. 11.55, developed by H. W. Leee (1922) with a maximum aperture of $f/4·8$. This suffered from appreciable pincushion distortion (§ 82), which was largely eliminated by the form shown in Fig. 11.56 where the front component is further split up and the two elements of the rear component separated. Nearly all modern telephoto lenses are derived from these basic forms. In the longer focal lengths, especially for miniature cameras, the separation between the elements is often made fairly great to decrease the optical interval δ (§ 152). The same principle is also used in the so-called teleconverters, diverging lens units fitted between a normal interchangeable camera lens and the camera itself (§ 183).

FIG. 11.56. LEE'S TELEPHOTO $f/3·3$

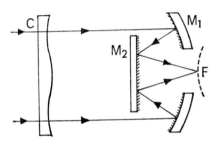

FIG. 11.57. SCHMIDT CAMERA

155. Mirror Optical Systems. In a telephoto lens the overall length of the lens construction in relation to its focal length is shortened by optical tricks. In a *catadioptric* or mirror system the same result is achieved more effectively by folding the light path back upon itself. Mirror optical systems have other interesting advantages. In the first place, light is not dispersed on reflection; hence a mirror system is free from chromatic aberrations, including the secondary spectrum (§ 75). This is particularly difficult to eliminate with long focus glass lenses, whereas the focal length of the mirror system remains constant over all wavelengths of light.

Catadioptric systems are derived in the first place from the Schmidt camera (Fig. 11.57) which in its simplest form consists of a spherical concave mirror M_1 and a plane mirror M_2 to

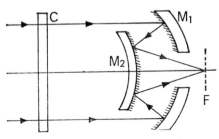

FIG. 11.58. CASSEGRAIN MIRROR SYSTEM

form the image in the focal plane F behind the spherical mirror M_1. The latter carries a central aperture for this purpose (B. Schmidt, 1931).

This system has two limitations: the focal plane F is curved, and the image suffers from spherical aberration. The latter was corrected in the original Schmidt camera by an aspheric corrector plate C, which however was difficult and expensive to make. To flatten the focal plane either a field flattening lens can be used or the plane mirror M_2 replaced by a convex mirror; this is the form of the Cassegrain system (Fig. 11.58).

To eliminate the need for an aspheric corrector plate, Bouwers coated the reflecting surface of the mirror M_2 in Fig. 11.58 on the convex face of a meniscus lens which also acted as a corrector. In certain specialised systems this permitted apertures up to $f/1$; in telephoto mirror lenses the apertures were appreciably smaller—for instance $f/8$ to $f/14$ in the Delca mirror optical systems which were produced in focal lengths up to 2,000 mm to cover image formats up to 6×6 cm (Fig. 11.59). The aperture of the lens was given by the ratio of the focal length to the equivalent diameter of the main mirror M_1; this equivalent diameter is obtained from the equation:

$$d_e = 2\sqrt{(r_1{}^2 - r_2{}^2)}$$

where r_1 is the radius of the main mirror and r_2 the radius of the central aperture in it. To avoid stray light the system also has to have a tubular baffle B. As a result of this arrangement it becomes highly impractical to adjust the lens aperture, and mirror lenses therefore use neutral density filters instead of an iris diaphragm to control the light transmission.

More advanced mirror optical systems for photography may use several correction lenses in front of the mirrors as well as auxiliary elements in the aperture of the main concave mirror.

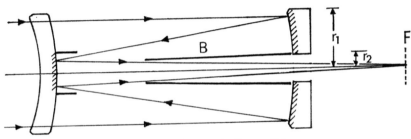

FIG. 11.59. BOUWER'S DELCA TC 200

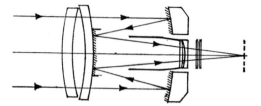

FIG. 11.60. MIROTAR MIRROR SYSTEM $f/4.5$
TO $f/5.6$

An example of such a configuration is the Mirotar (Fig. 11.60) which exists in focal lengths of 500 and 1,000 mm with apertures of $f/4.5$ and $f/5.6$ respectively. A number of German, French, Russian, American and Japanese manufacturers offer similar mirror lens systems, with focal lengths at times going up to 5,000 mm. The saving in constructional length is significant if we consider that in the Mirotar lens of Fig. 11.60 the overall length from the front of the lens system to the film plane is only about half the focal length—an appreciably greater saving than with an all-glass telephoto lens. (With a mirror optical system the overall length of the design is of greater relevance than the telephoto ratio, since the light path inside the system is very long.) Fig. 11.60 also shows the neutral density filters and colour filters behind the concave mirror; these filters are mounted on turrets for rapid selection and changing.

156. Inverted Telephoto Systems. The unsymmetrical disposition of the nodal points of a telephoto lens means that if the lens is turned back to front, it is the back focus which becomes much greater than the equivalent focal length. This follows from the equation in § 152.

Such an arrangement has certain practical advantages; it becomes essential when parts of the camera mechanism have to be located between the lens and the film while the lens has too short a focal length to accommodate them. Examples are the shutter system and film gate in cine cameras and more specifically the hinged mirror of a single-lens reflex when we want to use a short-focus wide-angle lens. From this consideration springs the use of the inverted telephoto design, also known as the *retrofocus* type of wide-angle lens. As the telephoto system essentially consists of a diverging lens system set behind a converging one, so the inverted telephoto layout is based on a diverging element or component in front of a converging one.

The resulting ray paths involved in image formation are shown in Fig. 11.61. The converging lens C has its focal point at f, corresponding to a focal length F_1. When a diverging lens D of focal length F' is placed in the ray path in front of the converging lens, it makes the parallel rays diverge so that they meet, after passing through C at a new focal point f'. The new focal length is then F_2, measured from the nodal plane NN'; the back focus of the combination, previously equal to F_1, now becomes E which is appreciably greater than F_2—even though F_2 is greater than F_1.

As with the normal telephoto lens, the separation between the negative and the positive elements determines the focal ratio (which has the same meaning as in § 152 but is now smaller than 1). For the nearer D moves to C, in other words the smaller the separation d becomes, the nearer the nodal plane NN' moves towards C and F_2 approaches E in magnitude. The greater d, the smaller becomes the focal ratio F_2/E.

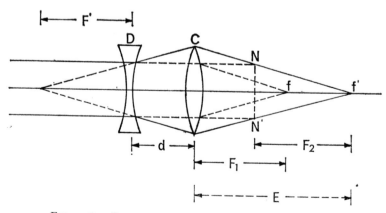

FIG. 11.61. PRINCIPLE OF INVERTED TELEPHOTO SYSTEM

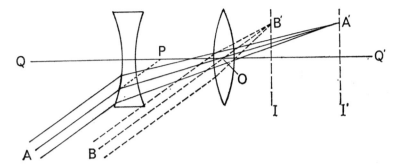

FIG. 11.62. ANGLE OF INCIDENCE OF SECONDARY RAY IN RETROFOCUS SYSTEM

The greater the separation between the two elements, the greater also becomes the need for correcting each element separately, and indeed the greater the degree of aberrations which cannot be corrected satisfactorily. As inverted telephoto or retrofocus designs are mostly used for wide-angle lenses, the potential aberration introduced by this design are appreciable, and need correspondingly complex systems of numerous elements to deal with them.

One practical advantage of the retrofocus design is however that it reduces the natural fall off in illumination (§ 86) towards the margins of the field, a substantial problem with wide-angle lenses. This arises from the fact that the angle at which the principal ray meets the image plane in a retrofocus lens is smaller for a given obliquity of the incident ray than with a normal lens. In Fig. 11.62 let the angle of incidence of the principal ray APQ be the same as of BOQ. Without the diverging element the angle at which this ray meets the image plane I is $B'OQ'$, which is the same as the angle BOQ. With the diverging element in place however, the angle at which the principal ray reaches the new image plane I' is now $A'OQ'$ which is smaller than APQ. Hence the intensity of illumination at A' is greater than at B'. Provided that the front element is large enough to eliminate artificial vignetting, the illumination at an angle ω to the principal axis will follow a $\cos^n \omega$ law, where n may be appreciably smaller than 4, depending on the focal ratio of the lens system.

157. Practical Retrofocus Systems. Early inverted telephoto lenses consisted of a diverging element placed in front of a converging group which itself was a triplet or a symmetrical (e.g. Gauss) derivative. This usually sufficed for medium-wide angle units like the Angenieux 35 mm retrofocus $f/2\cdot5$ (Fig. 11.63, an example

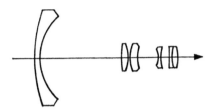

FIG. 11.63. ANGENIEUX RETROFOCUS $f/2\cdot5$

of a triplet derivative for the converging unit) or the $f/2$ Farrogon (Fig. 11.64—based on a symmetrical converging unit).

As however angles and speed requirements increased, both the diverging element and the converging group became increasingly more complex. Thus the Super-Angulon-R $f/4$ (Fig. 11.65) splits the diverging element into three separate lenses while the converging unit is a hardly recognisable symmetrical derivative, making a total of 10 elements in 8 components and using 16 air/glass surfaces. This lens covers a 91° angle on the 24 × 36 mm miniature camera format. The 18 mm Distagon $f/4$ (Fig. 11.66) even covers a 100° angle while a closely similar configuration is used on a 40 mm Distagon to cover an 88° angle on the 6 × 6 cm roll film format.

Extreme angles and extreme speed have not so far been combined except in cine camera

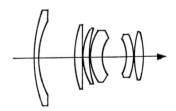

FIG. 11.64. FARROGON $f/2$

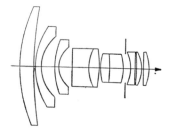

FIG. 11.65. 21 mm Super-Angulon-R $f/4$

lenses (and there only with the aid of aspheric elements). The compromises adopted are either an angle of 90°–100° with a maximum aperture of $f/4$, or moderate angles of around 65° with speeds of $f/2$. In between stages with angles of 80° and maximum aperture of $f/2\cdot8$ also exist.

The inverted telephoto principle is also inherent in some fish-eye lenses (§ 150).

The pupillary magnification (§ 107) of an inverted telephoto lens is greater than 1, which has its effect on depth of field and exposure factor calculations in close-up work.

158. Modern Convertible Lens Systems. While early convertible lenses of the kind described in § 146 could not compete in terms of quality with fully interchangeable lenses, the latter sometimes brought problems when used in smaller cameras such as 35 mm miniatures. One requirement was that for full optical versatility the camera had to have a focal plane shutter. With a diaphragm shutter fully interchangeable lenses have to be mounted in front of the shutter (unless the latter is changed with the lens); the shutter opening can then act as a rear stop and introduce distortion, quite apart from the possible limitation on the coverage of the lens. This is one reason for the current proliferation of telephoto and inverted telephoto designs (§ 154 and § 156).

The ideal location of a diaphragm shutter is

however as near as possible to the iris diaphragm, and modern convertible lenses make this possible with miniature and miniature reflex cameras. Here the lens consists of a rear group which is mounted behind the shutter, both being permanently built into the camera. This rear group is then combined with a number of alternative front groups to yield different focal lengths. Thus in Fig. 11.67 the rear group R with the front element A forms a Tessar lens of 50 mm focal length. The lens stop and the shutter are located in front of the rear group. By replacing the front element by the group B, the lens becomes an inverted telephoto system with a focal length of 35 mm; fitting instead the front group C produces a telephoto system of 85 mm focal length.

A significant point about these systems is that they must all have the same back focus, since the rear part of the lens is at a permanently set distance in front of the film plane. Focusing may be effected by moving the whole lens system (including the common rear group) forward and back or by adjustment of the front element or elements (front cell focusing—§ 159).

The design of such a set of interchangeable

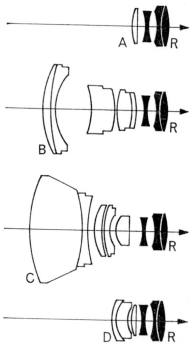

FIG. 11.67. Pro-Tessar Convertible System

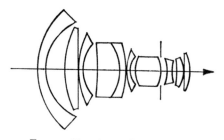

FIG. 11.66. 18 mm Distagon $f/4$

lenses requires some effort, since for each focal length the designer already has two parameters prescribed: the rear group and the back focus; he therefore does not have the same freedom in selecting the most convenient lens parameters for the whole system. On the other hand, convertible systems of this kind are often less expensive to produce since part of the lens is common to all units.

The Pro-Tessar system of Fig. 11.67 also includes a special unit: by fitting the front attachment *D*, the complete lens becomes a six-element symmetrical system useful for copying. This particular combination has only half the focal length of the normal lens (i.e. of the combination *A*) but as its distance in front of the image plane remains unchanged, it now can serve for close-ups and copying at a 1:1 scale of reproduction.

The basic lens of such a set can also be based on a 3-element triplet or a Gauss type symmetrical unit; convertible lens sets of this kind have been made by several manufacturers.

159. **Focus Variation: Front Cell Focusing.** The normal way of focusing a lens for objects at different distances is to displace the whole lens to change the lens-to-image plane distance. The same effect can be achieved by altering the focal length of the lens. If the focal length is decreased, but the lens-to-film plane distance kept constant, the lens is in effect set to a nearer distance—as in the case of the close-up unit of a convertible lens set (§ 158). In a simpler form this is the normal way of focusing many amateur cameras, since one of the elements of the lens is displaced relatively to the others by rotating the front of the lens mount. This produces a change of focal length and a displacement of the back nodal point in order to focus on objects at different distances. This was first effected by moving the front element of a triplet (H. D. Taylor, 1902), and later by moving the front element of a four-element lens (C. W. Frederick, 1920). In other lenses the back element has been moved (W. Gehrke, 1930). A very slight change in the separation of the elements is sufficient in many cases to produce an appreciable change in the focal length of the system, and thus the design of the camera may be considerably simplified. This method is not applicable to high aperture lenses, in which the performance would suffer appreciably from a change in separations.

160. **Variable Focus (Zoom) Lenses.** The most elegant way of having a range of focal

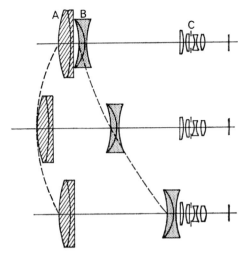

FIG. 11.68. NAUMANN'S VARIO-GLAUKAR
$f/2\cdot8$

lengths for a camera without the need to change lenses is a system in which the focal length itself can be varied by adjusting the position of one or more components in the optical system. This is similar in concept to the variable-power telephoto lens (§ 152) and of special interest in cinematography where the progressive increase in the focal length (by a suitable control on the lens) increases the scale of the image and decreases the field of view during an actual shot. This gives the impression, on projection of the film, of the camera moving smoothly along its own axis towards the subject, similar to a tracking or zooming shot. Lenses which make this possible therefore became known as zoom lenses.

For this particular application there is one important condition—not fulfilled by the variable-power telephoto lens (§ 152): the image must remain sharp during the zooming operation. In other words, the distance from the rear nodal point to the image plane must remain constant. So should the relative lens aperture at the different focal length settings. This is generally achieved by placing an afocal attachment—in effect a Galilean telescope—of variable magnification in front of a straightforward camera lens. One of the first systems of this type was designed by H. Naumann and appeared as the Vario–Glaukar (Fig. 11.68) with a zooming range from 25 to 80 mm and maximum aperture $f/2\cdot8$ (1931).

The magnification control is in effect obtained

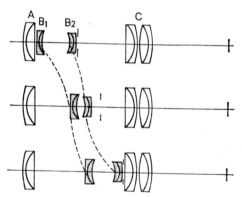

FIG. 11.69. WATSON TELEVISION ZOOM
LENS (1951)

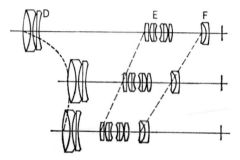

FIG. 11.70. WARMISHAM'S ZOOM LENS
(1932)

by the movement of the centre diverging component B between the front positive lens group A and the rear positive unit—the prime camera lens C (Fig. 11.68). The adjustment of the component B however still causes some shift in the plane of optimum image sharpness, so that the front component A has to be moved as well—though not necessarily in the same direction or to the same degree as component B. The differing paths of the two are shown by the heavy broken line in Fig. 11.68. To ensure the correct positioning of each group during zooming, the two movable components are linked together by a sliding or rotating cam system. Such an arrangement is known as *mechanical compensation*. In practice it is often more convenient to split the diverging middle component into two parts which change both their separation and their position (B_1, B_2) between fixed front and rear groups A and C respectively (Fig. 11.69). This has the advantage that the moving parts are better protected inside the lens.

Another approach by Warmisham had some points of resemblance to the variable power telephoto lens (§ 152), with a diverging element F (Fig. 11.70) behind the converging group E, with another diverging component D in front. All three groups here have to move to keep the sharpness constant at different focal length settings (the lens has a range from 40 to 120 mm), while the aperture did not stay constant either; it varied from $f/3.5$ at the shortest to $f/8$ at the longest focal length.

These early designs had 12 to 14 air-glass surfaces so that the light losses through reflection were considerable, while the number of elements was not sufficient to take care of all the optical correction problems posed by the focal length variation. Zoom lenses did not therefore become popular until lens coating (§ 89) became common after the late 1940s. The Zoomar designed by F. G. Back (1946) had altogether 16 components (32 air-glass surfaces) with in fact 22 elements. This lens had a focal length range from 17 to 53 mm, covering wide-angle to telephoto shots on 16 mm cine film. By changing the front component, the zooming range could be shifted to 35–106 mm without change of image position or light transmission.

The Zoomar also did away with the cam system of mechanical compensation; instead all the moving elements were rigidly linked together so that they moved as one unit—even though placed in different positions in the optical system. This is the principle of *optical compensation* which simplifies the construction of the lens mount (and eliminates sources of error due to possible wear on the cams). Thus in Fig. 11.71 the units A and C are linked together and move, while units B and D remain fixed in front of the prime lens E. To achieve a uniform correction of optical aberrations

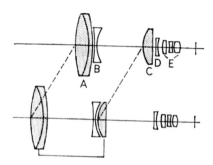

FIG. 11.71. ZOOM LENS WITH OPTICAL
COMPENSATION

throughout the zooming range, modern zoom lenses may have between 10 and 20 elements—or more.

161. Focusing with Zoom Lenses. A conventional focusing arrangement which involves adjustment of the lens-to-image plane distance is impractical with zoom lenses, since the distance adjustment would be different at different focal length settings. Zoom lenses therefore have a form of front cell focusing, involving alteration of the separation of the front component or components.

This involves the introduction of an additional focus variation whose degree must be controllable independently of the focal length adjustment of the lens system.

It is however also possible to design the lens in such a way, that a controlled focus shift takes place simultaneously with the focal length adjustment. If this focus shift corresponds to the change in the hyperfocal distance at different focal lengths, the lens always remains focused for maximum depth of field at the different focal length settings. This principle has been marketed under the name "Servo-focus" in the zoom lenses of narrow-gauge cine cameras by Eumig.

Various elaborations of this design are feasible. Thus the distance adjustment of the lens can be coupled with the focal length adjustment in such a way as to keep the subject sharp on the film when it appears at a given scale of reproduction.

This would imply that once the lens is focused at say 1 metre when set to a focal length of 50 mm, an adjustment to a 100 mm focal length would automatically shift the focus to a subject distance of 2 metres. Such an arrangement can be useful when filming moving subjects whose distance from the camera is liable to change rapidly and unpredictably, for instance small animals. To keep his subject sharp, the cameraman only has to make sure that the image scale of the main object remains constant—i.e. vary his zooming adjustment to keep the animal in a uniform size in his finder. In practice such coupled zooming and focusing systems involve the mechanical linking of separate zooming and focusing movements, since it would be too complex a job to incorporate such a compensation in the basic lens design. Moreover, the cross coupling will only work for one given scale of reproduction.

162. Zoom Lenses for Still Cameras. The zoom lens was originally conceived—and the majority of current types are made—for cine and television cameras. Zoom lenses for still cameras have to cope with additional problems. The main one is the bulk of the lens itself since the still camera lens has to cover at least an 18 × 24 mm frame, while the standard image angle with a still camera is usually twice as great as with a cine camera. (With the latter the focal length/diagonal relationship of § 134 does not apply.) Hence zoom lenses for still cameras must have all their dimensions appropriately scaled up. As they are already fairly big (in comparison with a normal lens) on cine cameras, the increase in weight and size becomes still more marked with the larger picture format.

One way of compensating for this is to restrict a still camera zoom lens to smaller maximum apertures—hardly any go above $f/2·8$—and to reduce the zooming range. So while zoom lenses for amateur narrow gauge cine cameras usually have focal length ratios up to about 8:1 (and professional cine zoom lenses up to 20:1), the range with still camera lenses is—with very few exceptions—between 2:1 and 3:1. One of the earliest still camera zoom lenses was the 36–82 mm Zoomar $f/2·8$ for 24 × 36 mm miniature cameras (Fig. 11.72) a 14-element, 11-component system with optical compensation.

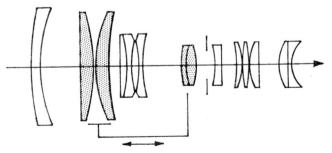

FIG. 11.72. 36–82 mm ZOOMAR $f/2·8$ FOR 24 × 36 mm FORMAT

The problem of scaling up is the main reason why still camera zoom lenses are virtually restricted to the 24 × 36 mm miniature format; a variable focus lens to cover a 6 × 6 cm roll film format becomes very cumbersome indeed. On the other hand zoom lenses would have been more useful with half-frame (18 × 24 mm) miniatures and ultra miniatures (12 × 17 mm and smaller), but these camera types are not sufficiently popular to justify the design and economic production of such lenses.

The zoom lens is largely tied to one camera type, the single-lens reflex, since the main advantage of a variable focal length is that the photographer can adjust the coverage of the lens by visual observation. (A separate variable focus viewfinder linked with the lens would again add greatly to the bulk.)

In terms of focal length range there are two distinct groups of zoom lenses: medium-range and tele-zooms. The former cover angles from a medium wide-angle to a medium long-focus lens—for instance 36 to 82 mm or 40 to 120 mm. In practice they are thus of more use for applications where the continuous focal length adjustment rather than a focal length range is important. In particular, the zoom lens cannot really replace a wide-angle optical system, for the minimum focal length is limited by the appearance of distortion. Owing to the highly unsymmetrical layout of the complete lens arrangement, there is no easy way of correction. For the photographer who does not require the continuous focal length adjustment, the use of a couple of separate lenses—a standard and a medium long-focus one—is far more convenient as regards bulk, less costly, and superior in performance.

The superiority is due to the fact that it is almost impossible to eliminate entirely a focus shift. The usual recommendation for the use of a zoom lens is to focus the subject at the longest focal length setting, and then adjust the focal length to the value required. The growing depth of field can then help to absorb some of the focus shift.

Tele-zoom lenses may (but do not have to) employ a telephoto system as the prime lens. They do however cover a distinctly long-focus range for the image format—for instance 80 to 250 mm with a 24 × 36 mm picture. The maximum aperture is usually $f/4$ or smaller, and as the angle to be covered is appreciably reduced, the lens system can be—at least comparatively—simpler. Generally a telephoto

zoom lens for a still camera is no bulkier than a normal lens of the longest focal length in the zooming range. So here the zoom lens offers the distinct advantage, that the photographer can with one lens replace optical systems of two to three times the total weight. The focal length may extend up to 500 mm; zooming ratios up to 6:1 also become more common in the tele range.

Since long focus lenses above about 200 mm are in any case nearly always used with the camera on a firm support, the bulk of tele zoom systems is not a problem.

Focus constancy—a constant separation between the rear of the lens and the image plane at all focal length settings—is essential in a cine camera which zooms during a shot; it is by no means necessary for a still camera zoom lens where the photographer can easily refocus after he has adjusted the focal length setting. Yet hardly any zoom lenses for still cameras exist without an attempt to provide focus constancy. A lens in which this is disregarded could be simpler, smaller and less expensive, but only a few such lens types are available.

163. Projection Zoom Lenses. Variable focus lenses are also used in cine and slide projection. Here their purpose is to allow an adjustment of the size of the projected screen image without having to move the projector forward and back along its axis. Hence the requirement of focus constancy is even less important since there is rarely a need for varying the image size during projection. It is perfectly adequate to adjust the size of the projected image and then focus the lens separately. Accordingly projection zoom lenses tend to be simpler in design, though the principle is the same. Most types use an optically compensated focal length adjustment (§ 160); often a variable focus attachment is used as a separate accessory to the projection lens (§ 184).

Focal length ratios are usually $1\frac{1}{2}:1$ to $2:1$; on the other hand projection zoom lenses are available to cover transparency sizes up to a (nominal) 6 × 6 cm format.

164. Lenses for Extended Spectral Ranges. Special lens systems are required for photography with radiations beyond the limits of visible light, in the ultra-violet and the infra-red regions.

Here two design problems have to be considered:

(a) the transmission limits of the glass or

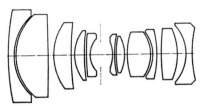

FIG. 11.73. 50 mm UV-PLANAR $f/2$

other medium involved—especially for ultra-violet radiation; and

(b) the chromatic correction of the lens system itself (§ 75).

While optical glass is transparent to infra-red radiation up to about 2.5 microns which covers largely the useful range of infra-red photography (as distinct from infra-red image recording by other methods such as thermography), the ultra-violet transmission limit is around 350 milli-microns, only just beyond the visible range. As the ultra-violet photographic range extends down to 200 millimicrons, special optical materials are here required. These include silica and various crystalline fluorides—which, however, are easily attacked by moisture and must be specially protected. A further limitation is that normal optical cements absorb ultra-violet, and so the lens elements are not cemented. Fig. 11.73 shows an ultra-violet transmitting lens con-sisting of quartz and calcium fluoride elements which not only transmits down to 200 milli-microns but is chromatically corrected for radia-tions from this limit up to 650 millimicrons near the infra-red limit.

Chromatic correction is a major problem. While lenses specially designed for ultra-violet and infra-red photography have been available for a considerable time, the same lens usually had different focal lengths according to the radiation employed. They therefore needed special calibration. This is acceptable where a specific wavelength or radiation is to be employed. When the designer does not have to make extensive compromises in chromatic correction, it is easier to correct other aberra-tions. Chromatic correction is however impor-tant when photography involves a wide range of wavelengths—for instance in spectroscopy and other scientific applications—and where focus adjustments for different wavelengths are not practical. The most highly corrected lenses available for such purposes cover a continuous wavelength of about 250 to 850 millimicrons with constant focus.

165. Lenses for Extreme Resolution. Process lenses used for photo-mechanical reproduction must possess high definition and freedom from distortion. Even higher definition is required in semi-conductor technology since the manufac-ture of integrated micro-circuits involves photo-mechanical steps of extreme reductions and hence calls for extreme resolution. Details clearly recorded on the final image may be under 1 micron thick. Such reductions usually take place in two stages, using process lenses of maximum quality for the first stage and micro-scope objectives for the second.

The lens designs themselves are fairly ortho-dox, based usually on symmetrical or Gauss derivatives. The high resolution—sometimes down to 1,000 lines per millimetre at a useful contrast level (see also § 171) is achieved by adjusting aberration corrections entirely in favour of high definition, at the expense of other aspects of less importance in this type of work. Such lenses are specially corrected for:

(a) Monochromatic light, preferably the short-est wavelengths of visible radiation. This reduces the need for chromatic correction; the sensitive materials used for this type of work are only blue-sensitive, and the shorter wave-length permits higher resolution with a more favourable diffraction limit.

(b) Fairly large apertures between $f/1\cdot2$ and $f/5\cdot6$. The use of large apertures also reduces the diffraction limit to resolution (§ 170).

(c) A narrow field of view. This eliminates the effects of many aberrations due to rays of appreciable obliquity.

(d) Fixed scales of reproduction—i.e. reduc-tion ratios between 1:10 and 1:70, according to the specific job required.

166. Aspheric Lenses. The surfaces of the glass elements of an optical system are nearly always spherical. By using non-spherical sur-faces for one or more of the elements it is possible to correct spherical aberration (§ 76) much more easily and with fewer components.

Such surfaces are however much more difficult and costly to manufacture. Aspheric surfaces may be simple—for instance sections of an ellipsoid (Fig. 11.74a), of a parabola (Fig. 11.74b) or a hyperbola; or they can be compound with curvature going in opposite directions in the centre and at the edge (Fig. 11.74c). Aspheric

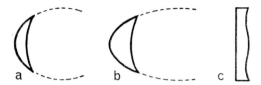

FIG. 11.74. ASPHERIC SURFACES

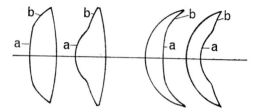

FIG. 11.76. BISPHERIC LENS SURFACES

elements were first used as corrector plates in astronomical telescopes (Schmidt, 1930); these had a shape corresponding to Fig. 11.74c (which is shown highly exaggerated). Methods of manufacturing simple aspheric lens surfaces were first patented between 1900 and 1922. In modern lens systems aspheric surfaces have been used to achieve extreme aperture lenses of high correction with comparatively few elements (§ 151 and Figs. 11.47 and 11.52).

In contrast to spherical lenses which can be ground and polished in large numbers at a time with automatic lapping equipment, high quality aspheric surfaces need individual treatment. Such surfaces are cut singly with extensively programmed cutting tools of extreme precision. It is the resulting complex machinery and comparatively slow operation which makes such lenses expensive. When considering aspherics for lens systems, the criterion is often whether the extra cost of producing the aspheric surfaces can be saved by using simpler systems giving equal or better performance. Thus in Fig. 11·75 a 25 mm $f/1.8$ wide-angle lens with only spherical components needs 9 elements; by introducing an aspheric surface a lens of similar performance could be produced with 7 elements and reduced dimensions. Although

this lens has an aperture of $f/2$, the light transmission is the same as of the $f/1.8$ lens owing to the reduced reflection loss with fewer surfaces. Certain ultra wide-angle and zoom lenses justify aspheric designs. Cheaply produced aspheric surfaces are widely used for condensers and concave mirrors in lighting optics (projectors, spot-lights, etc.) where no advanced optical correction is involved and lens elements can be moulded to the required shape.

A compromise between spheric lens production and aspheric correction possibilities is the bispheric lens (H. Kilfitt). Here the lens surface has two curvatures of different radius in the centre and at the edge, but both zones are spherical. Such elements may permit the better correction of zonal rays without the expense of designing and manufacturing complete aspheric surfaces. In Fig. 11.76 the surface sections a and b thus show different curvatures.

167. Plastic Lenses. Attempts have been made to replace optical glass by transparent plastics. The choice of materials is here much more limited, especially as far as refractive indices and dispersive powers are concerned. Two main plastics which have been used are polymethacrylates and polystryene. The former has a low refractive index (under 1·5) and a low dispersion—corresponding roughly to crown glass—while polystyrene has a somewhat higher index and higher dispersion.

Plastic lenses made by transfer moulding are used in some inexpensive amateur cameras. Their suitability for precision optical equipment is limited, owing to the comparative softness of the plastic, ease of distortion, tendency to optical inhomogeneity and dimensional change with temperature and relative humidity.

168. Lens Mount Types. Several types of mounts are employed for photographic lenses, according to the use to which they are to be put.

For cameras which are always used with a tripod (technical and view cameras), where there is no limit to the projection of the mount, a

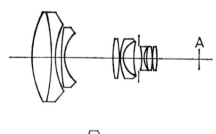

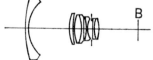

FIG. 11.75. SPHERICAL (A) AND EQUIVALENT ASPHERIC (B) WIDE-ANGLE LENS

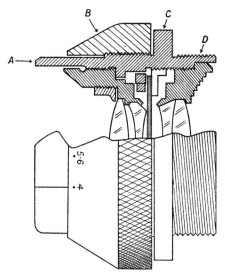

FIG. 11.77. SECTION OF MODERN LENS AND
IRIS DIAPHRAGM

A = hood.   *B* = diaphragm ring.   *C* = flange.   *D* = thread.

normal mount (Fig. 11.77), the simplest type of all, is usually fitted, the flange being attached to the rear of the lens mount, giving free access to the diaphragm. On cameras, where bulk has to be reduced, a *sunk mount* is often preferable, the flange being on the front part of the mount, which is thus sunk inside the camera in order to make use of the space corresponding to the thickness of the bellows (when closed). The diaphragm is then operated from the front by a cylindrical lining between the exterior mount and the actual body of the lens.

On cameras not fitted with a variable bellows extension for focusing, the lens mounting usually incorporates also a focusing mount. With interchangeable lenses this may be part of the camera or part of the lens—usually the latter. The commonest type is here the *helical focusing mount* which in effect screws the whole lens backwards and forwards via a screw thread. On modern cameras the helical mount often rotates independently of the lens, so that the latter moves forward and back without itself rotating. With such a so-called *rectilinear* focusing mount the other lens controls and scales—aperture, depth of field, etc.—always remain in the same place relative to the camera for easy reference.

Finally, for use with between-lens shutters the mount is reduced to two or three cells in which the lenses are bezelled or held in with

clamp rings, these cells being screwed into the female threads provided at either end of the shutter. For technical and view cameras where the lens is changed together with the shutter, the lens and shutter units are usually assembled by the maker of the lens to make sure of the required exact separation of the lens elements for optimum optical performance. Makers generally engrave their trade-mark, serial number, and lens characteristics on the front only. The back cells of lenses of the same series and mean focal length are not usually optically interchangeable, but as they are mechanically interchangeable some manufacturers avoid confusion by engraving on the back cell at least the number of the lens.

Where the camera lens is not interchangeable, any remounting—for instance after cleaning or repair—requires precision optical equipment to ensure correct alignment and positioning and is best carried out by the manufacturer. Fig. 11.78 shows a mount type for a lens with built-in diaphragm shutter and front cell focusing. In modern cameras the shutter unit is however so styled as to be part of the front camera housing.

Interchangeable lenses for miniature and roll film cameras may be attached by a screw thread or a bayonet fitting; for technical and view cameras the lens is often mounted in a panel to fit into the front standard of the camera. These mountings will be discussed further in connection with camera design.

The materials for lens mounts are usually

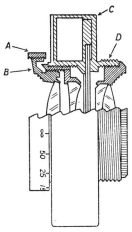

FIG. 11.78. SECTION OF LENS MOUNTED
IN SHUTTER WITH FRONT-CELL FOCUSING

A = focusing scale.   *B* = focusing mount.   *C* = shutter.   *D* = thread.

light alloys of aluminium and magnesium which have largely replaced the considerably heavier brass mounts. Pure aluminium, which was used for some time, had the drawback that the threads rapidly wore out. When a lens of long focal length is likely to undergo large changes of temperature (aerial photography at high altitudes) it is well to restrict the expansion and contraction of the mount by using the *invar* steels, or to adopt a compensating device like those frequently used on clock pendulums.

It is becoming general practice to finish lens mounts in black, either by anodizing or by lacquer. This has the advantage that aperture and distance scales can be engraved in white and thus become more readable. When copying, especially of originals under glass, a black finish is important to minimize reflections from the glass covering the original.

CHAPTER XII

LENS PERFORMANCE, TESTING AND DESIGN

169. Resolving power—test charts—line spacing and spatial frequency—spurious resolution. 170. Theoretical and practical resolution limit—effect of diffraction and of contrast of test targets. 171. Visual sharpness and edge gradient—brightness change across image boundaries—effect of edge gradient on resolution. 172. Spread function—shapes of spread functions. 173. Contrast transfer functions—maximum sharpness and maximum resolution—practical utilised resolution—contrast transfer function and lens aperture. 174. Frequency response and optical transfer function—evaluation by image waveform—sinusoidal test targets—automatic contrast transfer function measurement—modulation and optical transfer function. 175. Cascading functions—combining transfer functions for film and lens. 176. Simplified merit values—integration of transfer function curve—logarithmic quality grading. 177. Lens testing in practice—overall performance measurements—testing for production standard in manufacture—star tests for specific faults. 178. Aspects of lens design—calculation and ray tracing—the use of computers—spot diagrams—automatic computer programmes. 179. The care of lenses—storage—cleaning.

169. Resolving Power. The classical standard of lens definition was based on assessing how well the image obtained with the lens reproduced fine subject detail. The underlying consideration was that lens aberrations lead to loss of sharpness which reduces the recognizable detail.

For many years the criterion of sharpness was the *resolving power*—a measure of the fineness of detail which the lens could distinguish or resolve. This was established by photographing a resolving power test target, such as that in Fig. 12.1, at a specified scale of reduction. The target consists of black bars separated by white spaces of the same thickness as the bars themselves; the test chart contains a series of such bars of different fineness and separation.

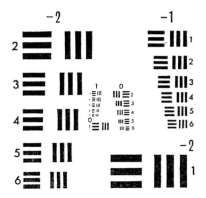

FIG. 12.1. RESOLVING POWER TEST CHART

151

The line spacing is expressed as the reciprocal of the width of a black bar and the white space between it and the neighbouring bar; for instance if the black bar in one set of the bars in the target is 0·5 mm wide (and the white space another 0·5 mm) the spacing of that set of bars is one line per millimetre. For a finer set of bars of for instance 0·25 mm width (plus the 0·25 mm white space between it and the next bar) the spacing is two lines per millimetre. This is also sometimes referred to as a *spatial frequency* of 2.

If such a test target is photographed at a reduction of 1:100 and the finest set on the target in which the bars are still distinguished as separate corresponds to the original spacing of 2 lines per millimetre, the image of those bars on the film will have a spacing of 200 lines per millimetre—and this would be the limit of the resolving power of the lens/film combination employed.

For resolving power chart tests a film must where possible be chosen with a resolution which is appreciably higher than that of the lens to be tested. Resolving power figures measured in this way normally vary at different points in the field of the lens; the resolution being highest in the centre of the field and dropping towards the margins.

Resolving power test targets nearly always carry two sets of lines, at right angles to each other, for each line spacing. This shows up any loss of resolution due to astigmatism.

In checking the limiting resolution on such

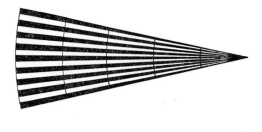

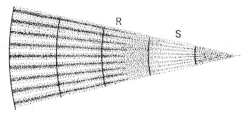

FIG. 12.2. SECTOR RESOLVING POWER
TARGET

a target, the number of resolved lines must also be correct, not only their spacing. For at line spacings (spatial frequencies) higher than the resolution limit lines may appear resolved once more. This is because a tone reversal occurs and the image shows two bars instead of three in the patterns of a resolving power test target like Fig. 12.1. These two lines correspond to the spaces between the three lines in the original. This is known as *spurious resolution* and arises from phenomena related to interference.

An alternative resolving power target popular in Europe is the sector type of Fig. 12.2. The concentric segment arcs with their calibration permit rapid estimation of the resolving power limit—for instance R in the lower part of Fig. 12.2. Spurious resolution is here seen to appear at S.

The actual resolving power figure obtained is influenced also by the type of test target used—i.e. the ratio of the length to the width of the lines and the number of lines in the test pattern. For comparisons, the same test pattern must therefore be used.

170. Theoretical and Practical Resolution Limit. In theory the resolving power of an optical system is limited by diffraction, in other words the fact that an image of a point object is never a true point but the ring pattern of an Airy disc (§ 85). The size of this depends both on the aperture of the lens and the wavelength of the light; hence these two factors again enter

into the theoretical limit of resolution. This relationship is given by the equation:

$$r = \text{approx.} \ \frac{2A}{\lambda}$$

where r is the spatial frequency (number of lines resolved per millimetre) and A the numerical aperture (§ 104) of the lens.

The numerical aperture of an $f/2\cdot8$ lens is $0\cdot175$. For green light of around 550 millimicrons ($0\cdot00055$ mm) wavelength the theoretical resolution limit would therefore be about $0\cdot35/0\cdot00055 = 640$ lines per mm. With an $f/1\cdot4$ lens (numerical aperture $0\cdot34$) the limiting resolving power becomes nearly twice as great with around 1,250 lines per mm. With light of shorter wavelength the limiting resolution is also improved; for instance with an $f/2\cdot8$ lens and light of 400 millimicrons at the blue-violet limit of the spectrum the theoretical resolving power goes up to about 880 lines per mm and at $f/1\cdot4$ to 1,700 lines per mm.

The practical resolving power of a lens depends on the contrast of the test target for which it is measured. This is where the significance of resolution as a sole criterion of sharpness begins to break down. High-contrast test targets of the type described, and the images usually photographed by most cameras, have very little in common. So it becomes necessary to look also at other—physiological as well as optical—aspects of sharpness.

171. Visual Sharpness and Edge Gradient. To the eye an image does not necessarily look sharpest when it clearly shows the finest details, but when the contrast across the boundaries of such details is greatest. If the brightness is plotted across the boundary between a light and a dark image area, the resulting curve should ideally have the shape shown in Fig. 12.3a. In actual fact the brightness change is much less abrupt and follows a curve as in Fig. 12.3b. The shallower the gradient of this curve, the less sharp the image appears. The edge gradient is given by the ratio AB/BC in Fig. 12.3b. This

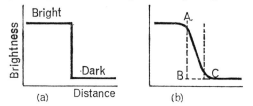

FIG. 12.3. EDGE GRADIENTS

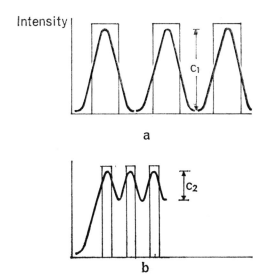

FIG. 12.4. CONTRAST AND RESOLUTION

is sometimes referred to as the acutance, though strictly speaking the latter is a mathematical expression of the edge sharpness across a boundary in a photographic film and is measured without reference to an image produced by a lens.

When we consider the image of a resolution test target, the edge gradients at each boundary between the black lines and the white spaces come into play, resulting in an intensity distribution as shown in Fig. 12.4a. When the bars are sufficiently wide and far apart, the contrast or intensity ratio between the black and white areas is not materially affected (C_1 in Fig. 12.4a); when however the lines are closer together, the edge gradient curves overlap and the overall contrast C_2 as in Fig. 12.4b becomes less. A point is therefore reached when the contrast is so low that the individual bars are no longer distinguishable—i.e. the lens does not resolve them. The lower the initial contrast of the subject, the sooner this resolution limit is reached. Hence the resolving power of a lens when imaging a normal subject such as a landscape is considerably lower than when a high contrast test target is used to evaluate the resolving power.

172. Spread Function. The edge gradient, i.e. the gradual drop of brightness instead of the ideal abrupt drop—as in Fig. 12.3b and 12.3a respectively—is caused by the fact that different light rays coming from an object point and passing through the lens do not always meet

in exactly the same image point. We have already seen that even with a perfect lens, diffraction results in the image point becoming a disc with an unsharp edge and an intensity distribution similar to that shown in Fig. 8.35 (§ 85). This is known as a *spread function*. As lens aberrations enlarge this image disc by the superimposition of larger or smaller discs, the actual shape of the spread function can vary appreciably. This affects both resolution and image contrast, and not necessarily in the same way.

For instance if the spread function has a narrow peak but a shallow edge gradient as in Fig. 12.5, the peaks are narrow enough to be distinguishable even when imaging a test target of comparatively high spatial frequency; the contrast however decreases appreciably, as we saw in Fig. 12.4b. A lens with this characteristic would thus have a high resolving power if we consider only the maximum number of lines per millimetre which can be distinguished in the image of the test chart. The spread function can however also have a shape more like that in Fig. 12.6a—with a steep edge gradient but a rather broad peak. The reproduction of a test target with a low spatial frequency (broad lines and spaces) would therefore still look very sharp, because the image contrast is high. In Fig. 12.6b the intensity ratio C_3 is greater even than C_1 in Fig. 12.4a which is based on the same line frequency. As the spatial frequency increases, i.e. the black lines get narrower and closer together in the test target, the broad peak of the spread function fully overlaps for each line as in Fig. 12.6c. So we have the paradox, that

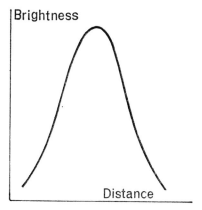

FIG. 12.5. NARROW AND SHALLOW SPREAD FUNCTION

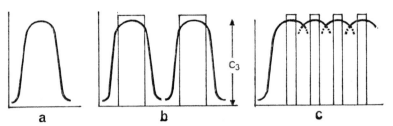

FIG. 12.6. BROAD AND STEEP SPREAD FUNCTION

a lens with a spread function as in Fig. 12.6a yields an image which appears sharper than that of a lens with the spread function as in Fig. 12.5, even though the latter offers a higher limiting resolving power.

173. Contrast Transfer Functions. For assessing the performance of the lens both its resolving power and the contrast of the image at different line spacings (spatial frequencies) of a test target are thus important. If we plot the contrast of the image at each spatial frequency against the spatial frequency itself, we obtain curves resembling Fig. 12.7. Here the dotted curve a shows the ideal relationship between contrast and spatial resolution; the contrast drop is due only to diffraction with increasing spatial frequency. Of the curves for actual lenses, b represents a lens giving good edge contrast but limited resolution, corresponding to a spread function as in Fig. 12.6a. Curve c on the other hand is a lens with a poorer contrast performance but a higher final resolving power—a spread function more like that of Fig. 12.5.

Such curves, when regarded simply as a plot of image contrast against spatial frequency, are known as *contrast transfer curves*. They are closely related to optical transfer curves (§ 174) whose derivation is however a little more complex.

With such curves we can make significant deductions of the lens performance for specific requirements. Thus if the lens is to be used for negatives which are unlikely to need big enlargement—or where we would look at such enlargements from an appreciable distance—resolution of high spatial frequencies is unnecessary if we assume a limiting utilized resolution or cut-off point at O in Fig. 12.7, the performance of lens b is obviously better than that of lens c—the image will look visually sharper. Where however maximum resolution of fine detail is important, irrespective of contrast at low spatial frequencies, a lens with the function of curve c in Fig. 12.7 would have to be chosen.

The exact shape of the contrast function curve depends of course on all factors which affect lens performance. Thus the curves of Fig. 12.7 apply to a specific lens aperture; Fig. 12.8 shows how the transfer function curves may vary for different apertures. Here the

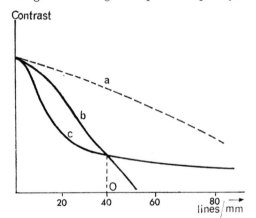

FIG. 12.7. CONTRAST TRANSFER FUNCTION CURVE

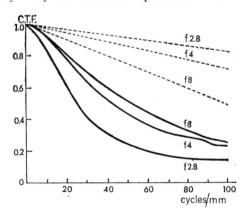

FIG. 12.8. CONTRAST TRANSFER FUNCTION AND LENS APERTURE

dotted lines are the ideal curves whose downward slope is due only to diffraction while the solid curves indicate the actual functions at the three selected apertures. It will be noted that while among the ideal curves that for $f/2\cdot8$ is highest and for $f/8$ lowest (as diffraction increases at small apertures) the actual $f/2\cdot8$ curve is the lowest since here residual lens aberrations have a greater effect than at the smaller aperture settings. (The actual positions of the curves may vary; thus it is possible to have a lens where the curve for a medium aperture would be highest and for large or small apertures lower; or a lens where the transfer functions at the different apertures are more or less the same, i.e. where the effects of residual aberration at larger apertures just balance the loss of resolution due to diffraction at the smaller ones.)

Moreover, the transfer function curve measured on the lens axis differs from the curve obtained near the edge of the field. To specify completely the performance of the lens a large number of curves would therefore be required. Different transfer curves would also be obtained if the lens is decentred, defocused, etc.—e.g. due to lack of precision in assembly.

174. Frequency Response and Optical Transfer Function. The derivation of the contrast transfer function is mathematically a little more complex and is based on the frequency analysis of an image. This means that the detail fineness and contrast can be analysed in terms of the frequency, amplitude and phase of a sine wave (§ 2). This is convenient because any curve of periodic fluctuations can be regarded as built up of sine waves of different amplitudes and frequencies. The signficance of this is that brightness variations in an image, plus corresponding fineness of detail (spatial frequency), can be evaluated by many means based on systems which respond to the amplitude and frequency of waveforms, for instance electronic test gear. In practice the transfer function can thus be obtained by analysing the spread function into spatial frequency components, and also be measuring the amplitudes of images of sinusoidal test targets. Such a target still consists of dark bands with light spaces in between them, but the brightness (or transmission) of these bands varies continuously in a manner which can be plotted by a sine wave (Fig. 12.9). The advantage of this kind of target for lens testing is that the brightness distribution of the image remains the same as

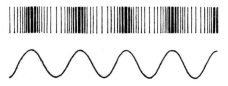

FIG. 12.9. SINUSOIDAL TEST TARGET

that of the object, differing only in amplitude (the height of the peaks and troughs in the sine wave). This makes analysis particularly simple.

One way of testing the transfer function characteristics of a lens is to project with it the image of a sinusoidal test target of continuously varying spatial frequency (Fig. 12.10). As this moves across the field of view of the lens, the brightness variation in the image is measured by a photo tube or similar device responding to light intensity. The tube is located behind a narrow slit in the image plane; the location of this slit determines the point in the lens's field at which the image quality is measured. As the image of the light and dark bands of the test target passes across the slit, the photo tube converts the brightness variations into current pulses. The frequency of these pulses corresponds to the line or spatial frequency of the test target, while the amplitude corresponds to the contrast with which the image reproduces the brightness of the target.

The output of the photo tube can be recorded in various ways; a convenient one is a cathode ray tube screen which may then show a trace similar to Fig. 12.11. The height of the trace at each cycle indicates the amplitude of the target image, the separation of the traces corresponds to the spatial frequency. The contour of the trace (the dotted line in Fig. 12.11) then corresponds to the transfer function. This dotted outline can also be regarded as a modulation curve, for it shows the decreasing modulation of the signal with increasing frequency. The

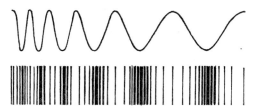

FIG. 12.10. SINUSOIDAL TARGET OF CONTINUOUSLY VARYING SPATIAL FREQUENCY

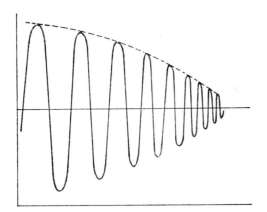

FIG. 12.11. CATHODE RAY TUBE TRACE
OF TRANSFER FUNCTION

transfer curve is therefore also known as the *modulation transfer function*.

In the reproduction a phase shift can also take place, where the position of the waveform is displaced. This is significant because the phase shift varies with increasing frequency; when the phase shift is equal to half a wavelength, we may get spurious resolution (§ 169). Curves indicating the modulation transfer function and the phase shift constitute the optical transfer function of a lens. When there is no phase shift the optical transfer function becomes identical with the modulation transfer function. As the phase shift is not of great practical significance, it is often ignored and the terms modulation transfer function (M.T.F.) and optical transfer function (O.T.F.) are used interchangeably.

175. Cascading Functions. When frequency response measurements are made on the image projected by the lens, the result is a transfer function of the lens on its own. When we however evaluate the image in a photograph— for instance by tracing the density variations in a photographic reproduction of a sinusoidal test target such as that of Fig. 12.9—the resulting response curve is the transfer function of the combination of the lens and the film.

This additive or cascading property is an important characteristic of transfer function curves. It enables us to allow for every stage involved in the reproduction from the original optical image to a final photographic picture (whether this is an enlargement or a projected transparency) and including even the visual impression on the observer.

Mathematically this is done by multiplying the transfer function curves of each stage with each other. For instance in Fig. 12.12 we have a film with a transfer function curve *a*, yielding high image contrast at low spatial frequencies and cutting off at *X* which is the resolution limit of the film. The transfer function curve *b* of the lens drops fairly rapidly already at low frequencies but has a high ultimate resolution limit. The combination yields the curve *c*. Each point on this curve is obtained by multiplying the values of the other two curves at that spatial frequency with each other. For example at a spatial frequency *Y* curve *a* has a value of 0·8, which means that the image contrast at that frequency is 0·8× the object contrast. The value at the same frequency *Y* for the curve *b* is 0·5; hence the corresponding value of the combined curve *c* will be 0·8 × 0·5 = 0·4. It becomes obvious from this, that the more stages are introduced in the transmission chain (camera lens—film—enlarging lens—paper emulsion etc.), the more the final transfer function deteriorates since each step in the reproduction chain contributes its own factor of information loss and definition loss.

It should be noted that the resolution limit of any one of the transfer functions involved in such a cascade automatically becomes the cut-off point for all the others: if the film cannot resolve more than *X* lines per millimetre, a photograph taken on the film—with however good a lens—obviously cannot do any better. From this it follows that when we are working with a film which has a fairly low resolution limit, it is better to choose a lens whose transfer function follows the shape of curve *b* in Fig. 12.7 rather than that of curve *c*, since the contrast rendering of curve *b* is better before

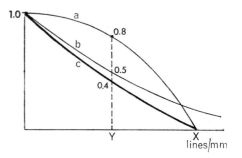

FIG. 12.12. TRANSFER FUNCTION FOR
LENS-FILM COMBINATION

the cut-off point while the higher ultimate resolution of curve *c* is not utilised.

176. Simplified Merit Values. The optical transfer function, and (ignoring phase information) the modulation transfer function gives fairly complete information of the performance of a lens, on its own or in a chain of reproduction. But it is somewhat cumbersome to handle when a simple comparative value is required. Numerous attempts have been made to derive from the transfer function such numerical merit or quality values. Some of these were aimed merely at combining a figure for limiting resolving power with edge sharpness or acutance (§ 171).

One possibility would be to integrate the modulation transfer curve, i.e. determine the area underneath it. To obtain a meaningful value, we have to choose suitable limits for this integration—covering for instance the spatial frequency range most likely to be needed in practice. These limits will then depend on the purpose for which the lens is required, but the merit values obtained can be used for direct comparison of the performance of different lenses for e.g. amateur miniature cameras. The usefulness of such a merit value has been confirmed by empirical tests with pictures taken by different lenses of varying performance and judged by panels of observers (Heynacher, 1963).

This is shown graphically in Fig. 12.13. An integration of the transfer function curve between the frequency limits *B* and *D* gives the area *ACDB* under the curve. Provided the lenses being compared have transfer function curves of more or less similar shape, such an integration gives a sufficiently reliable single value. The limit *B* should not correspond to too low a spatial frequency to avoid weighting the result too much in favour of low frequency resolution; the limit *D* should not go beyond the

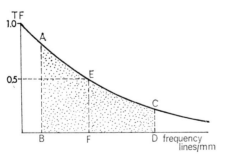

Fig. 12.13. Merit Value from Transfer Curve

point of practical utilization of lens resolution for the type of lens considered.

When a large number of lenses of the same type is to be tested, for instance when checking the quality of workmanship in lens production, it is even permissible to restrict the tests to a single selected frequency in the middle of the practically utilized spatial frequency range. The test is then reduced to a straightforward contrast measurement, which greatly simplifies the test equipment required and speeds up the procedure (§ 177). In Fig. 12.13 this figure of merit would correspond for instance to a measurement of the value (height) of the point *E* (0·5 in this example) at a selected frequency *F*.

A single numerical figure of merit is most useful if its increments represent just noticeable steps of definition difference. Heynacher has therefore suggested a further numerical quality grading *H* on a logarithmic scale given by:

$$H = C \times \log J$$

where *J* is the merit value obtained by integrating the transfer function curve as explained above and *C* is a constant.

177. Lens Testing in Practice. The quality and performance of a lens may have to be tested for a variety of different purposes; these determine also the methods that would be used in each case. We can conveniently group these approaches as:

(a) Testing overall performance;
(b) Testing for production standard; and
(c) Testing for specific aberrations.

Mathematical methods also permit prediction of the expected performance of a lens system from its design data. These are essentially a tool of the lens designer rather than of the lens user (§ 178).

Overall performance measurements are needed when the suitability of a lens for specific applications is to be evaluated. On a comparatively simple level this may be done by photographing a series of resolving power test charts—for example as in Fig. 12.1—distributed over the field of view of the lens (Fig. 12.14). Subject to the limitations of resolving power figures mentioned before (§ 171) and of the effect of the film on resolution (§ 175), such a test will at least show how resolving power varies over the field of view of the lens.

The test photograph is taken at a specific scale of reproduction; it may be repeated at different object distances and also at a range

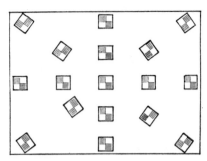

FIG. 12.14. RESOLUTION CHART LAYOUT
FOR TESTING

of slightly differing focus settings of the lens. From this it may be possible to draw conclusions as to how far the performance varies at different scales of reproduction, whether any definition loss away from the centre of the field is due to spherical aberrations or curvatures of field etc. and—by taking exposure series with different lens apertures—as to the effect of the lens diaphragm on the definition quality. If the test chart is photographed by monochromatic light of different colours and with a series of different focus settings of the lens (displacement of the focal plane) it is even possible to establish the degree of any chromatic aberration.

Such a complete test programme is necessarily lengthy and cumbersome, but even a single photograph of the chart layout can at least give a basis for quick comparison of different lenses.

For more advanced evaluation it is nowadays standard practice to determine modulation transfer functions. These may be measured optically by using a moving (e.g. rotating) test target of continuously varying spatial frequency. According to the design of the measuring set-up the result may be displayed as a transfer curve on a cathode ray tube screen (§ 174), plotted automatically by a recording system or even printed out by a computer output printer in the form of a graph. To cover the whole field of the lens, contrast transfer functions may have to be recorded with the slit (of the image plane—behind which the photo cell measures the transfer signal input) located successively in different positions of the lens's field.

As a simple photographic method the reproduction of a test target of continuously varying spatial frequency as well as contrast has been suggested. When such a chart (as shown in the upper part of Fig. 12.15) is photographed, the

resolution limit can be seen visually at different contrast levels and approximately traces out the shape of the contrast transfer curve (in the lower part of Fig. 12.15).

For lens testing in manufacture it is generally necessary to know whether a particular specimen of a production run falls within the laid down tolerances for assembly, centring etc. Since an optical manufacturer may have to test—if he checks his entire output—thousands of lenses a day, such tests are generally carried out by automated electronic instruments. Basically they rely on measuring the contrast of a test target of a specific spatial frequency. If the contrast—measured by photo cell circuits —is above a critical value, the lens is accepted; if it is below, the lens is rejected. Since such tests involve series of nominally identical lenses, such simple contrast measurements are a valid indication of the quality of the lens in respect of its manufacturing tolerances. The same applies to measurements of correct location in the mount, since a slightly defocused image would show a lower contrast than a correctly focused one. (This is where a simple merit value measurement as described in § 176 is justified.)

Specific lens aberrations and faults can usually be checked with a star test. Here the lens is used to project a pinpoint of light (for instance an illuminated pinhole) into its focal plane. The aerial image of this pinpoint is then observed with a microscope. The pinpoint may be moved into different positions in the lens's field and its image examined both for position and for shape. For instance, spherical aberration yields a light patch instead of a pinpoint image, and this patch may vary in shape and brightness distribution just in front of and behind the focal plane.

Spherical aberration in different zones of the lens can be examined by placing an annular diaphragm as in Fig. 8.16—with bands left free in different zones of the lens—in front. When the light point representing the object is moved to an off-axis position, the shape of the image point shows the presence of oblique spherical aberration and coma. Variations in the shape of the image as the microscope is focused on nearer and further planes may indicate the presence of astigmatism (§ 78), while the location of the smallest point image in different planes for axial and oblique rays would show up curvature of field (§ 81). Changes in the position of the image point when using light of different colours

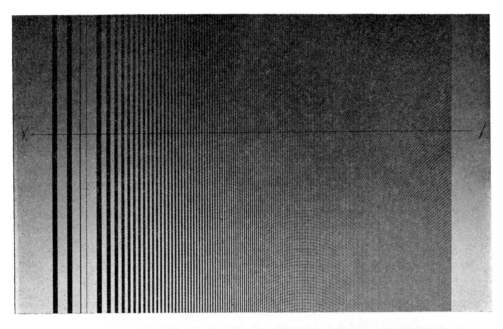

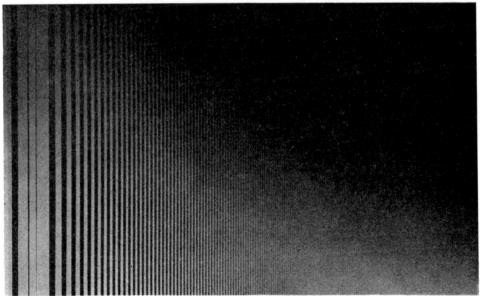

FIG. 12.15. VARIABLE CONTRAST RESOLUTION CHART AND ITS REPRODUCTION (COX)

will indicate the presence and the nature of chromatic aberrations. Finally, movement of the image point when the lens rotates on its own axis shows up centering errors.

178. Aspects of Lens Design. In designing optical systems it is essential to be able to predict lens performance from the optical parameters of the system; otherwise lens manufacture would be a purely speculative undertaking. There are two fundamental stages in optical design:

(*a*) Establishing the optical performance of a design, and

(*b*) Establishing a system for a required performance, or finding the change necessary to improve a system in specific directions.

The first of these can now be predicted with accuracy; the second is in many respects still a matter of trial and error.

To work out the performance and aberrations of a proposed optical system we must know the shape and light distribution of the image points formed by it. Some of the orders of aberration can be calculated mathematically, though such computation becomes increasingly complex with higher order aberrations.

The classical method of calculating required lens parameters (numbers of elements, their refractive indices and dispersive powers, curvatures of individual surfaces. thicknesses and separations of elements etc.) involves ray tracing. Here selected light rays are traced through the whole optical system, using the laws of refraction to calculate the change of direction of the ray at each optical surface until it meets the image plane. By tracing a number of rays in this way it is possible to show how far they meet—or fail to meet—in a single image point. When such rays are traced in sufficient number through representative zones of the lens, and from a sufficient number of object points, a reasonably complete specification of corresponding image points can be obtained.

Once the image quality and hence the performance of a lens is calculated in this way, the designer has to adjust selected lens parameters to improve the result in the direction required. This is where trial and error comes in: after each change in a parameter (and such changes have to be in small steps) the entire ray tracing procedure must be repeated. From the results the optical designer then sees whether his corrections or adjustments have taken the right direction.

The principal limitation of this method is the enormous time involved. Using trigonometrical tables, it takes a designer about 10–15 minutes to trace the path of a ray through one surface—so tracing say 2 or 3 dozen rays through a lens system of 10 to 12 surfaces could (and used to) require one to two working weeks—and the complete design of the lens might take many months. The use of desk calculators reduced this time by about half. But lens design took its big step forward with the introduction of electronic computers which could reduce the calculation time to one-millionth or less of that required by human calculation.

This immense acceleration of the process not only saved time, but permitted a much more complete analysis of the optical system. Present-day ray tracing procedures with computers are based on several hundred individual rays per lens.

The mechanization of ray tracing also permitted the generation of *spot diagrams*. These are magnified representations of the distribution of light rays from an object point reaching an image point. Here the results of computerized ray tracing are printed out by a special typewriter to form a pattern like Fig. 12.16 which represents an image spot showing a degree of coma. In this pattern each dot represents the meeting point of a light ray with the image plane; the more the dots are concentrated, the brighter the image spot at that point. When such spot diagrams are produced at different focus positions and in different locations of the lens's field, the aberrations arising can be evaluated directly. (The spot diagram in Fig. 12.16 is magnified about 500 times.)

From the data which produced the spot diagram, a suitable computer programme can record an optical transfer function and so

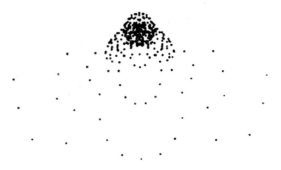

FIG. 12.16. SPOT DIAGRAM (COX)

give an indication of the lens performance in terms of contrast and resolving power.

Sophisticated programmes have been developed by which the computer automatically carries out changes in the lens parameters, repeats the ray tracing process and decides whether the adjustments made were in the right direction to improve the lens. The art of lens designing has thus largely become that of computer programming for such automatic adjustments and decision making, aiming at converging the calculations towards an optimum solution. The optical designer however still must specify the starting point and the required result as well as decide the programme to be used on the computer. But complex designs can be produced by computers which would have taken designers with only mechanical calculation methods several centuries.

179. The Care of Lenses. Interchangeable camera lenses, when not actually on the camera, should be kept in a clean and dry place, in dust-tight cases or at least with caps on both ends. A lens cap is also useful on lenses stored with the camera, as it protects the front element against dust and accidental damage. Lens caps are available usually in metal with a velvet lining, or in plastic.

Where a lens with cemented components is liable to be exposed to heat (for instance if employed on an enlarger), shield the lens from the light source by an opaque screen of card or metal, except when actually focusing or exposing. This applies particularly to camera lenses used in enlargers or projectors; special enlarging and projection lenses are generally designed to stand up to a reasonable amount of radiant heat.

Strict cleanliness of all surfaces is a necessary condition for obtaining clear images. A lens of which the surfaces diffuse the light either through condensation of steam or adherent dust, or grease marks due to contact with the fingers, will form a *halo* round all the highlights, and more or less completely veil the shadows.

Meticulous care is necessary in cleaning the lens surfaces. In the first place, atmospheric dust contains, among other things, numerous microscopic grains of sand, liable to scratch window or plate glass. Optical glasses tend to be considerably softer than other kinds, so that the rubbing of these grains on the surfaces of the lens, in the course of unskilful cleaning, causes the innumerable scratches seen on many

lenses after some years' service. This slight abrasion will considerably impair the qualities of the lens.

The lens coating is even softer than the glass, and particularly easily damaged even by hard rubbing in the course of normal cleaning.

In cleaning, all substances which are likely to deposit grease on the lens (such as chamois leather) should be avoided. Silk electrifies the glass and causes more dust to adhere. Linen cloth, taken from old linen garments, is very suitable for cleaning if recently washed and kept away from dust (preferably in a well-closed metal box).

Special lens-cleaning tissue is available and is cheap enough for a sheet to be discarded when once used. Avoid however cleaning tissues sold for spectacles; these are often impregnated with solvents which are harmless to spectacle lenses, but may affect the coating or the cement of camera lens systems.

Before cleaning, the surfaces should be dusted without applying pressure to the glass, e.g. with a very soft dry brush, kept for this purpose in a dust-proof case, and washed from time to time in denatured alcohol and immediately hung up to dry in filter paper.

The inner surfaces will not require dusting and cleaning so often as the outer surfaces, lens mounts with iris diaphragms being practically dust proof. Lenses other than convertible ones (§ 158) should never be dismantled anyway; reassembly requires extremely precise instruments to ensure accurate alignment, and cleaning and reconditioning of the inside of such lenses is best left to the manufacturer or a reputable optical workshop.

After dusting and dry cleaning, see that the surfaces are perfectly clean, which is best done in a room lighted by a single lamp, not too bright, looking at the lens held in a position slightly off the line joining the lamp and eye. If a dirty mark is seen, moisten it with a little soapy water and rub gently. If this does not remove it, moisten with a little denatured alcohol, taking care that none of it gets between the lens and its cell, as it might dissolve the Canada balsam used for cementing: after a few seconds, wipe dry.

In any case never try to polish the surfaces of a lens with a powder (chalk or rouge) or polishing paste, for the slightest wearing away of the glass which this polishing would produce would be sufficient to deform the surface and impair the quality of the lens. Long before a polishing paste deforms the lens surface, it will remove practically all the anti-reflection coating.

Never apply to the glass any alkaline solution, however weak, as optical glasses are extremely sensitive to action by chemical reagents and even to damp.

CHAPTER XIII

LENS ACCESSORIES AND ATTACHMENTS

180. Optical lens attachments. 181. Supplementary close-up lenses—near distances obtainable —variable power close-up lenses. 182. Negative supplementary lenses. 183. Tele-converters —advantages and drawbacks. 184. Afocal attachments—telescopes and field glasses in front of the camera lens—effective aperture—interchangeable tele and wide angle-attachments—afocal zoom units. 185. Anamorphic attachments—wide-screen effects—variation of compression. 186. Colour filters—effect of filter thickness on image position and light distribution. 187. The best position for mounting colour filters—in front of and behind the lens—supplementary filter lens. 188. Care of colour filters—cleaning and handling. 189. Polarisers—elimination of reflections—effect on skylight. 190. Soft focus diffusers. 191. Prisms and mirrors—relative advantages. 192. Lens hoods—optimum hood shapes—bellows hoods. 193. Graduated filters or sky shades.

180. Optical Lens Attachments. Optical attachments in this context are taken to mean items which affect the image scale, focus position or geometry—as distinct from units which redirect the light like mirrors or control its colour or intensity like filters.

Optical attachments in turn can be subdivided into:

(*a*) Positive supplementary lenses for close-up photography;

(*b*) Negative supplementary lenses for telephotography;

(*c*) Afocal adapters to increase or decrease the scale of the image without changing the back focus of the lens;

(*d*) Anamorphic attachments which change the image scale in one direction only and hence compress (or expand) the image uni-dimensionally.

181. Supplementary Close-up Lenses. Cameras of the fixed-focus type will produce a sharply defined image of the object only if it is at a sufficient distance from the camera, the picture being then on a small scale. In order to increase the usefulness of such a camera it is possible to mount positive supplementary lenses or magnifiers in front of the lens.

It must be emphasized in the first place that such magnifiers, and also the negative supplementary lenses referred to later, must be correctly centred with the camera lens. This excludes the use of all universal spring mounts, which can be adapted to filters or hoods of different diameters. The supplementary lens should be mounted in a small tube, which is either screwed into the inner thread of the lens

hood or on to the outer mounting of the lens, or it can be simply slipped tightly over the barrel of the lens.

For example, suppose that it is desired to photograph a subject at 1·50 m (5 ft) with a camera which is focused on infinity. It will then be sufficient to place a converging lens of 1·50 m (5 ft) focal length in front of the camera lens, that is a positive lens of 0·67 diopters. The subject will then be situated in the focal plane of such a supplementary lens. Rays of light coming from any point on the object to the magnifier are then transmitted from the latter and arrive on the camera lens as a beam of parallel light, i.e. in the form of rays coming from a very distant point. (In practice, if a fixed-focus camera has the focus set on the hyperfocal distance instead of infinity, the object should be arranged slightly on the far side of the focal plane of the supplementary lens.) It will thus be seen that if a set of supplementary lenses with properly chosen focal lengths is available, a fixed-focus camera can be used to photograph objects at all distances which are less than the minimum distance fixed by the limits of the camera. A point to remember is that each optical accessory increases the amount of stray light due to successive reflections from the glass surfaces.

With a camera which has a focusing adjustment but has an extension that is too short to allow a very near object to be photographed, the use of suitably chosen supplementary lenses will further extend its scope. If, for example, the camera cannot be focused on a distance less than 2 m and it is desired to photograph an object at a distance of 1·50 m the camera should be set at 2 m and a supplementary lens fixed on the front of the camera lens. This magnifying lens should have a power equal to the difference of the proxmity $\left(= \dfrac{1}{\text{distance}} \right)$ of the object and the point on which the camera is focused, i.e. in this case

$$\frac{1}{1 \cdot 50} - \frac{1}{2} = 0 \cdot 67 - 0 \cdot 50 = 0 \cdot 17 \text{ diopters}$$

This corresponds with a focal length of $\dfrac{1}{0 \cdot 17}$ = 6 metres.

With subsequent adjustment of the focus on a convenient distance, it is possible to use any magnifier whose focal length comes within the limit thus calculated and that corresponding to the use of the camera focused on infinity.

A more general equation for the focusing distance obtained with a supplementary lens is (neglecting the separation between the supplementary lens and the camera lens—i.e. assuming that the close-up lens is mounted as closely in front of the camera lens as possible):

$$u_s = \frac{u \times F_s}{u + F_s}$$

where u_s is the subject distance with the supplementary lens, u the distance on which the prime camera lens is focused and F_s the focal length of a supplementary lens. Thus with a camera lens focused on 1 metre and a supplementary lens of 2 diopters (focal length 0·5 m) the subject distance becomes

$$1 \times 0 \cdot 5/(1 + 0 \cdot 5) = 0 \cdot 33 \text{ metres}$$

If the camera lens is focused on infinity the ratio $u/(u + F_s)$ becomes equal to 1, and the object distance is then the focal length of the supplementary lens. Note that in all these cases the focal length of the prime lens does not enter into the calculation—the above formulae thus are valid for lenses of any focal length.

When using supplementary close-up lenses it must be realised that such lenses are usually uncorrected, and their use with a camera lens introduces aberrations into the resulting image (chromatic, spherical, astigmatic, etc.), which are more pronounced the stronger the additional lens. For this reason, if there is a choice between two supplementary lenses of different focal lengths, it is advisable to choose the one of the greater focal length, and to focus the camera accordingly. Supplementary lenses of high quality however often consist of cemented achromatic doublets to eliminate at least their effect on chromatic correction.

The focal length of a combination of a camera lens and positive supplementary lens is smaller than the focal length of the camera lens itself. So the latter would have a larger effective aperture than that indicated by the marking on the diaphragm. For purposes of exposure calculation, this apparent gain in lens speed is cancelled by the exposure factor required due to the increased lens-to-film distance (increased, that is, for the reduced focal length). In practice of course a small aperture is usually necessary to ensure adequate image sharpness with supplementary close-up lenses.

This reduction of the focal length also brings about, *ipso facto*, an increase in the depth of field, which at the same time is further increased since an incompletely corrected optical system has always a slightly greater depth of field (§ 122).

Positive supplementary lenses were sometimes called "portrait attachments," the implication being that such a lens permitted nearer subject distances with a fixed focus camera, to record large portrait heads. However, going close to a portrait subject in order to fill the frame with the head only, is liable to lead to unpleasantly exaggerated perspective effects (§ 135). Unless these are specially intended, it is better to enlarge a section of a negative carrying a smaller portrait image.

By using a combination of positive and negative elements of variable separation it is also possible to have a supplementary lens of adjustable dioptric power. This has the advantage in close-up work of providing a continuous near focusing range which spans that of the dioptric range. With single close-up lenses of fixed focal length the near focusing range is also limited and for different distances it is necessary to use different supplementary lenses. A close-up lens of variable power is however liable to impair the lens definition still further, and require appreciable stopping down to get a reasonably sharp image.

182. Negative Supplementary Lenses. In the same way that the focal length can be reduced by using a converging supplementary lens, so it can be increased by adding a diverging lens. For this the camera must however have provision for increasing the lens-to-image plane separation, for instance with bellows focusing. Negative supplementaries were at one time employed in landscape or portrait photography with such cameras, utilizing the softening of the definition resulting from the aberrations introduced by the supplementary lens for artistic effect.

It is possible to calculate the approximate value of the focal length (within 5 per cent) by assuming the power of the combined system to be equal to the difference between the powers of the camera lens and the supplementary lens. If a lens of 150 mm focal length, or 6·7 diopters, is coupled with a diverging lens of 500 mm focal length, or 2 diopters, the power of the combination will be approximately 4·7 diopters, i.e. a focal length of about 215 mm. In order to avoid excessive aberrations, and since an adjustment in focus is needed as when using an anachromatic lens, the power of the diverging attachment should not exceed half that of the camera lens, nor be below one-quarter of the power of the latter, since too weak a lens has no significant effect.

As with positive supplementary lenses, meniscus lenses—with the concave side towards the camera lens—are preferable to biconcave units.

183. Tele-Converters. While a negative supplementary lens can be used in front of the camera lens only when the camera has the necessary provision for increasing the lens extension, this extra extension can be provided automatically if the negative lens is fitted between an interchangeable lens and the camera itself. This is the so-called tele-converter, available for numerous miniature cameras. The tele-converter in effect converts the normal camera lens into a telephoto unit on the principle indicated in § 152. The effect of the tele-converter depends not only on the focal length of the camera lens L and the converter unit T in Fig. 13.1, but also on their separation S. A tele-converter consists of a negative lens or lens group in a tube whose length must be equal to F_2 in Fig. 13.1, i.e. the increase in the back focus as

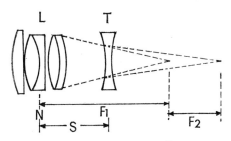

FIG. 13.1. TELE-CONVERTER PRINCIPLE

measured from the rear nodal plane N of the camera lens, taking into account the distance S between L and T.

Usually tele-converters are three- or four-element negative systems corrected as far as possible for chromatic aberration and certain other aberrations of their own, to minimize the loss of definition introduced by adding a lens system to the camera system. Generally they increase the focal length of the prime lens by a factor of $2\times$ or $3\times$. They can also be combined, with each converter unit further extending the lens-to-film distance and the focal length by its own factor. Thus a $2\times$ and a $3\times$ tele-converter together yield a $6\times$ factor, or a pair of $2\times$ converters a $4\times$ factor. There are also units with a variable converter factor—for instance from $2\times$ to $3\times$—achieved by altering the separation between two groups of negative components.

Tele-converters became very popular with users of miniature (and especially miniature reflex) cameras taking interchangeable lenses, since they greatly extend the scope of a limited number of such interchangeable lenses. If for instance the camera has only a standard 50 mm lens, a $2\times$ plus a $3\times$ converter provides a range of effective focal lengths of 50, 100, 150 and 300 mm; if a 135 mm lens is also available, the range of focal lengths is extended to over 800 mm. Moreover, such a combination is much cheaper than the corresponding tele lenses, while the combination of a tele-converter and a prime lens produces a much smaller and lighter unit than a regular tele-lens of the same focal length.

A further significant advantage is that the focusing range of a combination of prime lens with a tele converter is the same as that of the prime lens. Thus if the standard 50 mm camera lens focuses down to 50 cm (yielding a scale of reproduction of approximately 1:10), it will with a $3\times$ converter still focus down to the same distance. The scale of reproduction then grows to 1:3·3, while the near focusing limit of a regular 135 to 150 mm lens is usually around 1·5 to 2 metres. This near focusing limit is imposed by the mechanical movement range provided for the focusing adjustment of a regular long-focus or telephoto lens; with the tele-converter the focus adjustment is in effect carried out by varying the separation between the prime lens and the tele-converter, hence a shorter focusing travel covers a greater distance range. This however means that the focusing movement of the lens cannot be directly on the camera itself, which precludes range-finder coupling—the main reason why such converter lenses are primarily used with reflex cameras.

These advantages of tele-converters also have to be paid for with two important drawbacks. The first is the loss of image quality; the definition obtained with a combination of prime lens and tele-converter is usually inferior to that of a normal long focus or telephoto lens designed as a whole. Secondly, the converter increases not only the effective focal length but also the f-number. Thus a 50 mm $f/2$ lens used with a $3\times$ tele-converter becomes 150 mm $f/6$—appreciably slower than regular long-focus lenses of similar focal length. This may be a serious limitation when the camera focuses with a wedge type range-finder or a microprism grid in the focusing screen since these devices do not work below a limiting lens aperture.

184. Afocal Attachments. It has been known for a long time that by placing a telescope system, focused on infinity, in front of a camera lens—also focused on infinity—the image produced by the latter is magnified by a factor equal to the magnification of the telescope. The latter thus acts as a tele attachment, without however changing the distance from the prime lens to the image plane. The prime lens can then be focused in the normal way, and the same image magnification is obtained over the whole focusing range.

While normal astronomical or terrestrial telescopes are usually too large and bulky for mounting in front of a camera lens, the Galilean type telescope (see also §152) is more compact. The Galilean telescope consists of a converging front element and a diverging rear one. To achieve the condition of infinity focusing, where the rays leave the rear element (eyepiece) at the same angle as they enter the front element or objective, the separation between the positive and negative groups must be equal to the difference of their focal lengths. As previously noted, the magnification obtained is the ratio of the focal lengths of the front and rear elements or groups.

In practice the use of a simple Galilean telescope does not give very good results in photography, since such telescopes tend to introduce appreciable curvature of field and vignetting. A number of manufacturers of prism binoculars or field glasses do however produce special models suitable for attachment to camera lenses. The magnification obtained is then the magnifying power of the field glass (which for photographic use may be in the form of a monocular rather than a binocular). Thus an 8×30 glass effectively converts a 50 mm camera lens into a 400 mm lens.

The effective aperture of the camera lens is then limited by the size of the exit pupil of the field glass. The 8×30 designation signifies that the field glass has an $8\times$ magnification and a 30 mm diameter entrance pupil; the exit pupil is therefore $30/8 = 3.75$ mm. This becomes the effective entrance pupil diameter of the prime lens; if the latter has a focal length of 50 mm, the largest working aperture of the combination becomes $50/3.75 = f/13.3$. (As the elements of the field glass involve some loss of light, it is safe to regard the effective stop as $f/16$.) The iris diaphragm of the prime lens therefore does not affect the light transmission of the system until it is stopped down beyond about $f/14$. This is one of the main drawbacks of the use of field glasses.

While the magnification obtained with such an attachment does not depend on the focal length of the prime lens and does not influence the lens-to-image plane distance, the focal length of the prime lens does determine the maximum working aperture of the combination. Thus if the same field glass is used with a 12·5 mm lens of an 8 mm cine camera, the maximum working aperture of the combination becomes $12.5/3.75 = f/3.3$. In practice a 50 mm lens of a 24×36 mm miniature camera can be regarded as the useful limit for the utilization of field glasses of any reasonable power. The working aperture of nearly $f/22$ with for instance the 80 mm lens of a 6×6 cm reflex camera shows the impracticability of going any further.

The same principle is however used in providing afocal tele attachments of lower power for certain still and cine cameras. Ideally these

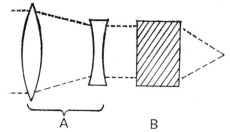

FIG. 13.2. TELE-ATTACHMENT PRINCIPLE
A = attachment
B = prime lens

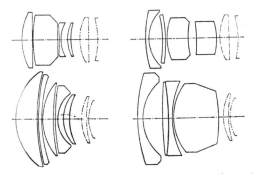

FIG. 13.3. MUTAR 1·5× (LEFT) AND 0·7× (RIGHT)
ATTACHMENTS

should be designed for a specific prime lens with which they are to be used, in order to reduce vignetting and loss of image quality to a minimum. This may lead to comparatively complex designs, like the Mutar 1·5× attachment (Fig. 13.3). Where the magnification of such an attachment is comparatively low and the entrance pupil diameter large, the exit pupil may be larger than the entrance pupil of the prime lens. In that case the effective pupil of the prime lens. In that case the effective lens speed is not impaired (except through reflection losses) and the iris diaphragm of the prime lens remains effective over its whole range.

The principle of the Galilean telescope can also be inverted so that it provides a reduction in scale (Fig. 13.4). The same conditions apply with respect to infinity focusing— i.e. the separation between the main planes of the negative and the positive unit must be equal to the difference of the focal length. Such a system can then act as a wide-angle attachment. Here the matching to the prime lens is even more important if the combination is to cover the wider angle of view without vignetting

and with not too much distortion. (In most wide angle attachments some barrel distortion is evident.) As the exit pupil of such a system is larger than the entrance pupil, no aperture limitations of the type encountered with telephoto attachments arise, unless these are introduced by vignetting.

Sets of afocal attachments for a camera with fixed lens thus give the camera some of the versatility of an interchangeable lens system. This may be useful when designing for full lens interchangeability poses unusual problems, as with twin lens reflex cameras. The Mutar 1·5× and 0·7× systems of Fig. 13.3 for a twin lens reflex are a typical example; here each Mutar unit consists of a pair of attachments matched to the taking lens and the finder lens of the camera.

In practice the magnification range of telephoto attachments for still and cine camera lenses goes up to about 2½× and of wide-angle attachments down to about 0·4×; the latter also exist as fish-eye attachments with the image scale and distortion characteristics of regular fish-eye lenses (§ 150).

When used with a zoom lens, the afocal attachment shifts the whole zooming range: thus a 2× attachment on a 40–120 mm zoom lens would turn the latter into an 80–240 mm system. On the other hand, as the zoom lens is essentially an afocal attachment of variable magnification in front of a prime lens of fixed focal length (§ 160), it seems logical to assume that the variable power portion could be used as a zoom attachment with camera lenses of fixed focal length. This is feasible, but still requires the zoom portion to be designed for use with a specific prime lens—otherwise it becomes very difficult to ensure acceptable image quality.

Such zooming attachments are used with cine cameras and with projectors. The combination of a prime lens with a zoom attachment specifically designed for it would also help to solve one practical problem when designing zoom lenses on still cameras: that of bulk. For normal shots requiring the standard focal length the prime lens might be used on its own, and the zoom section only attached when the greater focal length range is needed.

185. Anamorphic Attachments. These were designed to meet the requirements of wide screen cinematography. They are essentially a uni-dimensional wide-angle attachments, which extend the angle of view of the lens in a single (usually horizontal) direction instead of

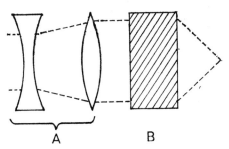

FIG. 13.4. WIDE-ANGLE ATTACHMENT
A = attachment
B = prime lens

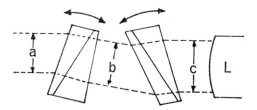

FIG. 13.5. PRISM ANAMORPHIC SYSTEM

both horizontally and vertically. This permits a cine camera frame with a 4:3 format proportion (an aspect ratio of 1·33) to cover a field of view with an aspect ratio of 2:1 or even 3:1. During projection the attachment—placed in front of the projection lens—expands the image horizontally to cover the required format proportion on the screen. In recent years this system has also gained some popularity in still photography where colour transparencies are produced and projected with the aid of anamorphic attachments yield wide screen pictures.

The anamorphic attachment usually consists of a pair of achromatised prisms arranged as in Fig. 13.5. The light beam passing through the prisms is narrowed down from c through b to a, thus reducing the scale of the image (and increasing the angle of coverage). This is based on the fact that a light beam passing through a single prism is always changed in width, unless it hits the prism at the angle of minimum deviation. Two prisms are used, to restore the direction of the axis of the system. By turning the prisms in opposite directions as shown by the arrows in Fig. 13.5 the degree of compression of the image can be varied.

A development of this idea is the use of two pairs of prisms, with their deflecting axes at right angles to each other—in other words a second prism pair in front of the pair in Fig. 13.5, but standing up from the plane of the diagram. By adjustment of the prism angles it then becomes possible to vary both the horizontal and the vertical compression at will. This yields a system which permits variation of scale without distortion, as well as selective distortion within a range of horizontal or vertical aspect ratios.

In place of prisms, cylindrical lenses can be used. This arrangement is similar in principle to that of the wide-angle attachment in Fig. 13.4, but the lenses are not curved in a plane at right angles to that of the paper. Cylindrical anamorphots require highly precise workmanship, for

their axes must be accurately aligned. The degree of compression can be varied by adjusting the separation between the components.

186. Colour Filters. Filters—coloured pieces of plate glass with plane-parallel faces or of coloured sheet gelatine used by itself or cemented between glass—are used to control the spectral composition of the light and to modify the colour or tone rendering of an image on the film (see also § 8). The practical use of filters will be considered later; here we are concerned only with their optical properties.

With the exception of the plain gelatine filters, which are too thin to modify the rays of light to any appreciable extent, any filter which is placed in front of or behind a camera lens alters the position of the sharp image, and introduces various aberrations into it.

If a pencil of light is made to converge at a point P by some optical system (Fig. 13.6), and a thick sheet of glass L, or some other transparent material with plane and parallel faces is interposed, it is easy to show that the image is displaced from P to P', its distance from the optical system being *increased*. If the inclination of the pencil is relatively small on the face of the sheet, the point P' is situated on the perpendicular drawn through P in a direction common to the two effective faces of the plate (L), and, if the latter is of glass, the displacement PP' of the image is approximately equal to a third of the thickness of the filter. A plate of thickness l of a substance of which the refractive index is n, is equivalent, from the point of view of the passage of rays of light, to a thickness of air equal to l/n; the difference between its actual thickness l and its effective thickness l/n, i.e. $l(n-1)$, represents the displacement of the sharp image, measured in the direction

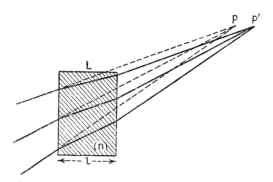

FIG. 13.6. EFFECT OF LIGHT-FILTER ON FOCUS

of the propagation of light. The glass used in the construction of filters (crown or plate glass) has a refractive index of about 1·5 so that the displacement of the image is about $l/3$.

If the filter is placed in such a way that the optical axis of the lens is perpendicular to its face, this being the necessary condition for the whole to constitute a centred system, the effect of the filter will be the same for every pencil of light. It will be sufficient to increase the distance between the plate and the lens by a third of the thickness of the filter, in order that everything may be in practically the same condition as before the introduction of the filter. If, on the contrary, the filter is not perpendicular to the lens axis, the differences of obliquity of pencils of light equally inclined to the optic axis cause deformation of the image. This may not be very considerable, it is true, but it would be particularly noticeable in negatives which had been taken through a badly placed filter, and which were required to give exactly superimposable images (three-colour work).

When the filter is placed between the subject and the lens, it is sufficient to consider the point P' (Fig. 13.6) as one of the points on the object, and it will be clear that, after passing through the filter, the rays will seem to come from the virtual point P, *which is nearer to the lens than the actual point on the object P'*. Thus, the whole object is brought virtually nearer the objective, and the amount of displacement is equal to about one-third of the thickness of the filter.

The image is formed *farther* from the lens than before interposition of the filter. If a camera is focused on an object and the object is reproduced on a scale of $1/m$, the *increase* in extension of the camera will be equal to the thickness of the filter divided by $3m^2$, a displacement which is negligible even for the thickest screens, when the object being photographed is not very near the lens. It is easy to show that the displacement of the image in this case is strictly equal to $l/\left(3m^2 + \dfrac{lm}{f}\right)$. The second term in the denominator is negligible compared with the first if m is appreciably greater than unity (reduction) and if the thickness l is only a small fraction of the focal length f.

In addition to the displacement of the image resulting from the interposition of a filter, the image is affected even if the filter is optically perfect ; these various aberrations, however, are fortunately small enough to have practically no disturbing effect. In the case of thick filters

mounted in front of a wide-angle objective, the chromatic aberrations may become of considerable importance, especially if the object is to superimpose the negatives taken through variously coloured filters; an appreciable barrel-shaped distortion is noticeable if the filter is between the lens and the image, while it is crescent-shaped if the filter is between the lens and the subject, slight curvature of the field occurring in both cases. For an equal thickness of filter, these aberrations are greater when the filter is on the same side of the lens as the nearer of the two conjugate planes. This is one of the reasons why filters are usually mounted in front of the lens for portrait or landscape photography —and in fact for any subject reproduced on a reduced scale.

The filter thickness can also have some effect on the light distribution in the image. In Fig. 13.7 an axial ray AB reaching the front surface of the filter at right angles suffers absorption only over a path l, equal to the thickness of the filter. An oblique ray CD with an angle of incidence α however travels a long way through the filter; its path m is equal to $l/\cos \alpha$. This means that with the filter the edges of the image receive less light (since the absorption inside the filter is proportional to the path length of the light through it) than central areas.

Generally solid glass filters are most satisfactory from the optical point of view, provided of course that their faces are both plane and parallel. Such filters have only two surfaces, so that reflection problems are reduced to a minimum, especially if the filter is anti-reflection coated (§ 89).

Gelatine filters can be produced in a wider range of absorption characteristics than mass-dyed glass. When they are mounted between glass plates for protection, this mounting needs particular care, as all six surfaces have to be parallel to each other. Excessive stress in the

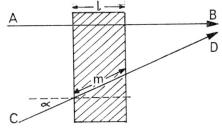

FIG. 13.7. LENGTH OF LIGHT PATH
FILTER

filter holder may distort glass mounted gelatine filters and upset the plane parallelism.

Gelatine filters mounted between commercial plate glass whose faces are usually neither plane nor parallel, are suitable only for visual use; filters for photography must consist of high quality glass with a high degree of flatness. This is particularly important when photographing with a long-focus lens, since with such lenses any inhomogeneity in the optical space between the lens and subject (or lens and image) has a much greater effect on image quality.

If the filter faces are parallel only one image is seen when looking at the reflection on the filter of distant objects, the line of vision being preferably glancing along the surface of the filter. If the faces are not parallel two separate reflected images will be seen.

187. The Best Position for Mounting Colour Filters. The efficiency of a light-filter is independent of it position in the beam of light. A filter always absorbs a definite proportion of each incident radiation, whatever the intensity of the light or its area of cross-section at the point where the filter is placed.

A light-filter may be placed (a) between the source of light and the object to be photographed; (b) between the object and the lens of the camera, and in this case it is usually mounted on the lens; (c) between the components of the camera lens; (d) between the lens and the sensitive plate, adjacent to the lens; (e) in front of the sensitive plate, almost in contact with it.

Position (a), generally used in micrography, has sometimes been used for the three-colour reproduction of colour transparencies. But it is impractical to have all the lights in a studio entirely covered by light-filters.

Position (c) should be rejected on principle, except when using gelatine screens of negligible thickness, which can be placed against the iris diaphragm after unscrewing one of the components of the objective. Every filter of appreciable thickness, being equivalent to two-thirds of its thickness of air, would produce very nearly the same effect as if the separation of the components of the lens had been reduced by a third of the thickness of the filter. This would seriously interfere with the definition unless the filter formed an integral part of the lens and was placed in position, with due regard to its effect, by the lens designer.

The fact that a filter, when used close to the nsitive film can be of mediocre optical quality without disadvantage has been put forward in favour of position (e). Unfortunately, any local defect in such a filter manifests itself on the image as a spot. Further, a "focal-plane filter" of indifferent quality is at least as expensive and immeasurably less workable than a "lens filter" of satisfactory quality, or, better still, a plain gelatine filter.

Usually the only two positions which need be considered are, therefore, those in front of (b) or behind (d) the lens of the camera.

In the circumstances usually occurring in practice, a filter placed in front of the lens does not alter the focus, which is a very appreciable advantage in the case of cameras whose focusing relies on a graduated scale. On all cameras this position of the filter lends itself most readily to taking on and off with the minimum of trouble. The filter can either be mounted in a ring, which is fitted over the lens like a cap, or provided with threads which allow it to be screwed into the lens hood. Most convenient when used with interchangeable lenses are bayonet-mounted filters. These are quick to fit or to detach, yet are secure when in position. Camera manufacturers are increasingly adopting this type of fitting.

In all cases where the object to be photographed is more than twice the focal length distant from the objective, the filter in front of the lens, in the case of thick filters, is least likely to introduce disturbing aberrations into the image.

A special case where a filter may be deliberately non-parallel is that of infra-red transmitting filters used to correct the infra-red focal length of a lens. Such filters are in fact very weak positive supplementary lenses with a converging power just sufficient to counteract the focal length increase of the lens to infra-red radiation. With such a filter it therefore becomes possible to focus the lens visually or by scale without using the filter, and then fit the filter without any further refocusing or adjustment. This is preferable to the use of an infra-red focusing index (§ 75) since the displacement of the image plane is not strictly the same at all focusing distances. The converging power of such focus correcting filters must be matched to the camera lens with which they are to be used and also to the principal wavelength of infra-red radiation to be corrected.

188. Care of Colour Filters. When not in use, all filters should be protected from the action of light, since the dyes with which they are made are sometimes affected by its prolonged action, and changes in their spectral absorption power may be caused in time.

When cleaning filters cemented between plate glass, the same precautions should be observed as when cleaning photographic lenses. Water should never be allowed to come into contact with the edges, since any wetting of the gelatine film would cause the latter to swell and might cause deformation of the filter and separation of the glasses.

Plain gelatine filters should never be handled except by their edges or between fine tissue paper ; any contact with the fingers invariably leaves fingermarks which cannot be removed and which seriously impair the definition. After being cut out, gelatine filters can be protected by dipping in a cellulose varnish. The filters must be protected from heat and damp, and when not in use should be kept between the leaves of a small notebook of white paper. When it is desired to cut out a circle of gelatine filter for fitting into a lens, breakage of the film can best be avoided by cutting it out between two pieces of strong paper, one of which has the circle to be cut out marked on it. As gelatine filters continually undergo slight expansions and contractions according to the humidity they should never be fitted into any kind of rigid frame. Lastly, gelatine filters should never be kept between plate glass unless suitably cemented on both sides, using e.g. Canada balsam solution in xylene. In this way multiplicity of reflecting surfaces and risks of tearing the gelatine will be avoided.

189. Polarizers. In normal light radiation, the light waves vibrate in all directions, perpendicular to the direction of propagation (§ 2). Various conditions can polarize light, that is, preserve only the vibrations parallel to a given plane, called the plane of polarization. For instance, the light diffused by a blue sky is polarized, and the clearer the sky the more complete the polarization. Light reflected from a non-metallic surface is polarized, the polarization being complete when the reflected rays are perpendicular to the refracted ones (reflection under an angle of 35° with the reflecting surface in the cases of glasses with a refractive index of 1·5). If the surface is transparent the refracted light is partly polarized, and it is then possible to decrease the proportion of non-polarized light by causing the light to pass through several thin plates in a stack. The light that has passed at the appropriate angle through

a suitable assembly of double-refracting colourless crystals (Nicol or Glazebrook prisms, made of Iceland spar) is totally polarized. Light that has passed a double-reflecting crystalline dichroic plate (Tourmaline, Herapathite or quinine iodosulphate) or a film holding in suspension a multitude of double-refracting, dichroic, ultramicroscopic crystalline needles similarly orientated (luteocobaltic periodosulphate; E. H. Land, 1934) is, at least in a spectral interval comprising the great majority of visible rays, formed mainly of polarized light. In recent years, polarizing foils, which have the advantage of not scattering any light, are prepared from stretched cellulosic materials.

Polarized light remains polarized after reflection from a polished surface, but it is de-polarized by diffusion on a matt surface or by passing through a ground glass.

If two polarizers are placed one behind the other, the light polarized by the first passes freely through the second if the planes of polarization are parallel. It is totally extinguished if these planes are mutually perpendicular, and partially extinguished in all the intermediate positions, and to an increasing extent as the angle between the two planes approximates to a right angle.

At first, the prohibitive cost and very narrow angle of field of effective polarizers restricted the use of polarized light in photographic practice. With the introduction of polarizing screens, which can be obtained in fairly large sizes, and with reasonably efficiency in the visible spectrum, numerous applications have been made possible.

The fact that these polarizers extinguish all components of vibration other than those orientated in the plane of polarization would, in the case of colourless polarizers, cause the exposure to be doubled. However, most polarizing screens used in photography have a certain density and may have a colour from grey to brown and these factors contribute to the need for a still greater exposure time.

For some purposes it is only necessary to use one polarizer, mounted on the lens. Others require at least two polarizers, one on the lens and one in front of each of the sources of light illuminating the subject.

By using one polarizer it is possible to decrease the luminosity of a blue sky without modifying the brilliance of other parts of the subject, and to decrease very considerably reflections on all brilliant non-metallic surfaces (glassware, water, earthenware, lacquered metal and other varnished objects). This is done by directing the axis of the lens at an angle of about 35° to the surface to be photographed. Thus, objects behind a transparent surface clearly become visible (Figs. 13.8 and 13.9), or the actual texture of the subject will become apparent. The correct orientation of the polarizer must be found by examining the image on the ground glass screen or reflex screen of the camera while rotating the polarizer in its own plane.

If a number of objects are illuminated by polarized light and photographed through another polarizer, reflections from all brilliant surfaces (including metals) can be decreased, whatever the values of the angles between the surfaces of the objects and the camera. These reflections can even be totally extinguished if the planes of polarization are crossed; this orientation is especially adopted for the photography of varnished paintings or of all documents under glass.

This same orientation permits the contrasts to be increased to a higher degree in the photography of documents on matt or granular paper than that of a glazed print as the structure of the paper is eliminated owing to the extinction of all light reflected by the rough surface. On the other hand it is possible to exaggerate these reflections if the polarization planes are parallel, the depolarized light diffused by the non-reflecting surfaces being then reduced in the proportion 2 : 1 relatively to the polarized light of the reflections.

190. Soft-focus Diffusers. Artistic photographers of the last century, obliged to work with lenses of far from perfect correction, often made a virtue of the limited definition, turning soft focus into a photographic style. This style is periodically revived, and lens manufacturers have at various times produced soft focus lenses with deliberate undercorrection of spherical and/or chromatic aberrations. A more convenient way of achieving a controlled softness of definition however uses soft focus attachments—which further have the advantage of permitting employment with any lens.

Essentially a soft focus attachment is a disc of clear glass or plastic with deliberately introduced surface irregularities which scatter light and cause the lens to produce a hazy unsharp image overlaying the basic sharp image.

The softening effect spreads light from bright image areas into neighbouring darker ones. When used during the camera exposure, the image spreads from the highlight portions of the negative into the shadows. When a soft focus unit is used during enlarging, it spreads light from the brightest parts of the projected image—i.e. the shadows of the negative—into the highlights.

The diffusing structure of a soft focus disc is usually a series of concentric embossed or engraved rings, or evenly distributed lenticular elements. With rings the diffusion effect gets smaller as the lens aperture is reduced, unless the rings are so spaced as to keep the relative areas of clear glass (or plastic) and ring pattern the same with different lens apertures. The diffusion with lenticular type soft focus discs does not depend on the aperture employed.

Soft focus attachments are generally available in different grades (degrees of diffusion) according to the effect desired. The effect of a given attachment is greater, the longer the focal length of the lens.

191. Prisms and Mirrors. We will consider here only the inaccurately named total-reflection prisms and the mirrors (at an angle of 45°) as used in commercial photography. They are employed either for directly obtaining a right-reading image (with certain methods of printing, reversed pictures would otherwise be obtained), or for the photography of ceilings, articles arranged on a horizontal table (jewels, natural history specimens), and, more particularly, for immersed objects.

The ideal—but costly—reflector is a metal mirror; optically worked glass mirrors, which are silvered on the surface, may be employed, it being possible to protect the silver, to a certain extent, by a very thin coat of celluloid varnish. Ordinary mirrors which are silvered on the back give rise to double images, except with very distant objects. The silvering on an unvarnished mirror will not adhere to the glass when damp. For periodical cleaning and re-polishing care should be taken to dry the mirror, the cloth, and the polishing rouge (optical quality) by warming. A more robust mirror is obtained by aluminizing or rhodiumizing the glass surface instead of the silvering.

A mirror has the following advantages over a prism : it absorbs less light ; does not cause the slightest aberration, and does not limit the angle of view. On the other hand, the reflecting surface of a mirror is more easily damaged.

The one advantage of a prism is the perfect stability of the silvering, which is applied

Kodak Ltd.

FIG. 13.8. PHOTOGRAPH TAKEN WITHOUT POLARIZER

Kodak Ltd.

FIG. 13.9. SAME SUBJECT PHOTOGRAPHED THROUGH AN EASTMAN
POLA SCREEN

externally on the hypotenuse (and which excludes all possibility of total reflection) without risk of any doubled image. Prisms, however, do not permit of an angle of field greater than about 30° being used without other reflections creeping in. The definition is often slightly inferior at the margins of the field from aberrations, which are the same as for a cube of glass with the side equal to the length of one side of the prism.

Both prisms and mirrors are best mounted in front of the camera lens, the mounting being on a small board which is interchangeable with the lens board. The reflecting surface should be turned to make an angle of 45° with the optical axis of the lens, in such a plane that, after reflection, the optical axis is either horizontal or vertical, according to the work in hand. This adjustment is only possible after repeated trials with the reflector mounted between the lens and the object to be photographed.

Ordinary mirrors have occasionally been used, in the absence of a wide-angle lens, for the photography of interiors. In this way the effective optical distance between the object and the camera can be doubled, but in the case of brightly illuminated or reflecting objects the definition usually suffers from doubling of the lines, etc. Surface-silvered mirrors have also been used in the construction of cameras which are designed to accommodate lenses of great focal length, so reducing the bulk of such cameras. In such cases, the part played by the mirrors may be compared with that of the prisms in prismatic binoculars for long-distance observation.

192. Lens Hoods. Any light reflected in the lens (§ 90) or which is scattered in the camera and distributed more or less uniformly over the image necessarily lessens the contrast and tends to veil the shadow detail. Scattering of appreciable quantities of light can usually be traced to two causes.

In the first place, small defects in the polish of the lenses and moisture or dust on their surfaces uniformly diffuse a certain proportion of the light which should go towards the formation of the image. Moreover, if the sun, though not necessarily included in the angle of view, is shining on the front of the lens, any defects on the surface of this lens (or on any accessory such as a supplementary lens or colour filter which is placed in front of the lens) will cause a considerable quantity of light to diffuse into the camera. The same effect is produced, although to a smaller extent, whenever a photograph is taken in the open air, since the lens receives light from all parts of the sky, apart from that within the angle of view.

In the second place, the image produced by a lens is usually larger than the area utilized. Any rays of light outside the useful field strike the interior walls of the camera, and these latter, even if matt black, always scatter an appreciable fraction towards the photographic material. The only really efficient means of protection, which is very difficult to apply to folding cameras and cameras which are fitted with lens movements (rising or cross fronts), consists in placing a series of diaphragms of progressively increasing aperture between the lens and the film plane. Many modern cameras incorporate internal baffles which aim to reduce such reflections inside the camera body. Even the pleated bellows of a bellows camera have a certain baffling effect of this kind. The baffle arrangement may be fairly elaborate on specialized camera types such as those used in aerial photography.

A lens hood is used to eliminate, or at least to diminish, the various causes of the incidence of stray light on the plate or film, by protecting the surface of the lens from light coming from above and by intercepting as far as possible any light that the lens would transmit to the sides of the camera. The use of this accessory is necessary for all out-door photography, especially for photographs taken against the light, and it is also of considerable advantage when working in a studio with walls having a high reflectivity.

It should be pointed out that of two lens hoods, each shading the lens to an equal extent, the one farther from the lens will be the more efficient from the point of view of protection from the sun. Thus, in Fig. 13.10, the two

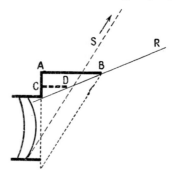

FIG. 13.10. ACTION OF LENS HOOD

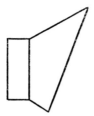

FIG. 13.11. CONE PATTERN OF LENS HOOD

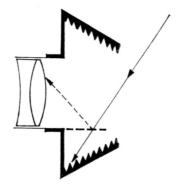

FIG. 13.12. LENS HOOD TO REDUCE
INTERNAL REFLECTIONS

opaque screens AB and CD both shield the lens from the ray R, but only AB, that is, the one farther from the optical axis, entirely protects the front lens from the direct rays of the sun in the direction S. It has been stated (C. Puyo, 1906) that for a lens hood to be effective in all cases, i.e. to protect the lens from the sun, whatever its position outside the angle of view, the lens hood should be extended to infinity along the bounding line R, a condition which is obviously impracticable. However, the farther the lens hood is placed from the optical axis, the more efficient it will be, and will remain effective as the sun approaches the limiting line R.

One of the best lens hoods would undoubtedly be a shade such as AB, hinged at A as high as possible, in such a way that the edge B can be raised or lowered to the limit of the field desired (B. T. J. Glover, 1920). Light from the sides is shielded by two small flexible curtains shown by dotted lines in Fig. 13.10. In practice, one is usually confined to fitting on to the lens either a lens hood, represented in section by an obliquely truncated cone (Fig. 13.11), or a cylindrical tube with the end cut obliquely, which is slipped on to the lens.

This form of lens hood protects primarily against light coming from above. As however stray light reflected from other directions—for instance the ground when photographing on the beach or in snow, should also be screened off, a cylindrical or rectangular lens hood is more frequently used. Of these, a rectangular hood, with its sides parallel to the lens format, is more efficient as it can be deeper without cutting off the light from the corners of the image. An ideal form is that shown in Fig. 13.12 which can not only be deeper than a straight-forward or cylindrical hood, but also prevents reflections from the internal surfaces of the hood (shown by the dotted lines in Fig. 13.12). The inside surface of the lens hood must in any case be matt black; a ribbed structure further helps to reduce reflections.

If the lens hood is made with a rectangular aperture parallel to the sensitive film, the dimensions of the opening can be calculated from the formulae

$$l = d + L\frac{D}{E} \qquad h = d + H\frac{D}{E}$$

where l and h represent the length and height of the opening, L and H, the corresponding dimensions of the sensitive film, d the diameter of the effective aperture, E the extension of the camera, and D the distance between the rectangular opening and the optical centre of the lens (or the diaphragm approximately). If the lens is raised by the amount e, the hood must be raised in the same direction by the amount $e\left(1 + \dfrac{D}{E}\right)$, both being measured from the centre of the image area.

On studio cameras the lens hood is usually formed by a piece of black cloth, supported in front of the camera by a removable metal frame; or the hood may take the form of a bellows connecting the lens front with an open-front frame. Such bellows hoods have the advantage of being adjustable in length to match different camera extensions. The hood may also be capable of being raised to correspond to the rising front movement of the camera.

193. Graduated Filters or Sky Shades. A device which used to be popular at one time for landscape photography was a selective filter which reduced the intensity of the light coming from the sky, without appreciably affecting the image brightness of the foreground. It was specially useful with earlier films whose sensitivity to blue light was appreciably greater than to light of all other colours.

A usual form of such graduated filters is that suggested by E. Joly in 1892, and consists of a uniformly graded filter of gelatine or glass, usually of a yellow colour. Such sky filters are made in the shape of a long rectangle, which is carried in a mount, allowing it to be raised or lowered according to the effect desired. The filter should be wide enough to cover the lens when placed at a short distance from it. The farther these screens are placed from the lens, the greater is their effect. The effect of a filter such as AB depends upon its differential absorbing capacity, which becomes greater as the aperture of the lens is reduced and the distance between the lens and the screen is increased (Fig. 13.13). The same results would obviously

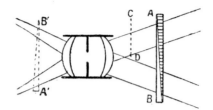

FIG. 13.13. ACTION OF GRADED LIGHT-FILTER

be obtained by placing a screen inside the camera (in the position shown by $A'B'$), but it is then difficult to adjust to its best position.

Neutral graduated filters and polarizers (§ 189) are the only ones suitable for decreasing the brillance of the sky blue in colour photography.

Index

The numbers refer always to the paragraph numbers in the text, and *not to the page numbers*.

The numbers refer always to the paragraph numbers in the text, and *not to the page numbers*.

The numbers refer always to the paragraph numbers in the text, and *not to the page numbers.*

The numbers refer always to the paragraph numbers in the text, and *not to the page numbers*.

The numbers refer always to the paragraph numbers in the text, and *not to the page numbers*.

The numbers refer always to the paragraph numbers in the text, and *not to the page numbers*.